A Visual Reference for
Evidence-Based Design

Jain Malkin
President
Jain Malkin Inc.
San Diego, California

 The Center for Health Design 2008

Copyright © 2008
by The Center for Health Design
http://www.healthdesign.org/
All rights reserved.

No part of this publication may be reproduced, stored in a retrieval system, displayed, published, or transmitted in any form or by any means, electronic, mechanical, photocopying, recording, or otherwise without prior written permission of the Publisher. Requests for permission should be addressed to Director of Marketing and Communications, The Center for Health Design, 1850 Gateway Boulevard, Suite 1083, Concord, CA 94520, (925) 521-9404, fax (925) 521-9405, Email: admin@healthdesign.org.

ISBN: 0-9743763-6-1

Printed in Korea

Cover Credits

Hospital entry/donor wall | Cabell Huntington Hospital, Huntington, WV

Architecture and Interior Design: Perkins + Will **Photography:** Chris Little

Supervising Editor: Jane Garwood **Consulting Editor:** Natalie Zensius **Copy Editor:** Lisa Richter

Design & Production by: Robert Anthony Strategic Marketing & Design

Creative Director: Jim Baehr **Graphic Design/Production:** Jamie Dandrea, Phuong Nguyen **Project Manager:** Lisa Ybarra

*This book is dedicated
to all who care so passionately about
improving patient care.*

Table of Contents

Foreword

The chief executive officer (CEO) was so proud. He radiated a glow as he took us on a tour of the new building. The lobby was huge, filled with new waiting areas, original artwork, and a long gleaming patient information desk. He pointed out the many varieties of plants and the soothing sounds of the large fountain in the center of the space. We were impressed. It could have been the lobby of a five-star hotel. The lobby, however, wasn't our focus that day, and our journey through the physical space became a learning journey for the CEO and his senior team.

Our mission that day was to walk in the shoes of a patient, to experience care as a patient or family member would. So we enlisted the guidance of a patient who arrived as we were admiring the beautiful entry space. The patient, a middle-aged man, was coming to the hospital for a cardiac stress test. We asked his permission for the hospital's leaders to accompany him on his visit, and he generously granted it.

The team watched as the patient approached the desk and was asked, "What is your name? Who is your doctor? And what are you here for?" The patient received paperwork and sat in the waiting area until called for the next step. This next step involved walking some distance and a repetition of the registration and waiting process. This pattern continued from cardiology to radiology to discharge.

By viewing the process through the patient's eyes, the leadership team saw and learned a tremendous amount. They saw drab design in the patient rooms and other care-delivery sites, design that contrasted starkly with the opulence of the public spaces. They noted the massive size of their waiting rooms, and wondered how they could reduce or even eliminate the need for waiting through innovative flow methods. They observed, with alarm, that patients walked as much just to get to the treadmill as they did during their stress tests. They saw that adjacencies and co-location of commonly used services were designed for staff convenience rather than the patient's. They noticed signage problems—staff directed patients to "EKG" when all the signs read "Electrocardiography." They overheard private, personal information disclosed in public spaces. They noted the poor design of handoffs involving information and patients. And they noticed how poor design presented obstacles to family involvement in care.

This is but one example of how care settings in the future need to consider the best of evidence-based design research to meet the needs of patients and staff. They will require a careful understanding of care processes and methods to make those processes more effective. Care settings in the future also need to demonstrate a deep connection with the needs and wants of patients and their families.

Having been involved in quality improvement for more than two decades, I know we can improve care. And I know we need to make care easier for staff to deliver and safer for patients to receive. Too often, in the design process, the key elements that contribute to safety, comfort, lower stress, and healing, are left on the budget-cutting floor.

In this book, commissioned by The Center for Health Design and published with funding from the Robert Wood Johnson Foundation, Jain Malkin powerfully argues for a closer focus on these evidence-based elements of facility design and, in doing so, has provided us with an exceptional guide to designing for the future.

So get out your walking shoes! It's time for your learning journey. I'm certain that the information in this book will be just as eye-opening for you as the patient tour was for the hospital leaders.

Maureen Bisognano
Executive Vice President and Chief Operations Officer
Institute for Healthcare Improvement
Boston

Acknowledgments

The author wishes to thank Kelly Kreuzinger and Bo Hearst for their work on the photo page graphics; Mary Anne Jones for typing the manuscript; and Jaynelle Stichler, Kirk Hamilton, Leonard Berry, James May III, Ann Hendrich, Roger Ulrich, Maureen Bisognano, and Anjali Joseph for their constructive comments and peer review of various chapters.

Like most books, this one could not have been written without help from many quarters. While it isn't possible to thank all who helped by name, some debts demand a more personal acknowledgement. Funding for the project was generously supported by a grant from The Robert Wood Johnson Foundation. I'm also indebted to The Center for Health Design for publishing the book and providing invaluable administrative support throughout the project.

Patient Room | Abbott Northwestern Heart Hospital
Minneapolis, MN. HKS, Inc. Photography: Ed La Casse

Introduction

It's risky business to be the first to write a book on a new topic, especially one that has a knowledge base in its infancy. Optimists will take comfort from the 1,000-plus studies that form the basis of this emerging body of information, while skeptics may not be convinced, as in the children's fable, that the emperor has new clothes. So consider this a snapshot in time. There is a need at this moment to capture the essence of what is going on around the country as major projects are unfolding and each healthcare organization tries to carry forth its mission in the face of daunting challenges: the rapidly escalating cost of construction, pay for performance, patient safety initiatives, integration of information technology, the re-engineering of patient care delivery, and—not least—figuring out what to build to optimize return on investment and enhance the patient's experience. A tall order, not for the risk-averse or the faint of heart.

FOCUS OF THIS BOOK

This book focuses on clinical areas in which direct patient care is provided: patient rooms, nursing core, and treatment and procedure spaces. The lobbies of hospitals and ambulatory care facilities have almost uniformly become appealing and uplifting environments. Suffused with natural light, water elements, gardens, music, coffee bars, fireplaces, works of art…these spaces are a celebration of wellness. And first impressions are important.

However, treatment areas, procedure rooms, corridors, and places that become the stage-set in the daily lives of patients have not fared so well. Many are bereft of any design detail or healing environment amenities that would bring a measure of joy to a weary or frightened patient. Even in a number of new hospitals opened within the last three or four years, design features drop off sharply as one exits the lobby and proceeds to patient care areas. Color and vibrancy disappear, and bland, conventional nursing unit design results.

Sometimes main artery circulation spaces are totally undifferentiated from service corridors, and by this, I don't mean that the service corridors look as good as those designed for main public circulation. Quite the contrary: both types lack landmarks or wayfinding cues despite the well-established body of research about how to make a complex building architecturally legible and easy to navigate. Color is the least expensive way to breathe life into an interior space, yet these corridors often have white floors, white walls, and sometimes even white doors.

In the early 1970s when I began my photo documentation of hospitals (long before any of us could even imagine how hospitals would be transformed through the advent of Planetree in the 1980s), I referred to those monotonous corridors as "infinity" corridors. They seemed to continue forever. White floors, walls, and ceiling, unbroken by anything but an occasional mop bucket or laundry cart, exaggerated the vanishing point. There was an unspeakably grim desolation, an institutional despair, an architectural expression of Edvard Munch's painting, *The Scream*. Sadly, after more than 30 years, these hospitals look much the same; it is a very expensive undertaking to replace aging facilities (Image page xvii).

In general, by the late 1980s, there were many examples of robust color and design in hospital interiors. Admittedly the lobbies weren't nearly as ambitious and grand as today, but there was more of a balanced focus on design of public space and patient care areas. But today, we see too many patient care areas—nursing units and even patient rooms—with no design features beyond the functional layout of equipment. Footwalls with no shelves or casework for flowers and plants, headwalls with little more than the perfunctory placement of medical gases, nurses' stations with the most basic casework design, lighting design with no imagination or regard for glare, and a total lack of color.

Far worse are the diagnostic imaging and procedure rooms, devoid of any positive diversion that would give an anxious patient some relief. Does it make sense to spend upward of $1.5 million on a piece of equipment and not reserve $10,000 to $20,000 for upgrades to the ceiling, flooring, and lighting—perhaps for the installation of backlit images of nature? The evidence is there. Research tells us clearly that reduction of stress for patients can even improve their immune response. Don't we have an obligation to create uplifting physical environments for patients?

The Underbelly of Mediocre Design

It is too easy to say that mediocre design results from the extreme financial pressures that hospitals now face. A glance in the rear-view mirror reminds us of the ravages of managed care plus a number of other stop-gap measures to control runaway costs that had us wringing our collective hands and wondering how hospitals could survive yet another budget cut, further Medicare payment reductions, or the increasing burden of the uninsured. Financial pressure has been a constant. Now the big threat is pay for performance. Medicare is not going to pay for care that results from medical errors. Despite these financial pressures, there are architects and hospital leadership teams who have figured out a way to achieve excellence in the design of their new projects. This has been true over the past 15 years and will continue to be true as evidenced by projects depicted in this book.

It can be assumed that all parties start a project with good intentions. Is there a group of more idealistic individuals than healthcare architects? Nevertheless, some of these well-meaning design professionals appear to be uninformed about what constitutes a good environment for patients. Another reason for mediocre work is that an architectural firm may accept a project at a fee too low to produce anything of substance, anything that requires deep study and analysis. Not uncommon in my experience is a budget that may have been appropriate for the initial program but, as the program grew, the budget was not adjusted. During value engineering, hospital executives and influential board members may not be well-versed in how to cut costs relating to the exterior skin of the building, or site features, or the mechanical system, but it is within everyone's knowledge base to reduce interior finishes or design amenities thinking that they can always be added in the future once the hospital is opened. But they never are.

Sometimes buildings are stripped of design features and amenities because the contractor lays cost-cutting options on the table for the owner without consulting the architect or the project budget may have been developed without a good understanding of appropriate evidence-based design benchmarks. Perhaps the hospital board is poorly informed about patient-centered care, focusing more on the architectural design of the building exterior and an impressive lobby.

I hope that this book will serve as a guide to emphasize important planning and design issues and provide insight into how numerous healthcare organizations have charted a course through difficult waters. Above all, the book is a manifesto about the importance of design amenities in patient care areas. These areas are not "back of the house;" they should receive the most thoroughly researched creative design even at the expense of the lobby, site features, or the types of exterior building materials used.

Limitations of this Book

This book focuses on acute care; however, the cancer treatment section, for example, has photos of radiation therapy and chemotherapy infusion facilities, which are, for the most part, always outpatient in nature. Diagnostic imaging facilities may be located in acute care or outpatient settings. This is not intended to be a complete compendium of every type of procedure or treatment room; the facilities depicted are representative of patient care settings, and the ideas expressed can be extrapolated to other environments. Truth be told, it was difficult to find good examples of diagnostic imaging facilities that went beyond a basic layout of equipment, four walls, and a ceiling. With the exception of magnetic resonance imaging (MRI), there are slim pickings; hence the chapter on diagnostic imaging is very small. Even most MRI projects are fairly uninspired. Radiation therapy rooms, on the other hand, are often designed with high-quality amenities and positive distractions.

The content is limited to adult care. Pediatrics and neonatal intensive care units were excluded because they are deserving of an entire volume—there is much to say and books such as those by Bruce Komiske (1999, 2005) and Mardelle Shepley and colleagues (1998) are excellent resources.

How This Book Is Organized

The book starts with a discussion of evidence-based design (Chapter 1), as that is the foundation for the content that follows. The following chapters—2, 3, and 4—discuss research methods, reducing infections, and incorporating research, respectively. The book then proceeds to a chapter on designing the experience, which relates to the entire milieu that surrounds healthcare services (Chapter 5). A small chapter on staff spaces (Chapter 6) leads to the largest chapter on patient unit design (Chapter 7). Certain projects have been presented as case studies because they have charted a new path in their approach to design. Two of these have already had a significant influence on other organizations planning new facilities, and the other two are not yet under construction but appear to have great potential. Subsequent chapters focus on diagnostics and procedures (Chapters 8 and 9), and the last chapter presents aspects of cancer treatment, limited to chemotherapy infusion and radiation oncology (Chapter 10).

Inpatient cancer units, including bone marrow transplant facilities, although worthy of inclusion, fall outside the limitations of this book. Similarly, inpatient units dedicated to neuroscience, cardiovascular disease, or orthopedics are not presented, because the discussion focuses more on acuity-adaptable rooms that can be assigned to various medical or surgical specialties at will. Specific patient rooms that exist in a new heart hospital, for example, are identified as such.

A Visual Reference

As the title of the book indicates, many photos of facilities as well as space plans support the text. Whenever possible, features are annotated or a commentary box explains how the relevant research has been embedded in the design. Research studies are not cited on the photo pages. Doing this would get very repetitive—how many times can I refer to the well-known studies documenting that natural light and views of nature are important? The evidence-based design chapter discusses the research and provides a guide to locating it. Insights from many interviews with architects, chief nurse executives, and chief executive officers discussing what worked and what did not have been laced throughout my commentary. Ten years from now, we will probably know a lot more about the effectiveness of same-handed patient rooms, acuity-adaptable rooms, and a variety of other concepts that are fairly new. And with the lens sharply focused on reduction of medical errors and patient safety, we will hopefully have a lot of evidence on what works. This book is the start of a long journey.

Selection of Projects

The net was cast widely to be as inclusive as possible. Some 50 healthcare architecture firms were contacted for project submittals. Time and resources limit the amount of research one can do to gather project photos, talk to persons of interest, and explore new ideas. It was very helpful to review issues of *Healthcare Design* magazine, and this led to the discovery of numerous projects worthy of inclusion. In addition, several of the organizations participating in The Center for Health Design Pebble Project research initiative have facilities that are noteworthy.

Despite tremendous effort to uncover the most visionary new projects, there is the frustration of wondering if the most significant project of recent years was not discovered. If this turns out to be true, it was not for lack of trying. At some point, research had to stop and the book had to be written. The many file cabinets and banker's boxes laden with journal, magazine, and newspaper articles beckoning to be included was a torment, as there is such richness of material on every aspect of healthcare design. Add to that numerous agencies producing statistics on all manner of topics from emergency room visits to the costs of treating nosocomial infections to the diseases affecting Baby Boomers. And then there are the many books that have been written on a variety of healthcare design topics, as well as on lean design, patient-centered care, and patient safety.

The landscape was much different in 1990 when I was doing research for my book, *Hospital Interior Architecture,* published in 1992. Most important, there is the Internet. In 1990, I had to contract with university-based libraries to research journal articles that were mailed to me. That book bundled together a lot of research focused on specific patient populations (rehabilitation, birthing, cancer, psychiatric, etc.) and offered application guidelines. The projects presented were truly cutting-edge and, at that time, there were few opportunities to be exposed to projects of this type since magazines such as *Healthcare Design* did not exist. Editors of professional design and architecture magazines that have annual healthcare editions have rarely understood the criteria for selecting and publishing excellent healthcare projects. In fact, it is amusing how often the featured projects are examples of what *not* to do.

Fast forward to today: despite many excellent books on healthcare design topics and a plethora of articles and studies being widely available, I hope that the format of this book makes it a valuable tool to encourage dialogue between healthcare organizations and their design professionals.

References

Komiske, B. K. 1999. *Designing the world's best children's hospital.* Mulgrave, Victoria, Australia: Images Publishing.

Komiske, B. K. 2005. *Children's hospitals 2: The future of healing environments.* Mulgrave, Victoria, Australia: Images Publishing.

Shepley, M. M., M. Fournier, and K. W. McDougal. 1998. *Healthcare environments for children and their families* (Association for the Care of Children's Health). Dubuque, IA: Kendall Hunt Publishing Co.

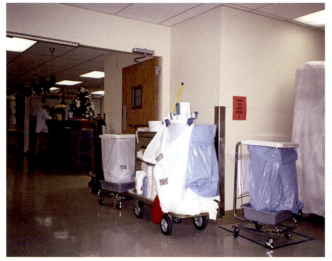

Photographer: Jain Malkin

Letting it all "hang out."

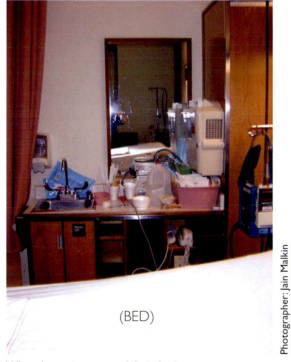

(BED)

Photographer: Jain Malkin

What the patient sees while in bed.

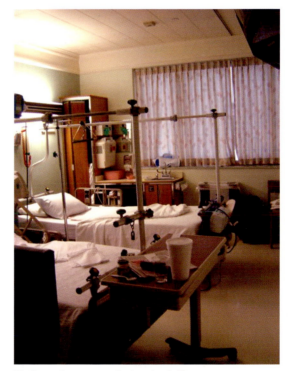

Orthopedic trapeze devices look like medieval torture racks.

Commentary

Housekeeping and laundry carts as well as mop buckets remain highly visible in many hospital corridors. Planning of new facilities demands a strategy for properly storing these where they are accessible but out of view. Older facilities (lower photos) with semi-private rooms lack adequate space to ensure clinical safety and expose patients to very cluttered views. The most conscientious staff cannot compensate for such tight spaces, not to mention the psychological toll on two strangers just three feet apart.

Oncology Clinic Corridor | Rebecca and John Moores Cancer Center
UC San Diego Medical Center, La Jolla, CA. Zimmer Gunsul Frasca Partnership. Photography: © Robert Canfield

Evidence-Based Design   1

The built environment is a powerful force in patient care. If properly designed, it enables care providers to do their work more effectively, and it has the potential to enhance patient safety. However, it's not a standalone. There is a continuous interplay between a building, its layout, and the work that is carried on within the walls. The workflow and care-delivery processes and the choreography of patients as they interact with the building and the caregivers must be in harmony. Aspects of this are discussed throughout this book in various chapters.

One can look at evidence-based design (EBD) in a narrow context as focusing only on research affecting the built environment or, in a more expansive context, as research coming from the neurosciences or lean design or a number of healthcare system research initiatives designed to improve patient outcomes. Design is a term that can be applied to care processes, architecture, the act of crafting the experience for patients as they interface with the medical center, or one can design a guest-relations program.

This is a time for great optimism. Never, in the past 30 years, have so many individuals, organizations, and regulatory agencies focused so intently on improving both the physical environment for patients as well as aspects of patient safety.

WHAT IS EVIDENCE-BASED DESIGN?

The Center for Health Design (CHD) defines EBD as "the deliberate attempt to base building decisions on the best available research evidence with the goal of improving outcomes and of continuing to monitor the success or failure for subsequent decision-making." An evidence-based model can be used for all design decisions. A report published by CHD (Ulrich et al. 2004) is a foundation for EBD. Some 650 studies (actually more than 1,000 in the current compilation) published in peer-reviewed journals can be sorted into three broad categories: safety, reduction of stress, and ecological health. (A separate abstracts table is available at the CHD website at www.healthdesign.org.) Although most of the recent evidence has come from patient safety and clinical outcomes, sources of evidence may come from widely varying domains including organizational and financial performance.

In some respects, it can be said that the concept of healing environments has evolved into EBD, but it's mainly in the area of reduction of stress that this overlap occurs. Research that underpins the concept of a healing or psychologically supportive environment is drawn from the neurosciences, evolutionary biology, psychoneuroimmunology (the effect of the emotions on the immune system), and environmental psychology. Some of these studies are part of the EBD report (Ulrich et al. 2004), but EBD goes beyond the healing environments dimension to consider the effect of the built environment on patient clinical outcomes in the areas of staff stress and fatigue, patient stress, and facility operational efficiency and productivity to improve quality and patient safety.

Evidence-Based Design Certification

Implementation of EBD requires that design professionals, healthcare planners, and healthcare organization management teams be familiar with the process to follow to identify research; create hypotheses; gather, implement, and report the data associated with their projects. To this end, CHD is inaugurating, early in 2008, a credentialing program called Evidence-based Design Assessment and Certification (EDAC). This will help healthcare organizations identify knowledgeable, certified practitioners. Once accredited, an individual will have an obligation to employ an EBD process in his or her work.

Key components of EDAC certification include:

1. Meaningful collaboration with the client/users
2. Recognizing and responding to the unique context of each project
3. Using best available credible evidence from a variety of sources
4. Using critical thinking to interpret the implications of the research on design decisions
5. Honoring a sacred trust to protect public safety and health
6. Commitment to share findings with the world

The Four Levels of Evidence-Based Practice

Hamilton (2003) identifies four levels of evidence-based practice, each successive level requiring more rigor and commitment.

Level-one practitioners

These practitioners stay current on literature in the field and interpret the meaning of evidence as it relates to the project at hand. They are learning from others as well as developing new examples for others.

Level-two practitioners

These practitioners take another step by hypothesizing the expected outcomes of design interventions and plan to subsequently measure the results. In this case, the design is less subjective and more challenging. The designer must understand the research and be able to interpret its implications and then be able to logically connect the design decision to an outcome that can be measured. This reduces the number of arbitrary design decisions and delivers solutions linked to outcomes. The designer must be prepared, however, to accurately report the findings regardless of whether successful or not. Sometimes there will be other discoveries that come out of this process in addition to the hypothesis being tested.

Level-three practitioners

Not only do these practitioners keep current with the literature, create hypotheses about intended outcomes, and measure results, they also report or publish their findings publicly. This may include speaking at conferences or getting articles published. This invites the scrutiny and possible criticism of others who may disagree with the findings and subsequently may lead the practitioner to become more rigorous in his or her approach. Or a designer may collaborate with a researcher to derive the benefit of working with someone who understands qualitative and quantitative research methods.

Level-four practitioners

These practitioners follow all of the steps previously mentioned but then attempt to get the research published in peer-reviewed journals. This generally requires that a design professional collaborate with scholars in academic or professional settings who understand the rigor of what is required to get an article accepted by a journal. This is the type of research that advances the field of evidence.

Hamilton labels "level-zero practitioners" as those individuals who understand the notion of EBD, but limit their study to isolated comments from magazine articles or conference presentations, using them subjectively to support their design, then claiming that the design is evidence-based. Without hypotheses and measurement, these individuals complete a project and search for positive outcomes. Since there was never a hypothesis, the necessary causal relationship is missing, thus, it's not evidence-based.

How Strong Is the Evidence?

The CHD report by Ulrich et al. (2004) identified more than 650 studies (more than 1,000 in the current compilation) in peer-reviewed journals that establish how hospital design can impact clinical outcomes. A graphic scorecard was developed to express, at a glance, the strength of the evidence (Center for Health Design 2005). Within each outcome area, bars are used to denote the quantity of studies that meet the criteria.

Topics with four or five bars are those for which the researchers found many strong studies linking environmental factors with the outcome. These are considered high action areas.

Topics with three bars are those that have relatively fewer studies associated with them; however, these are high-importance outcome areas in which additional research is needed.

Topics with one or two bars have few studies associated with them or few studies that conclusively provide a link between environmental factors and the outcome. These are important areas where additional research is needed.

Figures 1.1 through 1.4 depict the scorecards for quality, patient safety, patient stress, and staff stress, respectively.

▬ ▬ ▬ ▬ ▬	Topics with four or five blue bars are those where the researchers found many good studies linking environmental factors with the outcome or fewer strong studies that provided convergent evidence linking the environmental factor with the outcome. These are considered high action areas.
▬ ▬ ▬	Topics with three blue bars are those which have relatively fewer studies associated with them. However, these are high importance outcome areas and ones in which additional research in needed.
▬	Topics with one or two blue bars (e.g. reducing staff turnover, increasing handwashing compliance among staff) have few studies associated with them or few studies that conclusively provide a link between environmental factors and the outcome. These are important areas where there is need for additional research.

Quality Scorecard — Figure 1.1

Improve overall healthcare quality and reduce cost

Bars	Outcome
▬ ▬	Reduce length of patient stay
▬ ▬	Reduce drugs (see patient safety)
▬ ▬ ▬ ▬ ▬	Patient room transfers: number and costs
▬	Re-hospitalization or readmission rates
▬ ▬ ▬	Staff work effectiveness; patient care time per shift
▬ ▬ ▬ ▬	Patient satisfaction with quality of care
▬ ▬	Patient satisfaction with staff quality

Patient Safety Scorecard | Figure 1.2

Improve patient safety and quality of care

██ ██ ██ ██ ███	Reduce nosocomial infection (airborne)
██ ██ ██ ██	Reduce nosocomial infection (contact)
██	Reduce medication errors
██ ██	Reduce patient falls
██	Improve quality of communication (patient → staff)
██	Improve quality of communication (staff → staff)
██ ██ ██	Improve quality of communication (staff → patient)
██ ██	Improve quality of communication (patient → family)
██	Increase handwashing compliance by staff
██ ██ ██	Improve confidentiality of patient information

Patient Stress Scorecard | Figure 1.3

Reduce stress, improve quality of life and healing for patients and families

██ ██ ██ ██	Reduce noise stress
██ ██ ██ ██	Reduce spatial disorientation
██ ██ ██ ██	Improve sleep
██ ██ ██ ██	Increase social support
██ ██ ██	Reduce depression
██ ██ ██	Improve circadian rhythms
██ ██	Reduce pain (intake of pain drugs and reported pain)
██ ██ ██	Reduce helplessness and empower patients & families
██ ██ ██	Provide positive distraction
██ ██ ██ ██	Patient stress (emotional duress, anxiety, depression)

Staff Stress Scorecard | Figure 1.4

Reduce staff stress/fatigue, increase effectiveness in delivering care

██ ██ ██ ██	Reduce noise stress
██ ██ ██	Improve medication processing and delivery times
██ ██	Improve workplace, job satisfaction
██	Reduce turnover
██ ██	Reduce fatigue
██ ██ ██	Work effectiveness; patient care time per shift
██ ██ ██	Improve satisfaction

More Blue Bars = More Research Available

BENEFITS OF A HEALING (REDUCED-STRESS) ENVIRONMENT

At the start of this chapter, the interface between what has been called a healing environment and what is now called EBD was explained. In short, there is overlap in that most of the research associated with healing environments (also defined by Ulrich as "psychologically supportive design") falls into five categories, all with the common thread of stress reduction. Many of these studies are part of the EBD report (Ulrich et al. 2004), but some are not because the EBD report focuses on the impact of the built environment on clinical outcomes. Many studies from the neurosciences or evolutionary biology are not linked to the built environment but rather to the impact of various stressors on human physiology and biochemistry.

Here's an example: Pert (1997) discusses how our thoughts influence our biochemistry from moment to moment. She does research in neuropeptides and has documented the effects of stressors on the immune system. Although a scientist may take issue with generalizing this to the effects of the built environment, it would seem that anything that makes patients feel comfortable, including the setting in which a medical procedure takes place, would impact their thoughts and biochemistry. In fact, there is research in the EBD report (Ulrich et al. 2004) indicating that this has credibility, as explained below.

Research indicates that speedier recovery time at home may occur as a result of a less stressful hospital experience (Kiecolt-Glaser et al. 1998). In fact, physical comfort in the hospital setting may even reduce mortality and morbidity. Patients in this setting may require fewer narcotic pain medications, have less anxiety and depression, and have fewer postsurgical complications (Kiecolt-Glaser et al. 1998). A more comfortable, less stressful hospital experience leads to higher patient satisfaction which, in turn, is linked to increased patient compliance with drug regimens and recommended postsurgical care, including follow-up visits—all of which potentially affect clinical outcomes (Kiecolt-Glaser et al. 1998).

Feelings and Biochemistry: An Instant Feedback Loop

The most effective path to creating a healing (stress-reducing) environment is to inform design decisions by research. In recent years, the neurosciences have provided considerable insight into how the immune system can be experimentally suppressed or enhanced by a variety of interventions, and we have learned that feelings are inseparable from biochemistry. Our thoughts influence our physiology. What we perceive, think, and how well we cope are all set in motion by messages from the brain to the rest of the body.

One could say that our brains are writing a prescription for our bodies every minute of every day. Feeling sad or disheartened produces hormones that may affect the functioning of internal organs (Pert 1990; 1997). It doesn't require much of a leap to see how the healthcare environment—the total milieu—can influence one's emotional state and, according to neuroscientist Pert (1997), these messages can affect cell biology. In a number of studies, greater self-reported anxiety and stress are related to more postoperative pain (Kiecolt-Glaser et al. 1998).

Physiology of Stress

In 1956, Austrian physician and scientist Hans Selye pioneered a new frontier with his revolutionary discoveries about stress. His research demonstrated that hormones released during stress participate in the development of many degenerative diseases including brain hemorrhage, hardening of the arteries, coronary thrombosis, certain types of high blood pressure, kidney failure, arthritis, peptic ulcers, and cancer (Selye 1956).

His definition of stress refers to wear and tear on the body resulting from attempts to cope with environmental stressors; this was a new concept of mental and physical illness. He meticulously documented the enormously complex series of interactions between almost all systems of the body as a reaction to stress. Measurable and highly predictable physiological changes take place as a reaction to psychological and environmental stress (Frankenhaeuser 1980; Lazarus 1999; Rabin 1999), and this is the basis for the emerging field of psychoneuroimmunology (PNI). PNI is a term that refers to the role that the emotions play in the origin of physical diseases associated with immunological dysfunctions, especially autoimmune diseases as well as cancer, infections, and allergies. When people are under stress, their immune systems function less effectively (Kennedy, Glaser, and Kiecolt-Glaser 1990; Solomon 1990; Pert 1990; Pert 1997; Rabin 1999).

Stress involves the nervous system and the endocrine system. These two systems provide links between mind and body. Music has been known to have an analgesic or painkilling effect when pleasure centers of the brain stimulate the pituitary gland to release endorphins, the body's natural opiate (Campbell 1997; Taylor 1997). Many medical centers have experimented with aromatherapy (the inhaling of specific fragrances) to reduce nausea, decrease the amount of anesthesia needed in surgery, decrease pain, and lower blood pressure. Scent activates the limbic system, the emotional center of the brain. It should be noted that these are essential oils, highly distilled essences of herbs and flowers, quite different from the commercial fragrances marketed to consumers in stores selling products for the skin or bath.

Coping with stress

Stress results from any situation that requires behavioral adjustment such as invasions of privacy, no control over noise, acute or chronic pain, separation from family and things familiar, feelings of helplessness, and loss of control over events and the immediate environment. Add to this worries about medical errors—much in the news lately—and whether one's insurance will reimburse the costs of care, and it's easy to understand the high levels of stress and anxiety that can ensue. Under stress, muscle tension increases; all forms of pain are worsened because hormones produced during stress lower the threshold for pain; blood pressure and respiration increase; and the overproduction of stress hormones can cause cardiac arrhythmias, depression, and insomnia as well as delay wound healing (Kiecolt-Glaser 1998). It's interesting to note that the negative effects of stress can be measured hours after the stressful event occurred. Worse yet, stress impacts the immune system, which is perhaps the most compelling reason to design environments that reduce stress and help patients relax and feel comfortable.

Strategies for Reducing Stress in the Healthcare Environment

For a number of years the goal of healthcare facility design has been to create healing environments. Sometimes well-meaning individuals interpret this as the application of wallcovering, nice colors, carpet, and artwork. While these cosmetic features may create a certain ambience that is pleasing to patients, a healing environment is one that is based on research in the following areas.

Connection to nature

A large body of research is consistent with the proposition that humans are hard-wired to appreciate and benefit from exposure to nature. Based on our evolutionary past and the landscape features that were important for survival, research shows that humans have a deep need to connect to nature and that even a brief view of a garden or interaction with a water element, for example, can have immediate physiological benefits in terms of reducing stress and anxiety (Ulrich 1984; Ulrich 1999; Parsons and Hartig 2000). Patients who were shown a video of nature scenes (forest, flowers, ocean, waterfalls) during burn dressing changes had significantly reduced anxiety and pain intensity (Ulrich 1991; Miller et al. 1992, as reported in Ulrich et al. 2004).

Control (choice)

A considerable number of studies have documented that when individuals have options or choices, it reduces stress and enables them to feel more in control (Winkel and Holahan 1986; Evans and Cohen 1987; Steptoe and Appels 1989). A healing environment will offer as many choices and options to patients as possible in every setting, whether it is an outpatient waiting room or critical care unit. During hospitalization, patients have little control over significant, possibly life-altering events, such as surgery. Stressors that are perceived as unpredictable and uncontrollable are often associated with elevated stress hormones that may persist for several days prior to the procedure (Baum, Cohen, and Hall 1993, as reported in Kiecolt-Glaser et al. 1998). The ability to quickly return to one's neuroendocrine baseline after the event is beneficial for good health.

Viewed in this context, postsurgical recovery should be in a setting that is free of environmental stressors such as noise or a roommate who snores, and one should be able to enjoy nature programming on a wide-screen television and order favorite foods from a room-service menu as one recuperates. Access to guided imagery videos for postsurgical stress reduction, therapeutic touch, and a variety of other highly successful low-cost interventions should be made available.

Social support

It has been well documented that access to friends and family contributes to emotional and psychological well-being. According to Kiecolt-Glaser and colleagues (1998), social support is directly related to dimensions of autonomic, endocrine, and immune function, with family ties appearing to be a key source of support relevant to physiological functioning. Whether it is a social support group for breast cancer survivors or a family member sleeping overnight in a patient's room, sympathy and compassion offered by caring individuals are essential (Cohen and Syme 1985; Sarason and Sarason 1985; Ulrich 1991; Frampton, Gilpin, and Charmel 2003).

For example, myocardial infarction patients with high social support have more favorable recovery rates (Ulrich 1991). Male coronary bypass patients who received greater spousal support used less pain medication, were discharged from the surgical intensive care unit sooner, and spent fewer days in the hospital (Kulik and Mahler 1989, as reported in Kiecolt-Glaser et al. 1998).

Positive distraction

Humans are multisensory beings; research in the neurosciences demonstrates that various types of sensory experiences can actually be therapeutic and can boost the immune system (Pope 1995; Taylor 1997). Specific types of music, engaging moments spent in front of an aquarium or water feature, meditation, guided imagery, and visualization all provide distraction from pain and opportunities for developing coping skills (Ulrich 1991).

Elimination of environmental stressors

A growing body of environmental research indicates that stressors in the built environment can add to the burden of illness. Noise is perhaps the most deleterious of these, and hospital nursing units are notoriously noisy (Ulrich et al. 2004; Joseph 2007). Poor air quality and glare from direct (as opposed to indirect) light sources are other examples. In theory, much of this can be controlled by the owner and the design team working collaboratively (Ulrich 1991; Ulrich et al. 2004).

The acceptance of complementary therapies

There are, in fact, a range of complementary therapies in addition to music and aromatherapy—massage, acupuncture, meditation, art therapy, guided imagery, biofeedback, yoga, herbal medicine, and others—that have gained prominence in recent years and have been the subject of studies funded by the National Institutes of Health (NIH). Many of these are used to reduce stress and to restore harmony or balance.

Grants from the NIH are grouped into five major domains (National Center for Complementary and Alternative Medicine):

1. Alternative medical systems
2. Mind-body interventions
3. Biologically based treatments
4. Manipulation and body-based methods
5. Energy therapies

Collectively, diverse approaches to healthcare that fall outside conventional allopathic (Western) medicine are referred to as CAM, complementary and alternative medicine. Alternative medicine is used instead of conventional treatment, whereas complementary medicine is interwoven with conventional care. An extension of this is integrated medicine, which combines conventional medical treatment with evidence-based CAM, therapies known to be safe and effective.

The American Hospital Association hosts an annual conference on integrative medicine in which the focus is largely the business case—how to anchor these programs within the context of core services to achieve a more holistic approach to well-being. Healthcare organizations throughout the nation have implemented some or all of these low-cost, highly effective modalities.

NEUROSCIENCE PROVIDES INSIGHTS

The 1990s were often referred to as the Decade of the Brain in recognition of great strides made during that period in many areas of research as well as the ability to precisely locate areas of the brain responsible for various activities. This was in part made possible by improved imaging modalities such as PET scanners and functional MRI, which produce striking images showing specific parts of the brain that are activated when a person is asked to think about a certain subject. The brain holds many secrets yet to be revealed; despite the many successes, scientists express frustration about how much is still a mystery. The Neurosciences Institute in La Jolla, California, on its website (www.nsi.edu), refers to the brain as "the single most complex organ in the universe." The interaction between the mind and the brain is still hotly debated. How does the mind emerge from the brain? Is the mind a process that uses the brain as its instrument to experience the world? An excellent collection of readings on the brain can be found in Ornstein and Swencionis (1990).

Neurophysiology—Tapping into the Body's Own Pharmacopoeia

One of the most thought-provoking and insightful presentations on healing and healing environments was given by visionary hospital chief executive officer Patrick Linton (1992), whose originality of thought in 1991 defined and laid the foundation for a care delivery model that would tap into the "tremendously powerful healing potentials within each human being." Linton based his ideas on the research being done in psychoneuroimmunology (PNI), which he explains in the aforementioned presentation. Because this research is fundamental to understanding the science behind the intuitive notions people have about why certain types of environments are healing, a summary of observations follows, some from Linton (1992) and others as noted.

Psychoneuroimmunology

1. The mind and the brain, the nervous and endocrine systems, and the immune system are constantly interacting in a very dynamic way. To paraphrase Pert (1997): these systems are constantly having conversations with each other…what you are thinking at any moment is changing your biochemistry. Neuroscientist Esther Sternberg (2000) identifies the pathways connecting areas of the brain that are responsible for controlling immunity with those that generate feelings and emotions—how nerves, molecules, and hormones connect the brain and immune system.

2. Negative emotions may manifest as a physical disease, whereas positive emotions may positively affect one's health and, although this contention is controversial, in a variety of studies on cancer patients, they have been noted to reduce tumor growth, slow the progression of the disease, increase natural killer and T-cell activity, and increase antibody production (Linton 1992). Several large studies have found that happiness was a better predictor of future coronary problems than any other clinical variable (Rabin 1999; Lemonick 2005).

3. The brain and nervous system produce neurotransmitter cells that fit receptor cells like a lock and key. This connection engages the immune system. The same thing works in reverse. When the brain is engaged, it produces exactly the right "pharmaceuticals" needed, and they get to the correct place in just the precise dosage needed (Linton 1992).

Applying PNI to the effect of the built environment on a patient's experience of stress, neuroscientists have been able to document which areas of the brain are affected by the perception of a healing environment, a setting that feels comfortable or that provides pleasure (Rabin 2004). A pleasant environment keeps norepinephrine levels low so that patients actually experience less pain, have more restful sleep, less anger, less muscle tension, and lower risk of stroke (Rabin 2004). The other major stress hormone, cortisol, can actually damage neurons in the hippocampus and it also affects the rate of wound healing. Elevated levels of both norepinephrine and cortisol impair the immune system (Rabin 1999).

Neuroscience and Architecture

A collaboration between architects and scientists, initiated in 2003 by the American Institute of Architects (AIA), resulted in the Academy of Neuroscience for Architecture (www.anfarch.org). It is headquartered in San Diego because it is a nexus for neuroscience research. Scientists from the Salk Institute, the Neurosciences Institute (founded by Nobel laureate Gerald Edelman, MD, PhD,), and the University of California, San Diego's Division of Biologic Sciences, all located in La Jolla, California, are collaborating. The project's director of research planning, John Eberhard, has an office at the New School of Architecture in San Diego where neuroscience and architecture is a part of the curriculum. Although the focus of this research is not limited to healthcare facilities, this topic is expected to command considerable attention. Understanding how the brain experiences architecture is a complex undertaking.

As an example, the positive effects of natural light and window views are widely acknowledged but, from the research perspective, many questions remain unanswered (National Academy of Sciences 2002):

- What are the elements of visual stimulation that promote healing—light, movement, relief of boredom?
- Do these elements promote healing by blocking bad sensations?
- What neural pathways are activated by positive views?
- What are the hormonal responses to this activation, and how do they impact immune mediated diseases?
- Is memory involved in the beneficial effects of windows?

Heart Brain Medicine

In 2004, the Earl and Doris Bakken Heart Brain Institute was founded at the Cleveland Clinic Foundation. Bakken, the founder of Medtronic Inc., is well known for his affiliation with North Hawaii Community Hospital, a place where the spirituality of Hawaiian culture is integrated with architecture, the practice of medicine, and healing. The Heart Brain Institute will undertake research to explore the interconnections between cardiovascular and neurological medicine to establish a new field of medical knowledge. Instead of focusing on these two major organs as separate entities, it will support an interdisciplinary approach.

THE POWER OF THE BUILT ENVIRONMENT

Writing in the *Lancet* (August 2000), Colin Martin noted the correlation between evidence-based medicine and EBD. He predicted that "evidence-based design (EBD) is poised to emulate evidence-based medicine as a central tenet for healthcare in the 21st century." EBD focuses on the built environment, but, in addition, major forces guiding hospital design include patient safety, information technology interface, the family as a partner in care, and healing environments. They are actually overlapping in their impact.

For example, fewer patient falls are likely to occur when family is present. Breaches in patient safety exist as issues apart from the design of the built environment in the form of medication errors, nosocomial (hospital-acquired) infections, and so forth, but it is also known that a design issue—single bed rooms—and possibly the standardization of layout (avoiding mirror-image rooms) enhance patient safety (Chaudhury, Mahmood, and Valente 2003; Ulrich et al. 2004). In fact, single bed rooms have become the standard of care in the AIA *Guidelines for Design and Construction of Health Care Facilities* (2006). This is discussed in detail in Chapter 7.

Environment of Care

The "Environment of Care" chapter of the 2006 AIA *Guidelines*, which was developed with the input of CHD's Environmental Standards Council, identifies aspects of the overall care environment that influence patient outcomes and satisfaction as well as dignity, privacy, confidentiality, safety, patient and staff stress, and facility operations. Much of this is familiar to experienced healthcare design professionals, but it is most encouraging to see it established as the standard of care in an important document.

A few highlights

There is a major focus on the importance of natural light and views, access to gardens, and clarity of wayfinding. Giving the patient control over lighting and room temperature is emphasized, as are privacy, confidentiality, and reduction of noise. Cultural responsiveness is encouraged both in terms of the organization's internal culture as well as sensitivity to regional demographics. Finishes and color palettes, likewise, should address geographic appropriateness and be suitable for the patient population served. The value of sustainable design is also underscored in this chapter.

Water features are mentioned as they have become very popular, but they are also controversial due to the difficulty of managing infectious aerosols. They are not forbidden, but open water features are required to have this problem safely managed. In an appendix, it says that "open water features are not recommended within any enclosed space in healthcare environments."

Further, the AIA *Guidelines* (2006) state:

> If a water feature is provided, the design should limit human contact with the water and/or allow for the application of water disinfection systems. Materials used to fabricate the water feature should be resistant to chemical corrosion. Water features should be designed and constructed to minimize water droplet production. Exhaust ventilation should be provided directly above the water feature.

Clearly, the new AIA *Guidelines* will result in improved environments for patients. They give design professionals considerable support by elevating environmental amenities to the standard of care. In a value-engineering context, something that might have been easily dismissed as not essential to a project may be reevaluated as worthwhile.

RESEARCH—GETTING STARTED

It is easy to become overwhelmed by the sheer amount of reference material available: journal articles, books, magazine and newspaper articles, conference proceedings, and studies by various organizations such as the Institute for Healthcare Improvement, Institute for Family-Centered Care, or Planetree, to name a few.

Resources

Additional resources include infection-control data from the Centers for Disease Control and Prevention (CDC) or medical specialty professional organizations such as the Society of Critical Care Medicine. Online resources for accessing research journals include Medline and PubMed; Medscape provides a variety of articles on health topics; and a number of e-bulletins or newsletters are available from the Joint Commission (formerly known as the Joint Commission on Accreditation of Healthcare Organizations or JCAHO), The Center for Health Design (CHD) (www.healthdesign.org), and Premier Safety. The Institute of Medicine publishes data on quality and safety issues as does the Joint Commission. Hospitals for a Healthy Environment (www.H2e-online.org) and Healthcare Without Harm (www.noharm.org) are useful websites for pursuing green initiatives, as is the Green Guide for Health Care (www.gghc.org).

The Robert Wood Johnson Foundation (www.RWJF.org) offers a number of publications and resources associated with improving healthcare and has funded, with grants, various learning tools developed by CHD, including this book. *The Health Environments Research and Design Journal*, which published its inaugural issue in the fall of 2007, is the first interdisciplinary, peer-reviewed journal in the field of EBD for healthcare environments. As more issues are published, this will become an increasingly important resource.

The Environmental Design Research Association Journal should not be overlooked; although it is not focused specifically on healthcare, articles on wayfinding research and design for aging can often be found there as can studies related to man-environment issues (territoriality, attachment to place, and response to various types of environments). Other reference sources are association reports, manufacturers' testing information, and continuing education programs.

One caveat is that magazine and newspaper sources cannot be relied upon for accuracy in reporting research results unless it is clear that the writer has gone directly to the source as opposed to reporting information anecdotally from interviews. A good policy is to actually access and read the study or studies being discussed to be able to report the findings accurately. By so doing, one often discovers interesting tidbits.

For example, the findings may not have a high degree of validity for the specific population studied but it may have been highly significant for a subgroup of that population. One can never know this without reading the study. It's also important to know the number of persons in the study. Results from a study involving 15 subjects versus one involving 3,000 or 20,000 persons will have very different levels of significance. One would also want to know if there was a control group.

Dip a Toe in the Water

Start small. Ask clients what issues matter most to them. Hospitals already collect lots of data on quality and safety issues. Use this as a jumping-off point. Some hospitals have researchers on staff who can provide expertise. If not, there are advanced-degree nurses who monitor infection control and patient safety for the organization. They can be helpful in setting the research agenda and should be asked to commit to collecting postoccupancy data for comparison. CHD publishes a research matrix (Figure 1.5) that is used by its Pebble Project research partners to ensure uniformity of measurement and reporting to build a body of research using similar methodology. Start with the CHD report (Ulrich et al. 2004), selecting perhaps five studies to support each component of a design; then develop hypotheses based on this research platform that can later be tested. By doing this on each project, over time, a large number of studies will have become familiar and entered into a design firm's database.

A growing number of healthcare architecture firms are employing a director of research. This person is typically an architect with a doctoral degree in environmental design. The role of the director of research

Pebble Project Matrix							Figure 1.5
	Single Patient	Patient Groups	All Patients	Community	Staff	Organizational Culture	Family
Clinical, Observable Outcomes							
Safety Outcomes							
Economic Outcomes							
Patient-, Family-, Staff-Based Outcomes							
Sustainability							

The effects of the built environment are expected to impact five types of outcomes. The matrix relates outcomes to various stakeholders.
Source: Matrix courtesy of The Center for Health Design

is to prepare a research platform for projects in development, to mentor the design staff, to review design concepts for compliance with the research, to develop hypotheses, and to gather clinical-outcomes safety data from the hospital that are relevant to the new units being designed (data from existing facilities). Six to twelve months after occupancy, the director of research will coordinate or conduct postoccupancy evaluations, supporting or refuting the hypotheses, as well as compare clinical and safety outcomes from the existing units (if data are available) with the new facilities. An excellent article explaining the role of practice-based design researchers and the many ways in which research can inform design can be accessed on the InformeDesign website (http://www.informedesign.umn.edu) (Geboy and Keller 2007).

Lyn Geboy, director of research and education for a large architectural firm, found it difficult to get architects interested in reading research. The daily demands of meeting deadlines in a busy practice left little time for accessing studies. Most architects have not been exposed to research-based training and design in school and may feel ill-at-ease reading and interpreting studies. Geboy created a six-page educational document (similar to an executive summary) of the EBD data and, realizing that architects find visuals appealing, she developed a graphic representation depicting, with small photos, the 12 environmental factors that affect outcomes and contribute to a healing environment (Geboy 2007). The images are arranged in a wheel to express that they are conceptually linked and should not be applied as elective options.

InformeDesign

InformeDesign is an excellent web-based resource representing a collaboration between the University of Minnesota and the American Society of Interior Designers offering access to a wide number of studies on many design topics. Other offerings include a tutorial on research basics, a glossary of terms, and a monthly newsletter, *Implications,* that presents current research issues.

For those who are phobic about delving into research journals, in its database InformeDesign presents easy-to-understand research summaries of journal articles or studies which, by the way, are not limited to healthcare topics. Design criteria and key concepts are enumerated as are limitations of the study, followed by commentary and the full citation for the study. The traditional process of finding and reading the literature, interpreting the statistical analysis, and translating the research findings into design criteria, has been vastly simplified by InformeDesign to facilitate practitioners' use of research as a decision-making tool in the design process.

As one becomes more adventurous about reading research studies, going to the actual source and reviewing the study in its totality will yield a higher level of satisfaction and understanding. As an example, most studies of carpet performance that examine the issue of infection control fail to identify the specifications of the carpet. This is also true for the comparison products that are often identified as *sheet goods* or *sheet vinyl,* as if these generic terms covered all products. To make use of this research, designers need to know if the resilient flooring was sheet vinyl, linoleum, rubber flooring, or a hybrid in terms of composition. The thickness of the product, the finish, and the type of backing will also be of interest.

As for the generic term *carpet,* used in most studies, the fiber type should be described and whether it is solution-dyed, piece-dyed, or skein-dyed; whether it is cut pile, all loop, or loop and cut. And the pile height, stitch gauge, whether it is broadloom or carpet tile, and—very important—the type of backing should be described. Without this type of detail, studies involving flooring products are of little use to healthcare interior designers who are educated to understand the performance characteristics of specific products. A study comparing carpet versus hard-surface flooring sheds no light and also makes it impossible to replicate the study. By contrast, the study by Lankford et al. (2007) describes the finish materials being tested in enough detail to be very useful to interior designers and hospital environmental services managers. A good summary of these findings is offered by Leib and Rohde (2007).

Reading a journal article in its totality (as opposed to just citing the findings) allows one to understand how the study was conducted, the assumptions made by the investigators, and it provides a path to other journal articles on similar topics.

Research Methods "Classics"

Anyone who wishes to learn more about environmental psychology and research tools and techniques will want to read the new edition of *Inquiry by Design* (Zeisel 2005), *A Practical Guide to Behavioral Research* (Sommer and Sommer 2002), and the classic, *Post-Occupancy Evaluation* (Preiser, Rabinowitz, and White 1988). *Assessing Building Performance* is a recent book by Preiser and Vischer (2005).

Evidence-Based Design: The Corollary to Evidence-Based Medicine

Another approach to developing a research agenda for a project is offered by Hamilton and Watkins (2006), based on the classic text on evidence-based medicine by Straus, et al. (2005).

Step 1: Convert need for information into answerable questions.

Step 2: Track down best evidence with which to answer questions.

Step 3: Critically appraise the evidence for validity and applicability.

Step 4: Integrate with clinical expertise and unique biology, values, and circumstances of the patient.

Step 5: Evaluate effectiveness and efficiency; seek ways of improvement.

In Exhibit 1.1 Hamilton and Watkins (2006) in their conference PowerPoint slides outline the process used at WHR Architects for employing EBD, including a breakdown of roles and tasks for facility users and design professionals.

Exhibit 1.1 Sample Evidence-Based Process

Project: Outpatient Chemotherapy Area

Design for Safety (Guiding Principle)

What is the most serious issue that should be resolved in this type of facility? Example: Drug mix errors

Gather the Evidence Based on Research Questions:

> **Research Question = Design Issue:** *What evidence is there relating the environment to medication error, task reliability, safety, etc.?*

Critical Interpretation of the Evidence

> *Literature's relevance to this specific project and design concepts*

Design Based on the Specific Relevant Evidence

> *Reduce distraction, noise reduction, effective task lighting, air quality, fresh-air movement, temperature control, supportive technology (bar-coding reconciliation, integration software)*

Implement the Design, Measure, and Report the Results

> *Hypothesis of design's intended impact proved or disproved by data*

Will There Ever Be Definitive Evidence?

Occasionally there will be definitive evidence; some of the time studies will provide consensus, but this will be undermined by a number of studies with contradictory findings. What to do? Look for models analogous to the current project and contact experts for opinions about best practices. According to Hamilton (2004), "Evidence-based designers must use critical thinking to make rational inferences from a pool of information that will rarely fit precisely with their unique design situation. Nevertheless, an evidence-based healthcare project should result in demonstrated improvements in the healthcare organization's measures of clinical, economic, productivity, patient/staff satisfaction, or cultural success."

Figure 1.6 helps establish the criteria for the value of a potential research project.

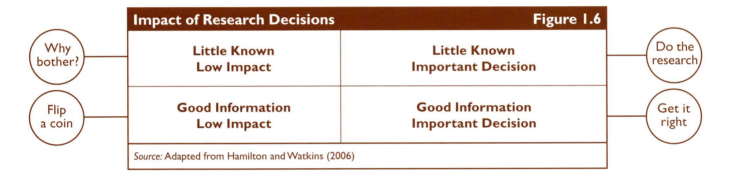

Impact of Research Decisions		Figure 1.6
Little Known **Low Impact**		**Little Known** **Important Decision**
Good Information **Low Impact**		**Good Information** **Important Decision**

Why bother? · Flip a coin · Do the research · Get it right

Source: Adapted from Hamilton and Watkins (2006)

Beware of false claims

Over the years, projects have sometimes been labeled a healing environment based on an art program (possibly not even one based on research) or a number of cosmetic changes in interior finishes. Healing environments sounds so nice, who wouldn't want to make a claim like this? However, several questions should be asked. Why would a specific design be expected to improve outcomes? Is the project anchored in research about reduction of stress for patients? Has anyone developed a hypothesis and attempted to measure outcomes before and after the interventions? Similar claims may, in the near future, be made about a project having been evidence-based. Articles are already starting to appear in magazines making this claim, and sometimes it is based on one or two research-based elements, but the project overall may miss the boat on many important issues. The evidence-based designation should be applied only when research has impacted the design with sufficient scope and hypotheses are tested in the process.

Despite this, there will be numerous aspects of design for which research does not exist and for which that project or hospital will be a pilot site to test ideas. Some projects may replicate studies to support or refute previous findings. According to Hamilton (2004), the minimum threshold for describing a project as evidence-based is the presence of hypotheses advanced and relevant measures to confirm or refute them.

It's the process of research that counts, not necessarily the results. Science is based on many trials, and many do not support the hypotheses. In fact, scientists often design studies to disprove a theory, as opposed to proving it. They try to find the flaw. But each successive evidence-based hospital project helps to build the body of knowledge that can be used by others. It's a laborious process that yields fruit after many years.

CONCLUDING REMARKS

The pursuit of EBD may lead to disappointment when hoped-for outcomes are not realized. This is the nature of scientific inquiry—design professionals should not internalize this as a failure; rather, they should congratulate themselves for having the courage to share the findings with colleagues. A hypothesis that is not supported is also valuable in adding to the body of knowledge. The expectation now is for hospitals to be transparent; should we expect any less of design professionals? Available research on a specific topic may reveal contradictory findings; this is not an easy process but the stakes are high. This is truly the dawn of a new era in healthcare architecture and design. Anyone who has been hospitalized or spent time with a very ill family member knows all too well the risks and anguish and what it means to be helpless and vulnerable. There are few callings higher than healthcare, whether one is a nurse, a physician, or a design professional working with providers to improve safety and performance.

References

American Institute of Architects. 2006. *Guidelines for design and construction of health care facilities.* Washington, DC: American Institute of Architects.

Center for Health Design. 2005. *Scorecards for evidence-based design.* Concord, CA: Center for Health Design.

Chaudhury, H., A. Mahmood, and M. Valente. 2003. Pilot study on comparative assessment of patient care issues in single and multiple occupancy rooms, unpublished report, Coalition for Health Environments Research/Center for Health Design.

Cohen, S., and S. L. Syme., eds. 1985. *Social support and health.* New York: Academic Press.

Evans, G. W., and S. Cohen. 1987. Environmental stress. In *Handbook of environmental psychology*, 2 vols., eds. D. Stokols and I. Altman, 571–610. New York: John Wiley & Sons Inc.

Frampton, S. B., L. Gilpin, and P. A. Charmel. 2003. *Putting patients first: Designing and practicing patient-centered care.* New York: Jossey-Bass.

Frankenhaeuser, M. 1980. Psychoneuroendocrine approaches to the study of stressful person-environment transactions. In *Selye's guide to stress research*, Vol. 1, ed. H. Selye, 46–70. New York: Van Nostrand Reinhold (now John Wiley & Sons Inc.).

Geboy, L. 2007. The evidence-based design wheel. *Healthcare Design* 7(2):41–42.

Geboy, L., and A. B. Keller. 2007. Research in practice: The design researcher's perspective. *Implications Newsletter* 4(11).

Hamilton, K. 2003. The four levels of evidence-based design practice. *Healthcare Design* 3(9):18–26.

Hamilton, K. 2004. Hypothesis and measurement: Essential steps defining evidence-based design. *Healthcare Design* 4(1):43–46.

Hamilton, K., and D. Watkins. 2006. The evolving art and science of evidence-based design. Lecture presented at HealthcareDesign '06, Chicago, IL.

Joseph, A. 2007. Sound control for improved outcomes in healthcare settings. Issue paper, Center for Health Design.

Kennedy, S., R. Glaser, and J. Kiecolt-Glaser. 1990. Psychoneuroimmunology. In *Principles of psychophysiology: Physical, social, and inferential elements*, eds. J. T. Cacioppo and L. G. Tassinary, 177–190. New York: Cambridge University Press.

Kiecolt-Glaser, J. K., G. G. Page, P. T. Marucha, R. C. MacCallum, and R. Glaser. 1998. Psychological influences on surgical recovery: Perspectives from psychoneuroimmunology. *American Psychologist* 53(11):1209–1218.

Lankford, M. G., S. Collins, L. Youngberg, D. M. Roone, R. Warren, and G. Noskin. 2007. Limiting the spread of infection in healthcare environments. Research report, Coalition for Health Environments Research/Center for Health Design.

Lazarus, R. 1999. *Stress and emotion: A new synthesis*, New York: Springer Publishing Co.

Leib, R., and J. Rohde. 2007. Are those room finishes and cleaners safe? *Healthcare Design* 7(3):12–17.

Lemonick, M. 2005. The biology of joy. *Time,* January 17.

Linton, P. E. 1992. Creating a total healing environment. Lecture presented at the Fifth Symposium on Healthcare Design, San Diego, CA.

Martin, C. 2000. Putting patients first: Integrating hospital design and care. *The Lancet* 356(9228):518.

National Academy of Sciences. 2002. Neuroscience and health care facilities workshop: Summary. Woods Hole, MA.

National Center for Complementary and Alternative Medicine. National Institutes of Health. http://www.nccam.nih.gov/health/whatiscan (accessed October 28, 2007).

Ornstein, R., and C. Swencionis, eds. 1990. *Healing brain: A scientific reader*. New York: The Guilford Press.

Parsons, R., and T. Hartig. 2000. Environmental psychophysiology. In *Handbook of psychophysiology*, 2nd ed., eds. J. T. Cacioppo and L. G. Tassinary, 815–846. New York: Cambridge University Press.

Pert, C. 1990. The wisdom of the receptors: Neuropeptides, the emotions, and body-mind. In *Healing brain: A scientific reader*, eds. R. Ornstein and C. Swencionis,147–158. New York: The Guilford Press.

Pert, C. 1997. *Molecules of emotion*. New York: Scribner.

Pope, D. S. 1995. Music, noise, and the human voice in the nurse-patient environment. *IMAGE: Journal of Nursing Scholarship* 27(4):291–296.

Preiser, W., H. Rabinowitz, and E. White. 1988. *Post-occupancy evaluation*. New York: John Wiley & Sons Inc.

Preiser, W., and J. Vischer, eds. 2005. *Assessing building performance*. Oxford: Butterworth Heinemann.

Rabin, B. 1999. *Stress, immune function, and health*. New York: Wiley-Liss.

Rabin, B. 2004. From psychoneuroimmunology to psychoneuroarchitecture. Keynote speech presented at HealthcareDesign '04 Conference, Houston, TX.

Sarason, I. G., and B. R. Sarason, eds. 1985. *Social support: Theory, research, and applications.* The Hague: Nijhoff.

Selye, H. 1956. *The stress of life*. New York: McGraw Hill.

Solomon, G. 1990. Emotions, stress, and immunity. In *Healing brain: A scientific reader*, eds., R. Ornstein and C. Swencionis, 174–181. New York: The Guilford Press.

Sommer, R., and B. Sommer. 2002. *A practical guide to behavioral research: Tools and techniques.* New York: Oxford University Press.

Standley, J. 1986. Music research in medical/dental treatment: Meta-analysis and clinical applications. *Journal of Music Therapy* 23(2): 58–122.

Steptoe, A., and A. Appels, eds.1989. *Stress, personal control, and health.* Chichester, England: John Wiley & Sons Inc.

Sternberg. E. 2000. *The Balance within: The science connecting health and emotions.* New York: W. H. Freeman & Co.

Straus, S. E., Richardson, W. S., Glasziou, P., and Haynes, R. B. 2005. *Evidence-based medicine: How to practice and teach EBM, 3rd ed.* Edinburgh, UK: Elsevier Churchill Livingstone.

Taylor, D. B. 1997. *Biomedical foundations of music as therapy.* St. Louis, MO: MMB Music Inc.

Ulrich, R. 1984. View through a window may influence recovery from surgery. *Science* 224: 420–421.

Ulrich, R. 1991. Effects of interior design on wellness: Theory and recent scientific research. *Journal of Health Care Interior Design* 3(1):97–109.

Ulrich, R. 1999. Effects of gardens on health outcomes: Theory and research. In *Healing gardens*, eds. C. Cooper Marcus and M. Barnes, 27–86. New York: John Wiley & Sons Inc.

Ulrich, R. S., C. Zimring, A. Joseph, X. Quan, and R. Choudhary. 2004. *The role of the physical environment in the hospital of the 21st century: A once-in-a-lifetime opportunity.* Center for Health Design: Concord, CA.

Winkel, G. H., and C. J. Holahan. 1986. The environmental psychology of the hospital: Is the cure worse than the illness? *Prevention in Human Services* 4:11–33.

Zeisel, J. 2005. *Inquiry by design: Environment/behavior/neuroscience in architecture, interiors, landscape, and planning.* New York: W.W. Norton.

Level 2 Trauma Room | Riverside Methodist Hospital
Columbus, OH. Karlsberger. Photography: Brad Feinknopf

Research Methods | 2

This chapter is an overview of research methods for design professionals to prepare them for discussions with investigators who may be engaged to conduct research on their projects. Understanding how to carry out research can be daunting for design professionals, but it need not be. This undertaking is no different from working with engineers and other specialized consultants. A researcher—perhaps someone affiliated with a university—should be engaged, whose role will be principal investigator. This is the person who will help to develop hypotheses with input from architects and the healthcare organization, because he or she will know what to study and measure. The researcher will see what data are already available and will design the study accordingly. Baseline data (if relevant) will be provided by the healthcare organization for comparison after the design intervention and, eventually, statisticians will analyze them. Depending on what is being studied, data may be gathered at intervals, such as 6 and 12 months after occupancy, to ensure that the findings are not the result of newness.

TYPES OF RESEARCH METHODS

Following is a brief outline of research methods (Zeisel 1991).

- **Observing Physical Traces:** Systematically looking at physical settings to note signs of previous activity that was not produced just to be measured by researchers. This provides insight into how people actually use an environment over a period of time and how it meets the needs of its users. It's also a clue about the culture of those who use the place and how they choose to present themselves.

- **Observing Environmental Behavior:** Systematically watching how people use their environments. This includes individual and group behavior. It offers an opportunity to see how activities relate to a space—whether the physical environment supports or interferes with ongoing activity.

- **Focused Interviews:** Developing questions to learn what people think, feel, do, believe, and expect. This provides insight into how people define a situation, what they consider important about it, and what effects they intended their actions to have.

- **Standardized Questionnaires:** Used to discover similarities among groups of people by comparing answers to the same set of questions asked of a large number of people. Questionnaires may be delivered by mail or be used to conduct interviews by telephone or in person. This research method is useful with well-defined problems, for example, looking at the degree of satisfaction among a group of people.

STUDY DESIGN

Study design may take several forms (Stichler 2006).

- **Qualitative Research:** Uses deductive reasoning (from general to specific), may involve looking at the past and finding current relevance or studying ethnographically a person's "lived" experience. Qualitative research provides insight into phenomena where a data deficit exists, and it provides a perspective otherwise untapped. An example might be examining the lived experience of nurses working in a specific type of patient unit design.

- **Quantitative Research:** A hypothesis is proposed and variables are defined. The *independent* variable (IV) is what is being manipulated. The *dependent* variable (DV) is the expected outcome. For example, if the hypothesis is that illumination levels affect the number of dispensing errors in a pharmacy, the IV is the level of illumination and the DV is the rate of prescription errors. These studies may be cross-sectional (measuring a specific variable at one point in time) or retrospective (looking at the past), prospective (looking at the future), or longitudinal (over a period of time). Subjects can be recruited to participate in a study and randomly chosen from a pool of appropriate persons or randomly assigned to specified groups. It is not always possible to have a randomized sample. In nonrandomized studies, subjects may be chosen purposely because of convenience (purposive convenience sample) or chosen because they exhibit specific criteria important to the study.

- **Correlational Studies:** Describes relationships between and among variables. This can be cross-sectional (one point in time), prospective (future), or retrospective (past).

- **Nonexperimental Research:** Relies on descriptive data through surveys and observation.

- **Quasiexperimental Research:** Does not have a control group or an experimental group. Instead, there is a comparative group and an interventional group, and the samples may not be randomized. Comparative studies measure differences in groups or observed data before an intervention and one or more times after the intervention.

- **Experimental Research:** A hypothesis is developed and subjects are randomly assigned to experimental or control groups, making this the strongest type of study. This is what is referred to as a *randomized controlled study.* Randomized studies have great generalizability. Depending upon what is being studied (e.g., a clinical trial examining the efficacy of a drug versus a placebo), the study may be double-blinded, meaning that neither the subjects nor the investigators know who received the active drug versus the placebo. In a 10-month study looking at 400 patients who had been hospitalized in a coronary care unit, and whether remote prayer (by strangers) reduced mortality, the study was double-blinded so that those doing the statistical analysis would not be influenced and neither the patients nor the caregivers knew who was in the experimental or control group. The group that had been prayed for had significantly fewer episodes of congestive heart failure, fewer cardiac arrests, less pneumonia, and required fewer diuretics and antibiotics (Benson 1996).

- **Meta-analysis** (Stichler 2006): Meta-analysis combines quantitative results from multiple studies. The findings are treated as one data set; subjects are not the unit of analysis—the studies are. The strength of the relationship among variables is averaged. This type of study provides a great deal of information on a research topic.

How to Critique Research (Stichler 2006)

1. Is the literature review adequate and appropriate?
2. Are the variables clearly identified and defined conceptually and operationally?
3. Are the intervention or instruments of measurement valid and reliable?
4. Is the hypothesis (or hypotheses) stated clearly and tested with the appropriate statistic for the study design?
5. Is the methodology clear enough to replicate the study? Is the sample defined clearly with inclusion/exclusion criteria?
6. Have the subjects' rights been protected with proper precautions and approvals?
7. Are the results and limitations clearly defined?
8. Have recommendations for further study been suggested?

The Center for Health Design (CHD) is an excellent resource for evidence-based design (EBD) research, most of which can be downloaded free. Anyone starting to build a reference library will want to include the references listed in Exhibit 2.1.

Exhibit 2.1 Research from The Center for Health Design

- "The Role of the Physical Environment in the Hospital of the 21st Century: A Once-in-a-Lifetime Opportunity," by Roger Ulrich, Craig Zimring, Anjali Joseph, Xiabo Quan, and Ruchi Choudhary (Ulrich et al. 2004), and its Abstracts Table Supplement (available at the CHD website at www.healthdesign.org)

- "The Impact of the Environment on Infections in Healthcare Facilities" by Anjali Joseph (Joseph 2006a)

- "The Role of the Physical and Social Environment in Promoting Health, Safety, and Effectiveness in the Healthcare Workplace," by Anjali Joseph (available at the CHD website at http://www.rwjf.org/files/publications/other/CHDIssuePaper3.pdf)

- "The Impact of Light on Outcomes in Healthcare Settings," by Anjali Joseph (Joseph 2006b)(available at the CHD website at http://www.healthdesign.org/research/reports/light.php)

- Designing the 21st Century Hospital: Environmental Leadership for Healthier Patients and Families Conference held on September 28-29, 2006, in Hasbrouck Heights, N.J. (content available at the Robert Wood Johnson Foundation website at http://www.rwjf.org/programareas/resources/product.jsp?id=21096&pid=1140&gsa=1)

- *Improving Healthcare with Better Building Design*, edited by Sara Marberry (Marberry 2006)

- "Limiting the Spread of Infection in Health Care Environments" by Mary Lankford, Susan Collins, Larry Youngberg, Denise Rooney, John Warren, and Gary Noskin (Lankford et al. 2007)

- *Color in Healthcare Environments*, by Ruth Brent Tofle, Benyamin Schwarz, So-Yeon Yoon, and Andrea Max-Royale (Tofle et al. 2004)

- "Pilot Study on Comparative Assessment of Patient Care Issues in Single and Multiple Occupancy Rooms," by Habib Chaudhury, Atiya Mahmood, and Maria Valente (Chaudhury, Mahmood, and Valente 2003)

THE PEBBLE PROJECT RESEARCH INITIATIVE

In 2000, CHD started a research initiative with a core group of four progressive healthcare organizations that has since expanded to more than 40. Referred to as the Pebble Project, it is anticipated that the specific projects undertaken by these institutions will impact and influence the healthcare industry much the way a pebble thrown into a pond creates a ripple across the entire body of water. In the healthcare arena, it is often a small demonstration project that leads to major change, such as the original Planetree project, a 13-bed medical-surgical unit that, in the early 1980s, led to the enormous patient-centered care revolution.

Although there are many reasons for healthcare organizations to join the Pebble Project research initiative, a common denominator is the conviction that the built environment affects the quality of care. These organizations are passionate about leading the way for the next generation of healthcare facilities.

Pebble Project Research Commitment (The Center for Health Design 2005)

- To document and critically analyze existing conditions and processes
- To use the existing evidence base to inform the design process and to conduct research and benchmarking studies to support innovative design decisions
- To clearly articulate the expected effects of EBD decisions or outcomes
- To measure the effects of innovations or changes made to existing environments or measure outcomes in the new environment post-changes

Pebble Project partners may be engaged in a new construction project or renovation; they may be in the visioning stage or at any point in the design process. Occasionally a project has just been completed. Resources for undertaking research may be ample or modest, yet each can make a contribution.

Types of Pebble Project Research Studies

Research studies fall into two broad categories: knowledge management and original data collection.

Knowledge management

Knowledge management involves existing data, critically analyzing it, and using that knowledge to inform the design, development, or operational performance of a healthcare organization. Types of projects within this category include:

- Evidence gathering: Gather all existing information about a topic and summarize it in a briefing paper. This is most useful at the beginning of a project.

- Benchmarking: Compare the characteristics or features of a design in an existing facility with what you plan to build in your new one. For example: how large is your patient room versus 10 recent best-practice examples? Or what is your nursing turnover rate versus others? Benchmarking is most appropriate in the initial stages of a project.

- Documentation and analysis of process and assumptions: Documenting existing conditions and processes is an essential part of EBD. Hospitals collect data routinely on a variety of quality and performance indicators either for internal purposes or to satisfy regulatory requirements. This can provide baseline data for comparison against changes or modifications. Some Pebble Partners are actually documenting their design process so that other healthcare organizations embarking on innovation will have a path to follow. It's important to document and understand how an evidence-based process differs from a traditional design process. This type of research starts with programming and continues through all phases of the project.

Original data collection

When the goal is to answer specific research questions and obtain knowledge, a variety of studies can be carried out. The research question should link specific environmental design factors with specific outcomes that may be related to clinical outcomes, financial outcomes, patient or staff satisfaction, or operational performance. Types of studies include:

- **Randomized controlled experiments:** This involves the manipulation of one factor (the independent variable) to test the effect on dependent variables. Usually there are two study groups—one that is exposed to the independent variable (the experimental group) and the control group that is not exposed to it.

- **Natural experiments:** Occasionally real-life situations may make it possible to study a specific existing condition. As an example, two identical intensive care units may differ only in that the nursing staff in one unit keeps corridors brightly illuminated and, in the other unit, corridors and nurses' station lighting are kept relatively dim. The research hypothesis may be whether staff speaks more softly in the unit with reduced light levels. Such experiments can be conducted in existing facilities, during new construction mock-up stage, or after occupancy of new facilities.

- **Before-after studies:** Data before and after are compared after an intervention has been implemented. If a single variable is considered, these studies can be carried out rather quickly. Large before-and-after studies that look at the effects of more comprehensive changes can be difficult to attribute the cause to any one factor because too many variables have changed at once (this is referred to as *confounding variables*). These studies can be executed at any stage in a design process.

- **Prospective studies:** New nonreplacement hospitals cannot record baseline data in the old facility. In a prospective study, characteristics of subjects are assessed and then analyzed later after they have been exposed to a change or new condition. For example, a hospital that has staff break rooms with different views (one of nature and one of a rooftop), could measure stress levels upon entering the break room and upon leaving it to see if the view of nature was more restorative.

- **Retrospective:** In retrospective studies, past behaviors or events are examined for relationships or patterns. These studies may be based on a review of medical charts for patients with a similar type of surgery or medical condition, perhaps examining the impact of different types of views on the use of pain medications or length of stay. The well-known study by Ulrich in 1984 on postsurgical cholecystectomy (gallbladder) patients was retrospective. This type of study can be carried out in an existing facility to compare sets of existing conditions or in a new facility.

- **Simulation studies:** During the design or construction phases of a project, mock-ups or simulated settings are often constructed to test spatial relationships, access to essential equipment, or to compare one model against another prior to building multiples of the room. This is a prudent strategy as it enables clinical staff, who often can't evaluate a concept in a drawing, to test drive the new idea or design.

- **Just-in-time studies:** As hospital projects are developed, staffs are often asked to make decisions that run the gamut from selection of furniture or finish materials to the evaluation of different nurse-station features. These studies are conducted during the design and construction phases of a project.

- **Ethnographic studies:** These studies help to identify how things work in a specific setting and what changes can be made to remedy conflicts. For example, an observer may study how nurses work and whether the current workstation facilitates or hinders their efficiency; or one could study specific times of day or specific tasks carried out by nurses such as preparation of medications or shift change, or one could study how the noise level changes with time of day. The observations would be systematically collected and analyzed to see where problems occur (environment, culture, process, or technology) to find solutions that enhance performance. Ethnographic studies are best conducted prior to visioning and conceptual design phases to inform the new design.

Evaluation of Pebble Project Research

The research conducted by the Pebble Project partners has been accruing since 2001. It is varied in the range of research questions studied as well as in the rigor of research methodologies employed. This is owing to the fact that some organizations have in-house researchers while others undertake these investigations with staff who have considerable clinical expertise in their fields but are not trained to conduct environmental research. CHD provides Pebble Project organizations consultation with researchers trained to carry out environmental research in healthcare settings. It provides guidance in identifying research hypotheses and in setting up a study. It continues to monitor the process as it moves through various phases. Pebble Project partners meet several times a year as a group to attend lectures and mentor each other on the research process or problems encountered. In addition, a CHD listserv just for Pebble Project partners' communication enables a member to throw out a question and get expert advice from a community of innovative thinkers.

An in-depth review of the Pebble Project (Joseph and Hamilton 2007) provides a look backward to the inception of this research collaborative as well as a matrix summary of research completed to date, and an analysis of key strengths and challenges, ending with a forecast of future directions. Pebble Project Partners have taken up the challenge to pursue research topics identified by Ulrich and colleagues (2004) as needing more study. Instead of focusing on areas for which many studies exist, Pebble Partners are trying to fill in the gaps. This continuous feedback loop between research sponsored by CHD and the CHD Pebble Partners has been a successful interface.

FABLE HOSPITAL

As CHD started to work with the four initial Pebble Project Partners, it became clear that a hypothetical model should be developed to guide the Pebble Project research initiative. Labeled *Fable Hospital,* it represents a 300-bed hospital that incorporates facets of EBD (Sadler et al. 2006). Located on an urban site, the hospital provides a comprehensive range of inpatient and outpatient services. The total cost of the project was estimated to be $240 million ($800,000 per bed). The design innovations and upgrades over conventional hospital design collectively added $12 million to the construction budget. The return on investment was just one year, based on conservative estimates of performance data provided by organizations participating in the CHD's Pebble Project research initiative. A detailed financial analysis is provided by Berry and colleagues (2004) and also by Sadler and colleagues (2006). A few highlights follow.

Design Innovations and Upgrades

- Oversized single patient rooms with dedicated space for family and large windows to provide enhanced access to daylight
- Acuity-adaptable room with standardized layout (same handed)
- Double-door bathroom access
- Decentralized nursing stations
- HEPA filters throughout HVAC system
- Noise-reduction measures
- Meditation rooms and patient education centers on each floor
- Positive diversions: artwork, gardens, fountains
- Flexible spaces for advanced technologies (e.g., robotic surgery)

Return on Investment

The return on investment was realized by looking at costs associated with the reduction of nosocomial infections, reductions in nurse turnover, fewer patient falls, decreased use of narcotic pain medications, increases in market share and philanthropy, and a decrease in patient transfers (when acuity changes). It's clear that a tipping point has occurred—a groundswell of understanding and acknowledgement—that EBD must be the foundation of the hospital of the 21st century.

CONCLUDING REMARKS

Doing research-based project design need not be a painful process. Like anything new, it may at first be uncomfortable and unfamiliar. In time, it will become rewarding, and design professionals will find themselves digging ever deeper into research on specific topics. An analogy is the Leadership in Energy and Environmental Design (LEED) accreditation process. Over the past few years, many firms have met the challenge to educate their design staffs to design green buildings, and they have learned to manage the process either within their own firms or by working with LEED-accredited consulting firms. Evidence-based design will have much the same path with the training of practitioners through Evidence-based Design Assessment and Certification and collaboration with researchers, whether independent or associated with a university.

References

Benson, H. 1996. *Timeless healing: The power and biology of belief.* New York: Scribner.

Berry, L. L., D. Parker, R. Coile, D. K. Hamilton, D. O'Neill, and B. Sadler. 2004. Can better buildings improve care and increase your financial returns? *Frontiers of Health Services Management* 21(1):3–24.

Center for Health Design. 2005. Pebble Project research commitment (http://www.healthdesign.org/research/pebble).

Chaudhury, H., A. Mahmood, and M. Valente. 2003. Pilot study on comparative assessment of patient care issues in single and multiple occupancy rooms. Unpublished report, Coalition for Health Environments Research/Center for Health Design.

Joseph, A. 2006a. The impact of the environment on infections in healthcare facilities. Issue paper, Center for Health Design.

Joseph, A. 2006b. The impact of light on outcomes in healthcare settings. Issue paper, Center for Health Design.

Joseph, A., and D. K. Hamilton. 2007. The Pebble Projects: Coordinated evidence-based case studies. British Research Institute (in press).

Lankford, M. G., S. Collins, L. Youngberg, D. M. Rooney, J. R. Warren, and G. Noskin. 2007. Limiting the spread of infection in healthcare environments. Research report, Coalition for Health Environments Research/Center for Health Design.

Marberry, S., ed. 2006. *Improving healthcare with better building design.* Chicago: Health Administration Press.

Sadler, B., D. K. Hamilton, D. Parker, and L. Berry. 2006. The compelling business case for better buildings. In *Improving healthcare with better building design, ed.* S. Marberry, Chicago: Health Administration Press.

Stichler, J. F. 2006. Research methods for evidence-based design. Lecture presented at HealthcareDesign '06, Chicago.

Tofle, R. B., B. Schwarz, S. Y. Yoon, and A. Max-Royale. 2004. *Color in healthcare environments.* Concord, CA: Coalition for Health Environments Research/Center for Health Design.

Ulrich, R. 1984. View through a window may influence recovery from surgery. *Science* 224: 420–421.

Ulrich, R. S., C. Zimring, A. Joseph, X. Quan, and R. Choudhary. 2004. *The role of the physical environment in the hospital of the 21st century: A once-in-a-lifetime opportunity.* Center for Health Design: Concord, CA.

Zeisel, J. 1991. *Inquiry by design: Tools for environment-behavior research.* Cambridge: Cambridge University Press.

Patient Bathroom | Oregon Health & Science University
Portland, OR. Peterson Kolberg & Associates Architects; Czopek & Erdenberger, Interior Design. Photography: Ed Hershberger

Patient Safety and Infection Control

3

Malcolm Gladwell (2000) defines the tipping point as **"that magic moment when an idea, trend, or social behavior crosses a threshold, tips, and spreads like wildfire."** It appears that this is happening with regard to concern about patient safety. Any number of articles in the press over the past five years with titles such as "Report: Medicinal Mix-ups Rampant" (*San Diego Union-Tribune* 2006) have consumers terrified to enter a hospital, and rightly so. When the Institute of Medicine (1999) released its report, *To Err Is Human: Building a Safer Health System*, hospitals were in denial. Near misses were rarely reported, and there existed a sacred covenant of secrecy in many institutions. The IOM report revealed that more people die each year from preventable medical errors than from motor vehicle accidents, breast cancer, or AIDS. The seventh leading cause of preventable death is admission to a hospital. An IOM study on drug errors asserted that, on average, a patient in a U.S. hospital can expect one drug error per day (Flower 2006).

The Rand Corporation conducted an extensive literature review, between 1993-1998, that covered eight years and more than 70 publications. The conclusion was, "there is abundant evidence that serious and extensive problems exist throughout American medicine resulting in harm to many Americans." An update to this study (Schuster et al. 1999 as reported in Institute of Medicine 2001) can be summarized by this excerpt:

Gaps between Ideal Care and Actual Care

The dominant finding of our review is that there are large gaps between the care people should receive and the care they do receive. This is true for preventive, acute, and chronic care, whether one goes for a checkup, a sore throat, or diabetic care. It is true whether one looks at overuse, underuse, or misuse. It is true in different types of healthcare facilities and for different types of health insurance. It is true for all age groups, from children to the elderly. And it is true whether one is looking at the whole country or a single city.

HOSPITALS ARE SCARY PLACES

"Any healthcare professional who spends much time around a hospital knows that you don't want to stay any longer than necessary," observes Daniel Beckham (1993). He quotes Clifton Meador, MD, who, during his tenure as Director of Medical Affairs at St. Thomas Hospital in Nashville, wrote a book of advice for his colleagues in which he warned: "A hospital is a dangerous place, use it wisely and as briefly as possible." Interestingly, this was said many years before the eye-opening publication of the IOM reports *To Err Is Human* and *Crossing the Quality Chasm*. Beckham continues: "It may not be as dangerous as Russian roulette, but it feels that way sometimes. Everyday you spin the cylinder. Click. Heavy sigh. Congratulations, you made it through another day without a complication."

Everyone Has a Story

When I told an acquaintance about the book I was writing, she immediately told me about a medical mishap experienced by her favorite aunt, a very spry 80-year-old living alone on the East Coast. Everyone has a story like this. She needed a "routine" hip replacement. The surgery went well and she was discharged after three days to a rehab facility where she spent 10 days. Either in the hospital or the rehab facility she contracted a potentially life-threatening infection, *Clostridium difficile* colitis, a pathogen that "explodes" in the gut and results in severe diarrhea and sometimes sepsis and even death. My friend's aunt was sent home with antibiotics for four days and then rushed to the hospital where she remained for 21 days, critically ill from the infection. At a low point she refused food and stopped interacting with family members. She was then discharged to a second rehab facility for another eight days after which she had a long and difficult recovery at home. And this happened to a person who, by her niece's account, was feisty, active, and had a passion for life. Imagine how many persons with less zest for living would have given up and died. Somewhat later, the aunt's life-long best friend was admitted to a hospital after a bad fall and she contracted MRSA (Methicillin-resistant Staphylococcus aureus). Patients who survive this often spend months in the hospital and endure several surgeries to cut out infected tissue.

FOCUS ON PATIENT SAFETY

One organization in particular has moved mountains to get hospitals around the nation motivated to report errors, share information, and use evidence-based clinical protocols to reduce variability among practitioners.

The Institute for Healthcare Improvement (IHI) kicked off the "100,000 Lives Campaign" in 2005 in which more than 3,000 hospitals signed a pledge to implement six evidence-based patient safety initiatives. This resulted in saving 123,000 lives in an 18-month period. More lives could have been saved, but only 39% of hospitals implemented all six interventions. Other IHI initiatives are discussed in Chapter 7.

The Movement Gains Momentum

Virtually every healthcare newsletter and publication has numerous articles on aspects of patient safety and reduction of errors. The National Quality Forum's *Safe Practices for Better Healthcare* report (2003) has proposed a common set of standards and measures for quality developed by a panel of experts who created a synthesis of the research. Clinical, operational, and financial performance are interconnected and interdependent.

The Leapfrog Group, a coalition of Fortune 500 companies and other large private and public healthcare purchasers, has been working to drive improvements in patient safety. They have embraced the National Quality Forum's list of 27 Never Events, incidents that should never happen in a hospital.

In the context of pay for performance, Never Events could mean never a payment. Hospitals reporting to the 2007 Leapfrog survey and that choose to complete the section on Never Events must agree to apologize to the patient and/or family affected, waive all costs related to the event and refrain from seeking reimbursement from the patient or a third-party payer for costs related to it, report the event to at least one of three regulatory agencies within 10 days of becoming aware of the occurrence, and they must perform a root cause analysis to determine the causal factors of the event and improve processes based on this analysis (Aetna 2007).

It is evidence of a tipping point having been reached when insurers jump on the bandwagon. WellPoint, the nation's largest health insurer (Appleby 2007), as of 2007, provides an incentive bonus to its 42,000 employees to meet specific screening and treatment goals for its 34 million policyholders to make sure they get the right care. Employees are coached to contribute to the health status of members (Appleby 2007). Making use of its databank of patient medical claims, laboratory test results, and prescription information, the insurer will verify if members are being screened for various types of cancer, are compliant with their diabetes medications, or are getting their children vaccinated. This is a clear and welcome cultural shift for a payer.

Another hopeful initiative is computer-automated tracking of infections before they spread widely through a nursing unit or hospital (Carpenter 2006). A Web-based system, Setnet, sends e-mail messages to the users when a potential outbreak is detected. Another system, MedMined, locates sources of infections through a sophisticated system that tracks, cross-references, and analyzes signs of infections. The service then alerts infection-control staff, which lessened the rates of infection in many hospitals by more than 20%. Financially, patients with nosocomial infections require 8.7 days of treatment at an average cost of $14,000, much of which is unreimbursed, especially for Medicare and Medicaid patients and the uninsured (Carpenter 2006).

On the Verge of Major Upheaval

For at least 15 years there has been talk about reforming healthcare. Nothing is more complex, has more moving parts, and could be more of a challenge. Will it at last happen? Will universal coverage happen? It may take 10 years to see information technology really integrated with care delivery and to see systems in place that will significantly reduce medical error. Many smart people are working hard to make this happen. But, as healthcare futurist and humorist Ian Morrison ponders, will it be yet another example of Pimp My Ride? This show on MTV shows cars that have been enhanced with all manner of cosmetic accoutrements but, like our healthcare system, they never do anything to the chassis or engine – it has a great sound system and seats, but you can't drive it anywhere.

Report Card: Five Years after *To Err Is Human*

An extraordinarily well-written assessment of the status of patient safety in the nation's hospitals by Leape and Berwick (2005) five years after the IOM released its riveting report is well worth reading. As would be expected from two of the most respected health policy leaders in the nation, the article is laced with interesting statistics, gives credit to the federal agencies and regulatory bodies such as the Joint Commission that have worked hard to implement high-impact evidence-based safe practices, and chronicles successes and failures. Most interesting is the discussion on barriers to progress and why physicians, by culture and training, find it so hard to support patient safety initiatives. As always, Leape and Berwick end on a positive note with an achievable plan of action.

Hospital-Acquired (Nosocomial) Infections

These clinical issues are the least well known to design professionals but are so important that they have become the new imperative in healthcare design. To not understand the sources of healthcare-acquired infections (HAIs) and how they are spread exposes a designer or architect to liability and may expose patients to avoidable risks. This is the reason a detailed discussion of these issues is provided.

Infections that have been nearly eradicated in some countries are rampant in hospitals throughout the United States due to poor hygiene; 1 of every 20 patients contracts a nosocomial (hospital-acquired) infection (McCaughey 2005). Hospitals in Denmark, Finland, and the Netherlands dramatically reduced their rates of infection to less than 1% through the vigorous enforcement of handwashing, the meticulous cleaning of equipment and hospital rooms, and the use of disposable protective clothing to reduce carrying the pathogens from room to room (McCaughey 2005). Frequently, stethoscopes and blood-pressure cuffs are contaminated with live bacteria; yet physicians and nurses almost never clean these items as they move from patient to patient. Clothing such as ties and uniforms pick up pathogens 65% of the time when doctors and nurses lean over patients (McCaughey 2005; Neely and Maley 2000).

At one hospital in New York City, the outbreak of *Clostridium difficile (C. diff)* colitis was traced to care assistants who carried out two tasks without changing clothes: emptying bedpans and delivering food trays. *C. diff* is transmitted from feces by oral ingestion.

The ability of the most drug-resistant microorganisms to survive on dry environmental surfaces is quite remarkable: *Enterococcus* (including vancomycin-resistant enterococci [VRE]), *Staphylococcus aureus* (including Methicillin-resistant *Staphylococcus aureus* or MRSA), *E.coli*, Klebsiella, and *Pseudomonas aeruginosa,* can survive for months. Spore-forming bacteria, including *C. diff,* can also survive for months. *Candida albicans* (the most important nosocomial fungal pathogen) can survive up to four months on surfaces (Kramer, Schwebke, and Kampf 2006). Patients in any room of the hospital, and healthcare workers as well, may become infected by contact with environmental surfaces if regular surface disinfection is not carried out.

Patients with compromised immune systems due to age, disease, recent surgery, and anesthesia are more susceptible to nosocomial infections. Both adult and pediatric intensive care units have infection rates three times higher than other hospital patients (Weinstein, as reported in Joseph 2006). A considerable body of research indicates that the built environment can be a contributing factor in the transmission of HAIs, one third of which have been found to be preventable (Weinstein, as reported in Joseph 2006).

There have been a large number of studies investigating clinical evidence of the role of environmental surfaces in the transmission of nosocomial infections. Some of these studies evaluate different types of fabric content and materials such as plastics, steel (bed rails and grab bars), wallcoverings, and even fabrics used in workers' uniforms, all of which are discussed later in this chapter. Research indicates that contaminated hands can transfer viruses to five more surfaces or 14 other subjects (Kramer, Schwebke, and Kampf 2006). Unfortunately compliance rates for handwashing by healthcare workers is reported to be 50% in one source (Kramer, Schwebke, and Kampf 2006) and commonly fall in the range of 15% to 35% in another (Ulrich et al. 2004), even though this is one of the best strategies for reducing transmission of infections. According to the latter source, physicians and nursing assistants have the lowest rates of compliance.

There are a number of strategies that may influence handwashing compliance. According to Ulrich et al. (2004), providing alcohol-gel hand-cleaner dispensers at the bedside usually improves compliance, as does increasing the ratio of the number of sinks to beds. Provision of hand-gel dispensers next to patient room doors may not be effective, and automated (infrared) water and soap dispensers may not increase compliance.

According to Murphy and Whiting (2007), hospital leaders significantly underestimate the extent of HAIs and the degree to which they impact cost and operating margins. In presenting the business case for reduction of HAIs, Murphy and Whiting report on a study of 1.69 million admissions from 77 hospitals: HAIs reduced overall net inpatient margins by $286 million or $5,018 per infected patient. The average additional incremental direct cost for patients with an HAI was $8,832.

Dispelling the myths

The three myths Murphy and Whiting (2007) examine and seek to dispel are:

1. HAIs are an expected byproduct of treating an older, sicker patient population.
2. The additional cost of an HAI is largely offset by reimbursement, making the infection revenue neutral or positive.
3. The number of HAIs in most institutions is not significant, making the cost savings associated with reduction not worth the investment.

Examining the evidence

HAIs cost between $5 billion and $6 billion annually and result in 100,000 deaths in the United States (Murphy and Whiting 2007). In presenting a case study of Allegheny General Hospital in Pittsburgh, Pennsylvania, and its goal of achieving zero central-line associated bloodstream (CLAB) infections, Murphy and Whiting report the following: the average loss per case was $26,839 (the difference between actual cost and reimbursement) for treating a patient with CLAB infection, and the hospital was able to achieve a 90% reduction in CLAB infections.

The hospital also set out to reduce ventilator-associated pneumonias (VAPs), which averaged a loss of $24,435 per case. In this effort, it was able to achieve 82% reduction. Looking at CLAB infections and VAPs together, the hospital achieved cost savings of $2.2 million. Most notably, the cost to obtain this level of savings was just under $35,000; the cost per ventilated patient was just $17. Can any hospital ignore these issues when the mortality associated with VAPs and CLAB infections is 20% to 60%?

In addition, HAIs consume many additional patient days. In 2005, in Pennsylvania, the average length of stay was five days for a patient without an HAI and 23 days for a patient with an HAI (Murphy and Whiting 2007). Zero tolerance for HAIs can make available a significant number of bed days that potentially can result in greater reimbursement.

A Day in the Life of 1,237 Hospitals

In a survey conducted by the Association for Professionals in Infection Control and Epidemiology, a day in the life of 1,237 hospitals and long-term care facilities revealed that the number of MRSA cases was 8.6 times greater than 2005 estimates by the Centers for Disease Control and Prevention (CDC) (Russell 2007). This represents a snapshot of MRSA rates on a single day. Although it is often thought that intensive care patients are especially vulnerable to MRSA, causing infection-control efforts to be focused there, the alarming news in this study is that 67% of the cases were among patients hospitalized for nonsurgical medical conditions.

The Elements of Transmission

The transmission of infection within a hospital requires three elements: a source of infecting microorganisms, a susceptible host, and a means of transmission for the microorganism (Garner 1996).

Source

Sources of infection may be other patients, personnel, and visitors, and may include persons in the incubation period of a disease, persons colonized by an infectious agent but with no apparent disease, or those who are chronic carriers of an infectious agent. Inanimate objects may also be a source of contamination and are referred to as *fomites*.

Host

Resistance to pathogenic microorganisms varies greatly among persons. Some persons may be asymptomatic carriers. Age, underlying disease, certain types of antimicrobial treatment, immunosuppressive agents, irradiation, in-dwelling catheters, surgical operations, and anesthesia may cause patients to be more susceptible to infection.

Route

There are five main routes of transmission: contact, droplet, airborne, common vehicle, and vectorborne (neither of the last two play a significant role in typical nosocomial infections). *Common vehicle* refers to microorganisms transmitted by contaminated food, water, medications, devices, or equipment. *Vectorborne* refers to transmission by insects and rodents.

Multidrug-Resistant Microorganisms in Healthcare Settings

There are a number of multidrug-resistant microorganisms that can be found in both inpatient and outpatient settings that have developed resistance to antimicrobial drugs (CDC 2000):

- *Clostridium difficile*-associated disease
- MRSA — Methicillin-resistant *Staphylococcus aureus*
- VRE — Vancomycin-resistant *enterococcus*
- ESBLs — Extended-spectrum beta-lactamases
- PRSP — Penicillin-resistant *Streptococcus pneumoniae*

According to the CDC (2000), these patients can safely be cared for in outpatient settings if appropriate infection-control measures are followed. Outpatient settings include physicians' offices and clinics, especially pediatric settings, hemodialysis centers, and residential settings such as long-term care and skilled nursing facilities. In the outpatient setting, transmission often occurs if the patient has draining wounds or difficulty controlling body fluids.

Clostridium difficile-associated disease

The incidence and severity of *Clostridium difficile-associated disease (C.diff)* are increasing, possibly due to a new strain (Sunenshine and McDonald 2006). Hospitals are struggling to deal with this epidemic, and interior designers need to understand enough about it to be able to specify appropriate interior finish materials, upholstery fabrics, and furnishings for patient rooms. Patients with *C. diff* may be found in a standard patient room, which means that CDC contact precautions will be employed.

This infection almost always follows the use of antimicrobials (antibiotics), which kill many of the beneficial flora in the intestine, creating optimal conditions for *C. diff* to flourish. It is transmitted via fecal-oral route (ingestion) following contamination of the hands of healthcare workers and patients. For patients who are otherwise healthy, there is a good prognosis; but for those with diabetes or pulmonary disease or heart disease, treatment regimens can be complex. The disease can quickly advance in severity, sometimes leading to death (Sunenshine and McDonald 2006).

Moderate to severe diarrhea is associated with *C. diff*. This means that the floor and patient chairs are especially vulnerable to becoming sources of contamination. Nonporous surfaces that can be cleaned with a dilution of bleach and water or a product such as Virex are essential. Patient chairs with an opening between the seat and back will be easier to clean, and there should be no edge welting or cording and as few seams as possible. Mesh fabric with a tubular metal frame may be an appropriate choice or an upholstered chair with a smooth vinyl cover. Over time, most vinyls can be expected to deteriorate from repeated cleaning with strong or caustic agents. This is truly a new age in terms of environmental issues associated with transmission of infection. Designers have to refine their strategy because these patients may be found in any room of the hospital, not necessarily in isolation rooms.

Alcohol gel is not effective in killing *C. diff* spores, which can live on dry surfaces for several months (Sunenshine and McDonald 2006). The only effective means of decreasing the spread is handwashing with a triclosan-containing hand soap and increased environmental cleaning; however, *C. diff* is highly resistant to routine disinfectants (Sunenshine and McDonald 2006). Hands must be washed prior to gloving and washed again after removing gloves. The rate of surface contamination increases in proportion to the *C. diff* status, severity of diarrhea, and incontinence of patients in the area. No well-controlled trials of disinfectants have been conducted; however, use of both unbuffered and phosphate-buffered hypochlorite solutions (bleach) have been shown to decrease rates of contamination as well as lower *C. diff* rates (Sunenshine and McDonald 2006).

According to Sunenshine and McDonald (2006), it should be noted that no disinfectants with a claim to *C. diff* spore inactivation are registered with the Environmental Protection Agency. However, the Healthcare

Infection Control Practices Advisory Committee (HICPAC) (2003) guidelines recommend "meticulous cleaning followed by disinfection using hypochlorite-based germicides as appropriate." The HICPAC guideline specifies the dilution and mixing of bleach solutions.

HICPAC guidelines recommend that contact precautions be implemented for symptomatic patients. For patients, this includes a private room and toilet or cohorting with other symptomatic patients; and for healthcare workers, it means donning disposable gowns and gloves before entering the room. A strategy implemented by one hospital involved placing a mobile isolation cart with all supplies needed outside the door. A cut-out graphic of hands affixed to the room-number sign immediately cues healthcare workers that this is a *C. diff* patient and alcohol gel cannot be used. A sign placed on the wall near the door has instructions for caregivers and visitors with a colored band at the top that says "handwashing only." This hospital monitors handwashing practices by healthcare workers with a version of mystery shoppers. This same practice is employed to observe how thoroughly housekeepers clean rooms: high performers get a pay raise. Every room has its own equipment (blood pressure cuffs, disposable stethoscope, IV pumps) to reduce contamination that occurs when moving equipment from one room to another. An unresolved issue mentioned by the nurse in charge of infection control to the author during an onsite interview on May 1, 2007, is the need to secure multidose medications (e.g., inhalers), which should not be put back in the Pyxis dispensing machine. A locked drawer would work, but the interior of this drawer would have to be disinfected between patients.

Methicillin-resistant *Staphylococcus aureus* (MRSA)

Methicillin-resistant *Staphylococcus aureus* (MRSA) has become a prevalent nosocomial pathogen. Infected or colonized patients are the reservoir by which it is spread, and it is often carried by healthcare workers from one patient to another (CDC 2004). Contaminated hands may carry the pathogen by (a) contact with colonized or infected patients; (b) colonized or infected body parts of the hospital personnel themselves; or (c) devices, items, or environmental surfaces contaminated by body fluids containing MRSA. This type of bacteria causes staph infections that are resistant to treatment with the usual antibiotics. "MRSA in healthcare settings commonly causes serious and potentially life-threatening infections, such as bloodstream infections, surgical site infections, or pneumonia" (CDC 2006). MRSA can also affect people in the community at large, generally as skin infections that look like pimples or boils; these often occur in otherwise healthy people (CDC 2006).

Multibed rooms are harder to decontaminate after a patient is discharged. More healthcare workers enter the room to care for two patients and can touch the same contaminated surfaces. A study by Boyce and colleagues as reported in Ulrich et al. (2004) found that 42% of nurses who had no direct contact with a patient infected with MRSA but who had touched contaminated surfaces had contaminated their gloves with MRSA. This was the result of the nursing unit simply having had patients infected with MRSA. This shows how easily MRSA can be carried by hand contact from one place to another.

People infected with MRSA are likely to have longer and more expensive hospital stays and may be more likely to die as a result of the infection. According to CDC data, MRSA infections increased from 2% of the total number of staph infections in 1974 to 22% in 1995 and 63% in 2004 (CDC 2006).

Standard precautions, as described in Garner (1996), should control the spread of MRSA in most instances (CDC 2004); however, if the MRSA is "judged by the hospital's infection-control program to be of special clinical or epidemiologic significance, then Contact Precautions should be considered" (CDC 2004).

Vancomycin-resistant Enterococci (VRE)

Enterococci are bacteria normally present in human intestines and the female genital tract and are also often found in the environment (CDC 2005). The antibiotic *vancomycin* is used to treat infections caused by these bacteria, which in some instances have become resistant to this drug; hence the name VRE. Most of these infections occur in hospitals (CDC 2005). VRE is spread by contact (hands or contaminated surfaces) with stool, urine, or blood containing VRE. It is usually not spread by casual contact such as touching or hugging, nor is it spread by coughing or sneezing. Although not reported in U.S. hospitals until 1989, in 2004 VRE caused one of every three infections in intensive care units according to data from the CDC (2005).

Extended-spectrum beta-lactamases (ESBLs)

Extended-spectrum beta-lactamases (ESBLs) are enzymes commonly produced by *E. coli*, *Enterobacter*, *Salmonella*, *Pseudomonas aeruginosa*, and other gram-negative bacteria; they are associated with broad multidrug resistance. Detecting ESBLs in the laboratory has been problematic and has led to avoidable therapeutic failures in patients who received inappropriate antibiotics (Thomson 2001).

Penicillin-resistant Streptococcus pneumoniae (PRSP)

Pneumococcal infections are a leading cause of morbidity and mortality in the United States. Infection with PRSP is higher in families with children attending daycare and has been associated with recent overuse of antibiotics according to the CDC (1996). Overuse of antibiotics is recognized as the cause of the antibiotic-resistant strain that causes pneumonia, bacteremia, and meningitis.

Pseudomonas aeruginosa (PSAE)

Pseudomonas infection may affect the urinary tract, lungs, and respiratory system; soft tissue; joints; skin; gut; and the linings of the heart and can also lead to bacteremia, septicemia, and other systemic infections (Leib and Rohde 2007). PSAE is so resistant to antibiotics that it may result in the death of approximately half of patients hospitalized with cancer, cystic fibrosis, and burns who happen to contract the infection (Leib and Rohde 2007). From an environmental standpoint, it can survive outside the body on dry surfaces for lengthy periods. Ten percent of all HAIs are PSAE according to Todar's online *Textbook of Bacteriology* (University of Wisconsin, Madison, Department of Bacteriology).

CDC Infection Control Guidelines

Standard precautions (Garner 1996; CDC 2004)
The CDC recommendations for standard precautions include:

1. Handwashing: Wash hands before and after gloving and whenever touching blood or bodily secretions; it may be necessary to wash and reglove between procedures on the same patient to prevent cross-contamination of different body sites.

2. Gloving: Remove gloves promptly after use, before touching noncontaminated items and surfaces, and before going to another patient.

3. Masking: Wear a mask and eye protection or a face shield during procedures likely to generate splashes or aerosols of blood, body fluids, or secretions to protect mucous membranes.

4. Gowning: Wear a gown (clean, nonsterile is adequate) to protect skin and soiling of clothes during procedures and patient care activities likely to generate splashes or aerosols of blood, body fluids, or secretions.

5. Appropriate device handling: Handle soiled, used patient care equipment in such a way as to prevent transfer of microorganisms to other patients and environments. Ensure that reusable equipment is not used for the care of another patient until it has been appropriately cleaned and reprocessed and that single-use items are properly discarded.

6. Appropriate handling of linen: Handle, transport, and process used linen soiled with blood, body fluids, secretions, and excretions in a manner that prevents exposure to skin and mucous membranes and transfer of microorganisms to other patients and environments.

7. Environmental control: Employ adequate procedures for cleaning and disinfecting environment surfaces, beds, bedrails, bedside equipment, and other frequently touched surfaces, and ensure that these procedures are being followed.

8. Occupational health and bloodborne pathogens: Prevent needle-sticks, injury by scalpels or sharp instruments; place needles and disposable syringes in puncture-resistant containers located as close as practical to the location where items were used.

9. Patient placement: Place a patient who contaminates the environment in a private room.

Contact precautions (Garner 1996)

In addition to standard precautions, contact precautions are employed for patients known or suspected to be infected or colonized with epidemiologically important microorganisms that can be transmitted by direct contact with the patient or indirect contact (touching) of environment surfaces or patient care items in the environment.

1. Patient placement: Place the patient in a private room; if not available, place patient with other patients who are actively infected with the same microorganism but with no other infections. The door to the room must remain closed.

2. Gloving and handwashing: In addition to standard precautions, wear gloves when entering the room; change gloves after contact with infective material (especially fecal matter and wound drainage); remove gloves before leaving room and wash hands immediately with an antimicrobial agent or a waterless antiseptic agent. After handwashing, do not touch potentially contaminated environment surfaces. Note that alcohol gel does not kill *C. diff* spores (Sunenshine and McDonald 2006), which are spread by contact.

3. Gowning: In addition to standard precautions, wear a gown when entering the room if clothing will contact the patient, environment surfaces, or items in the patient's room or if the patient has diarrhea, a colostomy, or wound drainage not contained by a dressing. Remove the gown before leaving the patient's room.

4. Patient transport: Limit the movement and transport of the patient from the room to essential purposes only. If transported, take precautions to minimize risk of transmission to other patients and minimize contamination of environmental surfaces or equipment.

5. Patient care equipment: When possible, dedicate noncritical patient care equipment to a single patient to avoid sharing between patients.

6. Additional precautions for VRE: Consult the HICPAC report (2003) for strategies.

Airborne precautions (Garner 1996)

In addition to standard precautions, use airborne precautions for patients known to be or suspected of being infected with microorganisms transmitted by the airborne droplet nuclei of evaporated droplets containing microorganisms that remain suspended in the air and that can be dispersed widely by air currents within a room or over a long distance.

1. Patient placement: Place the patient in a private room that has (1) monitored negative air pressure, (2) 6 to 12 air changes per hour, and (3) appropriate discharge of air outdoors or monitored HEPA filtration of room air before it is circulated to other areas of the hospital. When a private room is not available, place the patient in a room with another who has the same infection.

2. Respiratory protection: Wear respiratory protection (N95 respirator) when entering the room. These respirators fit over the head like a hood and have a battery pack. Susceptible persons should not enter the room of patients known to have or suspected of having measles or chicken pox.

3. Patient transport: Limit the movement and transport of the patient from the room to essential purposes, and minimize dispersal of droplet nuclei by placing a surgical mask on the patient.

4. Additional precautions for preventing transmission of tuberculosis (TB): consult the CDC's *Guidelines for Preventing the Transmission of Mycobacterium Tuberculosis in Health-Care Facilities* (1994).
   [Author's note: Healthcare workers will wear a hood with a respirator and a HEPA filter. The room requires negative air pressure.]

Droplet precautions (Garner 1996)
In addition to standard precautions, use droplet precautions for a patient known to be or suspected of being infected with microorganisms transmitted by large-particle droplets that can be generated by the patient during coughing, sneezing, talking, or the performance of procedures.

1. Patient placement: Same as above for contact precautions except the door may remain open.
2. Masking: In addition to standard precautions, wear a mask when working within three feet of the patient.
3. Patient transport: Follow same guidelines as for airborne precautions.

Other sources of information include: National Institute for Occupational Safety and Health (http://www.cdc.gov/niosh/), for information on protecting healthcare workers, and the Association for Professionals in Infection Control and Epidemiology (http://www.apic.org//AM/Template.cfm?Section=Home).

Implications of CDC Infection Control Guidelines for Design Professionals
What are the design implications associated with the CDC guidelines for standard, contact, airborne, and droplet precautions?

- The placement of glove boxes, alcohol-gel dispensers, and sharps containers are a matter of safety as well as aesthetics. Designers should locate them accordingly as they plan the room. What often happens is that they are installed by hospital engineering staff after construction has been completed. The placement is sometimes haphazard and not based on a careful analysis in terms of CDC infection control guidelines.

- Masks, gowns, and eye protection are recommended even for standard precautions for procedures likely to generate aerosols or splashes of blood or body fluids. Consideration must be given to storage of these items.

- Patients with multidrug-resistant microorganisms may be found in any room in the hospital, not necessarily an isolation room. Storage of protective gear that can be accessed *before* entering the room is essential for contact precautions. Figuring out how to accomplish this is a challenge if the goal is to use something other than a mobile cart. Caregivers treating patients with airborne or droplet-type infections are dressing in "space suits" with respirator hoods, gowns, boots, and gloves. Where are these items going to be stored, labeled, and easily found? If decentralized storage rooms are where they will be placed, then these rooms must be easily accessible and larger than standard. If placed at decentralized nurse workstations that serve one or two patient rooms (as in Image pages 7.4, 7.8, 7.56, and 7.65), then this casework will need to be more extensive. The nurse charting alcove on Image page 7.23 would accommodate this storage. Another solution is the vertical supply cabinet to the right of the nurse workstation on Image pages 7.52 and 7.54.

- Waste receptacles in patient rooms will need to be larger and carefully placed to accommodate the increased amount of disposable protective gear.

- The way that soiled linen is handled until it may be removed from a patient room is important in preventing microorganisms from being transferred to other surfaces in the room. This needs to be discussed with the environmental services manager and the hospital infection control officer as the room is being planned. If a mobile cart for soiled linen is provided in the room, is it built into a cabinet that requires the lifting of a lid or door to gain access to it? Depending on how it is designed, this may create another opportunity for contact transfer of pathogens.

- The location of the handwashing sink is important. It should be close to the room entry (Image pages 7.35, 7.46, 7.55, and 7.59) and preferably not behind a door (Image page 7.78) or partition (Image page 7.45).

THE BUILT ENVIRONMENT AS A RISK FACTOR FOR INFECTION

The focus on patient safety and the magnitude of HAIs demand that design professionals become well versed in knowing where risks occur, how they occur, and what they can do to reduce or minimize them. For many years, the primary goal has been to reduce the institutional appearance of hospitals—to make them less threatening through the careful selection of interior finish materials; the use of furniture with wooden frames and woven upholstery fabrics (as opposed to vinyl); and the introduction of texture, water features, artwork, and vibrant color. Materials selected for this purpose have to meet fire codes and be durable and easy to clean.

Since such an array of products that meet these general requirements is available, designers have usually not had to go beyond the specifications and manufacturers' printed literature to feel confident in their selections. Occasionally a call to the technical department about whether one product versus another is the best choice for a given situation is required. For example, hospitals often have moisture problems associated with both on-grade concrete slabs and below-grade slabs. This results in problems with many types of resilient flooring, which can lead to substantial risk—and possible litigation—for contractors, architects, and designers.

The situation today is quite different. The goal for design professionals needs to be enhancing patient safety; however, designers cannot necessarily rely on manufacturers' claims and recommendations as in the past because new environmental threats exist. The study by Lankford et al. (2007), summarized by Leib and Rohde (2007), points out that manufacturers are sometimes out of touch with the cleaning agents and methods actually used by hospitals and that manufacturers' recommended cleaning processes may not result in eradicating pathogens. Nor can designers rely on an antimicrobial label to feel confident that these products will prevent the growth of pathogens (disease-causing germs).

The Antimicrobial Controversy

There is considerable ongoing debate about the appropriateness and effectiveness of products enhanced with antimicrobial properties for use in hospitals. Types of products currently being marketed include paint, upholstery and cubicle drape fabrics, ceiling tile, patient gowns, door handles, solid-surface material (used for countertops), as well as coating that can be applied to a variety of surfaces. Carpet with antimicrobial preservative has been available for a number of years. The debate or discussion is occurring between infection control specialists, microbiologists, and hospital facility managers who want to know whether such products are effective, safe, and worth the additional cost. Certainly, the ideal would be a variety of products that extinguish pathogens on contact. This would do much to solve the current infection control crisis in hospitals, at least in terms of pathogens transmitted from environmental surfaces by contact. So kudos to manufacturers for trying to make this work.

The issue, however, is that antimicrobial agents come under the jurisdiction of the Environmental Protection Agency (EPA) Federal Insecticide, Fungicide, and Rodenticide Act, as opposed to public health products such as antiseptics and germicides, sterilizers, disinfectants, and other sanitizers also regulated by the EPA and the Food and Drug Administration.

The EPA requires data to support claims of efficacy against specific microorganisms as well as labeling that details the safe and effective use and also hazards associated with the product. Manufacturers are prohibited from making a public health claim for any product unless it has been approved and registered by the EPA or is exempt from registration (Kaiser Permanente 2006).

One has to read the claims on labels carefully. The antimicrobial properties may apply to the stability of the product itself (shelf life), prevention of odors due to mold or mildew, prevention of staining, or prevention of infection.

A large manufacturer of modular carpet tile (and a company that has been a leader in the green movement in terms of manufacturing practices as well as the lifecycle impact of its products) makes these claims for Intersept, an antimicrobial preservative used in its own carpet brand and sold to other companies for incorporation into air filters, paint, fabrics, wallcoverings, ceiling tiles, adhesives, and HVAC equipment (Interface 2002).

- It inhibits the growth of a broad spectrum of fungi, molds, mildews, bacteria, and odor-causing microorganisms that can affect carpet.
- It is registered with the EPA for use in carpeting and other products.
- It is guaranteed to maintain antimicrobial preservative effectiveness for the life of a properly maintained floorcovering.
- It is low in toxicity and contains no arsenic, heavy metals, phenols, or formaldehyde

The emphasis in the Interface technology brief is on Intercept's antimicrobial "preservative protection," however, photos of petri dish cultures are included in the brief and point to the zone of inhibition around the treated sample, showing no microbial growth. According to the brief, Intersept "works by destabilizing cell membranes of bacteria and fungi, and inhibiting their ability to reproduce…and it is a broad-spectrum biostatic preservative, not a toxic pesticide…and has been certified to meet the three most recognized environmental quality standards."

This sounds convincing to a nonscientist, but the controversy continues. Kaiser Permanente, in an internal 2006 position paper on antimicrobials, revealed that the "antimicrobial action of surfaces can only effectively treat the first cell layer of pathogenic material." Beyond that, only mechanical debridement (scrubbing) with detergent and water will disinfect the surface. The conclusions of the Kaiser study (2006) are:

- There is no scientific evidence that environmental surface finishes or fabrics containing antimicrobials help prevent infections.
- No studies linked gowns made from antimicrobial fabrics to effective prevention of HAIs in the patient setting.
- The impregnated silver ion particles found in some of these products are heavy metals and environmental toxins. "Whether these materials leach enough silver ions into rinse water upon cleaning or into the soil upon disposal has not been assessed here, however, it would be prudent to prevent a known hazardous material from entering into a product's lifecycle during manufacture, use, maintenance, or final disposal."
- "It is our considered opinion that due to the unproven benefits of antimicrobial healthcare finishes and fabrics…coupled with their cost and potential environment concerns, these products do not recommend themselves for use in healthcare facilities for the purpose of greater infection prevention and control. This position is subject to change as additional scientific-based evidence becomes available."

Another leading manufacturer of healthcare carpeting outlines, in a white paper, a number of the issues mentioned in the Kaiser brief and, in fact, disputes the claims made by the manufacturer of Intersept (Evans 2005). Is this a battle of Goliaths for a larger share of the market or a true and sincere philosophical difference?

The increased burden on design professionals

The burden of understanding where the environmental risks lie and evaluating a variety of products against evidence-based studies is what design professionals will now be expected to do. This involves reading studies in their entirety to pick up all the nuances. Simply reading an abstract or summary of the findings will not provide the level of expertise needed.

Manufacturers of finish materials, fabrics, and furniture are working hard to incorporate various technologies into their products so that they extinguish pathogens on contact. For example, according to the product literature, AgION antimicrobial silver ion technology has a trimodal method of killing microorganisms: it interrupts the reproductive cycle, structurally breaks the cell wall, and affects cell metabolism. A number of fabric manufacturers have incorporated this into upholstery and cubicle drapery fabrics, but the evidence thus far has not demonstrated effectiveness in the patient care environment.

Nanotechnology has been applied to the manufacture of solid-surface materials used for sink countertops and other surfaces to kill pathogens on contact; however, as we learned from the Kaiser study, only the first layer of cells is affected. In addition, an infection control officer at a large medical center shared her concerns that, perhaps two years after installation of the countertop, there might be a new strain of pathogen and the microorganism might not be sensitive to the agents embedded in the countertop (personal communication with author).

No doubt, there is frustration on all sides of this equation: manufacturers see a great opportunity for the development of enhanced products to deal with a very serious problem, while scientists and those responsible for patient safety hunger for evidence-based proof. According to a recent article (Fields 2007), researchers at North Carolina State and Emory University have developed a "thinner-than-microscopic protective layer, called nano-coating, that can be applied to most any surface; that purports to kill 99.9% of most microbes through a chemical reaction caused by exposure to visible light." The company developing the technology, LaamScience, is hoping to introduce it to hospitals on a variety of products by the end of 2007.

Nanotechnology: Untold promise, unknown risk

A *Consumer Reports* (2007) investigation of the promise and risks associated with nanotechnology discusses the tremendous potential of this technology to change our world as profoundly as electricity did. The article raises questions, however, about the substantial risks, which according to a number of scientists have not been explored. These include risks to both human health and the environment. According to physicist Andrew Maynard, science advisor for the Project on Emerging Nanotechnologies at the Woodrow Wilson Center, a nonpartisan public policy institute in Washington, DC: "The more we know about nanomaterials' risks, the more we worry about what we don't know" (*Consumer Reports* 2007).

Limited laboratory and animal research conducted thus far raises these concerns:

- Benign materials can become toxic when nanosized because microscopic particles tend to react more readily with human tissues and other substances.
- Nanoparticles can enter the body and its vital organs, including the brain, much more easily than can larger particles. These nanoparticles are already used in food additives, cosmetics, and other products that are ingested or applied to the skin, such as sunscreens. The government does not require labeling to indicate the presence of nanoparticles. According to a report from insurance industry giant, Swiss Rex, "humankind has never been exposed to such a wide variety of substances that can penetrate the human body apparently unhindered." (This company is involved in risk assessment.)
- Some nanomaterials seem to linger in the environment—especially in the water supply.
- Nanomaterials pose very different risks from the same materials at conventional size; therefore, standard safety-assessment tools are inadequate.
- Manufacturers are not required to disclose the presence of nanomaterials in their labeling.

The promises of nanotechnology are many. Nanodelivery systems may be able to precisely target tumors to improve the treatment of cancer. Solar cells, produced at a fraction of current costs, will use nanoparticles of a new semiconductor material printed on thin metal sheets like ink on paper. Automobile fuel lines made with carbon nanotubes may be able to reduce the risk of explosions. The *Consumer Reports* article details dozens of nanotech inventions currently under way and also explains the chemical and molecular science involved in this remarkable technology.

Nanotechnology in upholstery for healthcare applications

An article in a magazine for textile industry professionals (Gurian 2007) cites evidence that nanotech-treated upholsteries held up to repeated use of disinfectants, based on a controlled laboratory study of 100% solution-dyed nylon and 100% recycled polyester. The disinfectants used in this study were three phenolic and three quaternary germicides that were recommended by the CDC as well as ammonia, hydrogen peroxide, and a 4:1 dilution of bleach. (It should be noted that the author of this article is a technical specialist employed by DesignTex and the sample fabrics tested were treated with their proprietary Nano-tex coating.) The conclusion of the study is that stain resistance of the treated fabrics was unaffected by multiple cleanings with strong disinfectants.

What to do?

The debate about developing technologies and their effectiveness in extinguishing pathogens on contact will continue until unassailable scientific evidence exists. In the meantime, design professionals and hospitals will have to make informed decisions based on available studies and individual infection control policies employed at institutions.

Pathogens Associated with Building Construction or Maintenance

An essential part of the planning process for new construction, and especially for remodeling within an occupied facility, is an assessment of risk associated with infections transmitted by air, water, or the environment. An infection control risk assessment is a requirement outlined in the AIA *Guidelines for Design and Construction of Health Care Facilities* (2006).

A number of risks are associated with mechanical ventilation systems that are not operating optimally. Joseph (2006) offers an in-depth discussion of this topic, including HEPA filtration. The most effective way of maintaining clean air is to remove air pollutants (chemicals, dust, microorganisms) at the source. Indoor air quality can be greatly enhanced through the use of HEPA filters, but this comes at a higher cost than standard 90% efficiency filters. A cost analysis and comparison is provided by Joseph (2006).

Aspergillosis and legionellosis

The association between construction and the development of aspergillosis in immunocompromised patients is well established, as is the association of hospital-acquired legionellosis and potable water (Noskin and Peterson 2001). Recall a number of years ago a large outbreak of Legionnaire's disease on a cruise ship, which was traced to a fountain. These bacteria are found in manmade moist or aquatic environments and enter hospitals most frequently through aerosols from cooling towers, condensers, showers, faucets, hot-water storage tanks, and respiratory therapy equipment and humidifiers. Amplification is stimulated by stagnation and warmth (Rogers 2006).

To avoid stagnation, fountains inside buildings should never be on a time clock with the pumps turned off after hours. Twenty-four-hour circulation of water is essential, as is proper treatment with additives, an ultraviolet light, and various other measures used to control biofilm (bacterial) growth. Ice machines used in hospitals are another source of legionellosis if they are not routinely cleaned and maintained. Vacant hospital rooms with faucets that have not been used in a 24-hour period should be flushed by running the water prior to handwashing or drinking the water, according to a number of microbiologists.

Effective methods of disinfecting the hospital water supply include chlorination, thermal eradication, ultraviolet light, and metal ionization. Northwestern Memorial in Chicago, Illinois, installed a copper-silver ionization system and also has 100% HEPA-filtered air in its new hospital to control aspergillosis and legionellosis (Noskin and Peterson 2001).

Aspergillus are fungi found in decaying vegetation and dust. Spores are easily suspended in the air and can survive for extended periods. They are easily inhaled and can lead to invasive infections of the upper and lower respiratory tracts (Noskin and Peterson 2001; Ulrich et al. 2004). Older hospitals sometimes have outbreaks of aspergillosis when they remove ceiling tiles and do work above the ceiling. Proper cleaning and maintenance of HVAC ducts and the use of HEPA filters are essential. It is increasingly common in new hospitals for the entire building to have HEPA-filtered air (see Image page 7.28 for a discussion of advanced HVAC features). Prevention of aspergillosis is especially important for patients undergoing solid organ or bone marrow transplantation. Patients undergoing these procedures should be placed in rooms with positive air pressure in relation to the corridor, windows should be tightly sealed, and the air exchange rate should be at least 15 air changes per hour (Noskin and Peterson 2001).

Tuberculosis (TB)

Patients requiring isolation for tuberculosis (TB) should be placed in a room with negative airflow, and the air should be exhausted to the outdoors without recirculation. At least 12 air changes per hour should occur. Doors to the rooms should be self-closing and walls, windows, ceiling, floor, and penetrations well sealed (Noskin and Peterson 2001). In addition, rooms should be monitored to ensure that they retain negative pressure. The placement of negative air-pressure rooms, when a hospital is being designed, should ideally be located where high-risk patients will be cared for: the emergency department, recovery room, bronchoscopy suite, ambulatory clinics, and medical inpatient units (Noskin and Peterson 2001).

Interior Finishes

There is considerable debate about the use of carpet in hospital inpatient corridors, although it has been used for many years. Proponents of carpet appreciate the non-institutional ambience it provides and, from the designer's perspective, it is the principal way to introduce pattern and texture in a corridor and to reduce noise. Footsteps and the clatter of carts on hard-surface flooring can force patients to keep their doors closed and can interrupt sleep. Healthcare workers, on the other hand, point to carpet as a potential source of back injury from pushing patients on heavy beds on surfaces that offer resistance. Environmental service managers often find it easier to keep a hard-surface floor clean. Infection control officers almost always weigh in against carpet. However, hospital chief executive officers (CEOs) often favor it because of the ambience it creates. All of these viewpoints are valid.

On behalf of carpet, it should be said that contemporary carpets developed for the healthcare market (as opposed to carpets that may have been used in studies from the 1980s) have advanced backing systems that prevent moisture (spills) from leaching into the slab. They have agents that extinguish odors as well as stain-resistant coatings applied during the manufacturing process for appearance retention. Many of these carpets can be soiled with any number of stains such as mustard, catsup, coffee, soft drinks, blood, and urine and easily cleaned with no residual spotting. However, unusual spills should be cleaned in a timely manner, and therein lies the rub. Many health systems have reduced, not added to, their housekeeping staffs and responding to a carpet spill or stain may not get priority.

Carpet manufacturers have worked hard to develop patterns and color palettes that camouflage soiling. Whether broadloom or modular carpet tile, installation methods with no volatile organic compound adhesives are standard. But…carpet must be properly maintained, which means having the proper equipment and maintaining a schedule for frequent cleaning by steam-extraction method. Vacuum cleaners with HEPA filters are also recommended.

Carpet and infection control issues

The CDC *Guidelines for Environmental Infection Control in Health-Care Facilities* (HICPAC, 2003) cites the advantages of using carpeting for its humanizing qualities, reducing falls and resultant injuries, and reducing noise. It also states that carpet is harder to keep clean and makes it harder to push wheeled equipment, including wheelchairs. (It should be noted, in this regard, that many hospital carts have not been fitted out with large wheels intended for carpet. Sometimes that can make quite a difference.) The *Guidelines* disallow carpet in hallways and patient rooms housing immunosuppressed patients or in patient-care areas where spills are likely to occur (operating rooms, burn therapy units, intensive care units). When carpet is used in areas other than these, there are certain caveats such as the need to clean spills of blood or body fluids promptly and to replace carpet or carpet tiles that remain wet after 72 hours. Research results cited in the *Guidelines* section on carpeting include:

Despite evidence of bacterial growth in carpet, only limited epidemiologic evidence demonstrates that carpet influences HAI rates.

- The number and variety of microorganisms in carpet tend to stabilize over time.
- Vacuuming and cleaning the carpet only temporarily reduces the bacterial count, which quickly returns to precleaning levels.
- Dry bonnet buffing machines used to clean carpet can disperse aspergillus spores into the air.
- Carpet-cleaning equipment, especially for wet cleaning, can become contaminated with waterborne organisms such as *Pseudomonas aeruginosa* if not properly maintained and can transfer these organisms to the carpet.
- According to the Occupational Safety and Health Administration, carpeting contaminated with blood or other potentially infectious materials cannot be fully decontaminated. Therefore, the CDC suggests carpet tile may be a good option for high-activity patient care areas at high risk for spills.

A number of studies indicate that carpet, although colonized with a variety of pathogens, provides no direct link to patient infections (Lundstrom et al. 2002; Skoutelis et al. 1994; Joseph 2006).

Hard-surface flooring may take many forms from the commonplace vinyl composition tile (VCT) to linoleum, rubber flooring, or vinyl sheet goods. In all types except VCT, manufacturers offer a wide range of products that do not need waxing, which saves considerable expense and labor over the lifecycle of the product. It does require a visual adjustment to become accustomed to floors without a mirrorlike shine. This is a hard sell to some CEOs, who often equate cleanliness with a bright shiny floor.

Hard-surface floors, cleaned with various types of surface disinfectants, have been described to have no significant impact on the incidence of nosocomial infections; however, disinfection of surfaces in the immediate proximity to patients has been known to reduce acquisition of pathogens such as VRE (Kramer, Schwebke, and Kampf, 2006). Since people don't touch the floor whether it is carpeted or hard-surface, it seems not to be a source of contamination.

A very interesting study by Lankford and colleagues (2007) evaluates 14 specific types of flooring, wall finishes, and upholstery fabrics after contaminating them with PSAE and VRE. Using the manufacturers' recommended cleaning methods, samples were cultured after one day, three days, and one week. The method of transmission was freshly washed hands. All surfaces contaminated with VRE remained contaminated for a week; however, contamination levels dropped for 11 of the materials except for VCT, microvented perforated vinyl wallcovering, and continuous monofilament polyethylene textile paper-backed wallcovering. All of these finishes maintained contamination levels after one week.

Selection criteria for finishes used in patient care areas include that they be smooth with little texture. A counterintuitive finding in this study was that smoother surfaces were, on the whole (with the exception of vinyl upholstery), less effectively cleaned and/or more likely to transmit infection to hands. A possible explanation is that smooth surfaces make it easier to transmit pathogens to hands and that absorptive surfaces keep disinfectants in contact with the pathogens longer. Different cleaning methods were used on each product per manufacturer's instructions (Leib and Rohde 2007).

This study will be very useful to interior designers, because the materials and the cleaning methods tested are identified in a meaningful way. An easy-to-read summary of the Lankford study has been written by Leib and Rohde (2007).

Materials tested (Leib and Rohde 2007)
Upholstery
1. 100% woven solution-dyed nylon fabric (A-M*)
2. Polyester and acrylic-blend woven Crypton (A-M*)
3. 100% jacquard woven polyester with proprietary water-based polymeric coating (A-M*)

4. Vinyl upholstery (A-M*)

Flooring

5. Tufted 6.6 solution-dyed carpet with woven synthetic backing (A-M*)
6. Tufted 100% solution-dyed proprietary nylon carpet with recycled vinyl backing
7. VCT
8. Linoleum
9. Vinyl sheet goods
10. Rubber tile

Wall finishes

11. Latex paint with eggshell finish
12. Vinyl wallcovering, Type II, 20 oz.
13. Vinyl microvented perforated vinyl wallcovering Type II, 20 oz.
14. Continuous monofilament polyethylene textile paper-backed wallcovering

*A-M indicates antimicrobial treatment claims.

Findings

Painted surfaces cleaned with a mild detergent still had some contamination, whereas vinyl wallcovering had none after being cleaned with a strong quaternary soap solution. The other two wallcoverings (#13 and #14) tested also had no contamination after being cleaned according to manufacturer's recommendations. Interestingly, solution-dyed 6.6 nylon carpet had no contamination after cleaning, whereas vinyl sheet goods, VCT, and rubber tile had spotty contamination. Further, antimicrobial additives did not appear to enhance clinical performance.

Furniture and Fabrics

Furniture is thought to be a minor infection risk (Noskin and Peterson 2001), but prolonged survival of VRE, *C. diff*, and other pathogens on chairs makes the patient high-back chair a potential reservoir for contact contamination. In the Lankford study (2007), solution-dyed fabric, Crypton fabric, and vinyl showed no contamination after cleaning. The types of strong disinfectants used by hospitals and the bleach solution required to kill *C. diff* spores can destroy wood furniture frames and arm caps as well as cause deterioration to fabrics, including vinyl upholstery. Chairs with mesh seats and powder-coated steel frames may be better able to withstand harsh cleaning solutions. It has been this author's experience that regulatory agency inspectors who never used to comment on furniture are now interested in patient room seating. They may want to examine a log book to see what was used to clean the chair fabric after a patient with an infection was discharged, and they may expect that chair fabrics be cultured occasionally after cleaning to see if cleaning methods were effective.

From a practical standpoint, chairs will be easier to disinfect and clean if there is a space or opening between the seat and back (this also prevents bodily fluids from collecting in the crevice), and if they have no welting or cording on the edges and no upholstered paneled arms that create a crevice for bodily fluids.

A Canadian manufacturer has introduced a line of unupholstered chairs coated with colorful silicone, which is known to be inert, impermeable to fluids, and inherently flame retardant as well as incapable of supporting microbial growth. According to the manufacturers, it can be cleaned with soap and water and will withstand the harshest hospital cleaners. It's a different look than the "soft" upholstered chairs we have become accustomed to in healthcare but, if the priority is to reduce sources of contamination, this is worth considering.

Cubicle or privacy curtains are frequently touched by caregivers and are a potential source of contamination; yet, these are infrequently changed or washed. A study investigating five common hospital fabrics: 100% cotton (clothing), 100% cotton terry (towels), 60/40 cotton/polyester blend (scrub suits and lab coats), 100% polyester (cubicle curtains), and 100% polypropylene plastic (splash aprons) as sources of transmission of nosocomial microorganisms concluded that fabric type may influence survival of pathogens (Neely and Maley 2000). Most of the bacteria tested survived longer on polyester cubicle drape fabric than on cotton. *Staphylococci* and *enterococci* survived for days to months on this fabric, suggesting that these drapes can be a reservoir for bacteria. Fabric blends (on which bacteria survived for at least a day) are most commonly worn by healthcare workers, and these fabrics can become vectors for spreading infections as the sleeve of a lab coat touches one patient before moving to another (Neely and Maley 2000).

Other Sources of Contamination

There are any number of surfaces that need to be disinfected but may occasionally be overlooked by housekeeping staff who are under pressure to clean a room in a specified time limit. For example, a hospital outbreak of MRSA was traced to a stretcher and a hand-held shower. An electronic ear-probe thermometer was implicated in an outbreak of VRE (Neely and Maley 2000). Admission of a VRE-free patient to a hospital room previously occupied by a patient colonized with VRE was found to be an independent risk factor for nosocomial acquisition of VRE by the previously uncolonized individual (Neely and Maley 2000). Stethoscopes and blood pressure cuffs are rarely disinfected as nurses and physicians move from patient to patient. Think about the patient bathroom and the number of hands touching the door handle, light switch, faucets, toilet seat, towel bar, towels, and shower drape (if any). When caregivers empty bedpans in the toilet, there is an aerosol when the toilet is flushed. Particles of fecal matter may contaminate surrounding surfaces.

Patients with *C. diff* infections often have diarrhea. Imagine the possibilities for infection when touching faucets and light switches upon entering and exiting the bathroom. Multiply this times two for semiprivate rooms and exponentially for families and visitors. A strategy to reduce contamination may be to use infrared sensor faucets and soap dispensers and to activate bathroom lights with a motion sensor. The telephone next to the patient's bed may be a reservoir for pathogens in the small holes of the mouthpiece. The device is touched by many hands, the mouthpiece may touch a mucous membrane (the mouth) and aerosols from speaking or coughing may contaminate surfaces of the phone.

Steel grab bars

Grab bars commonly used in bathrooms and showers are Type 304 18-gauge stainless steel and many of them are shot-blasted or peened to make the surfaces more slip-resistant. In a report evaluating common satin-finish stainless steel grab bar material, rough-peened grab bar finish, anodized aluminum, and polyamide 6 nylon grab bar material, the results showed that the satin finish grab bar had so much porosity as to provide a reservoir for microbial incubation; the rough-peened finish fared even worse. The anodized aluminum sample had less porosity than either of the aforementioned grab bars and the polyamide nylon had no significant surface porosity (http://www.unsafegrabbars.org). Since grab bars are placed in humid and damp locations and subject to chlorine-treated water in showers, which is known to cause pitting and crevice corrosion in Type 304 steel (according to the Stainless Steel Development Association), this seems like an issue that needs to be investigated further.

CONCLUDING REMARKS

Clearly there is a new mandate for the design of healthcare facilities. It starts with a thorough understanding of patient safety and infection control issues, which must be interlaced with new layouts of patient units based on the research findings of the IHI's *Transforming Care at the Bedside* (2004) and Ascension Health/Kaiser Permanente's "Time and Motion" study of nursing work patterns. The ambience of patient care areas is also important. Design features as appealing as those in the lobby and public areas must be carried into procedure and treatment spaces as well as into patient rooms, bathrooms, and core areas.

References

American Institute of Architects. 2006. *Guidelines for design and construction of health care facilities.* Washington, DC: American Institute of Architects.

Appleby, J. 2007. WellPoint ties bonus to goals for care. *USA Today,* April 4, 1B.

Carpenter, D. 2006, Tracking infections. *Hospitals & Health Networks,* February, 59–61.

CDC. See Centers for Disease Control and Prevention.

Centers for Disease Control and Prevention. 1994. Guidelines for preventing the transmission of Mycobacterium tuberculosis in health-care facilities, October. http://www.cdc.gov/MMWR/PREVIEW/MMWRHTML/00035909.htm (accessed November 20, 2007).

Centers for Disease Control and Prevention. 2000. Multidrug-resistant organisms in non-hospital healthcare settings, December. http://www.cdc.gov/ncidod/dhqp/ar_multidrugFAQ.html (accessed April 27, 2007).

Centers for Disease Control and Prevention. 2004. Information about MRSA for healthcare personnel, August 31. http://www.cdc.gov/ncidod/dhqp/ar_mrsa_healthcareFs.html (accessed April 27, 2007).

Centers for Disease Control and Prevention. 2005. Vancomycin-resistant *Enterococci* (VRE), April 5. http://www.cdc.gov/ncidod/dhqp/ar_vre.html (accessed April 27, 2007).

Centers for Disease Control and Prevention. 2006. MRSA in healthcare settings, October 6. http://www.cdc.gov/ncidod/dhqp/ar_mrsa_spotlight_2006.html (accessed April 27, 2007).

Consumer Reports. 2007. Nanotechnology: Untold promise, unknown risk. July.

Evans, P. 2005. Antimicrobial research. White paper, Tandus Technologies.

Fields, L. 2007. Break through! Germ-killer coating. *The Reader's Digest*, March.

Flower, J. 2006. Headed for a tipping point? *Hospitals & Health Networks.* http://www.hhnmag.com (accessed November 21, 2006).

Garner, J. 1996. Guidelines for isolation precautions in hospitals. Centers for Disease Control and Prevention. http://www.cdc.gov/ncidod/dhqp/glisolationptII.html (accessed April 27, 2007). Also published in *Infection Control Hospital Epidemiology.* 1996. 17:53–80 and *American Journal of Infection Control.* 1996. 24:24–52.

Gladwell, M. 2000. *The tipping point.* New York: Little, Brown and Co.

Gurian, M. 2007. Nanotechnology in high-performance upholstery for sports arena and healthcare applications. *American Association of Textile Chemists and Colorists Review* 7(4).

HICPAC. See Healthcare Infection Control Practices Advisory Committee.

Healthcare Infection Control Practices Advisory Committee. 2003. *Guidelines for environmental infection control in health-care facilities.* Recommendations of the Centers for Disease Control and Prevention (CDC) and HICPAC. U.S. Department of Health and Human Services, CDC. http://www.cdc.gov/ncidod/dhop/pdf/guidelines/Enviro_guide_03.pdf (accessed January 6, 2007).

Institute of Medicine. 1999. *To err is human: Building a safer health system.* Washington, DC: National Academy of Sciences Press.

Institute of Medicine. 2001. *Crossing the quality chasm: A new health system for the 21ˢᵗ century.* Washington, DC: National Academy of Sciences Press.

Interface. 2002. *Technology brief: Intersept antimicrobial preservative protection.* La Grange, GA: Interface Flooring Systems.

Joseph, A. 2006. The impact of the environment on infections in healthcare facilities. Issue paper, Center for Health Design.

Kaiser Permanente. 2006. Antimicrobial position paper, Kaiser Foundation Health Plan Inc.

Kramer, A., I. Schwebke, and G. Kampf. 2006. How long do nosocomial pathogens persist on inanimate surfaces? *BMC (BioMed Central) Infectious Diseases.* (6):1–17. http://www.pubmedcentral.nih.gov/articlerender.fcgi?tool=pubmed&pubmedid=16914034 (accessed February 2, 2007).

Lankford, M. G., S. Collins, L. Youngberg, D. M. Rooney, J. R. Warren, and G. Noskin. 2007. Limiting the spread of infection in healthcare environments. Research report, Coalition for Health Environments Research/Center for Health Design.

Leape, L., and D. Berwick. 2005. Five years after *To Err Is Human*: What have we learned? *JAMA* 293(19): 2384–2390.

Leib, R., and J. Rohde. 2007 Are those room finishes and cleaners safe? *Healthcare Design* 7(3):12–17.

Lundstrom, T., G. Pugliese, J. Bartley, J. Cox, and C. Guither. 2002. Organizational and environmental factors that affect worker health and safety and patient outcomes. *American Journal of Infection Control* 30(2):93–106.

McCaughey, B. 2005. Coming clean. *New York Times*, June 6. http://www.nytimes.com/2005/06/06/opinion/06mccaughey.html?oref=login (accessed June 6, 2007).

Murphy, D., and J. Whiting. 2007. Dispelling the myths: The true cost of healthcare-associated infections. White paper, Association for Professionals in Infection Control and Epidemiology Inc.

National Quality Forum. 2003. *Safe practices for better healthcare*. Washington, DC: The National Quality Forum.

Neely, A., and M. P. Maley. 2000. Survival of *Enterococci* and *Staphylococci* on hospital fabrics and plastic. *Journal of Clinical Microbiology* 38(2):724–726.

Noskin, G., and L. R. Peterson. 2001. Engineering infection control through facility design. *Emerging Infectious Diseases* 7(2). http://www.cdc.gov/ncidod/eid/vol7no2/noskin.htm (accessed June 10, 2007).

Rogers, J. 2006. The debate over fountains in healthcare environments: How great is the risk? Lecture presented at the Center for Health Design Pebble Project Partner Meeting, Milwaukee, WI.

Russell, S. 2007. High staph infection rates in hospitals stun public health officials: New study reports lethal drug-resistant bacteria widespread. *San Francisco Chronicle.* June 25.

Rutherford, P., B. Lee, A. Greiner. Transforming care at the bedside. White paper, IHI Innovation Series, Institute for Healthcare Improvement. (Available on http://www.IHI.org)

San Diego Union-Tribune. 2006. Report: Medicinal mix-ups rampant. New York Times News Service. July 26: A1.

Skoutelis, A. T., G. O. Westenfelder et al. 1994. Hospital carpeting and epidemiology of *Clostridium difficile. American Journal of Infection Control* 22(4):212–217.

Sunenshine, R. H., and L. C. McDonald. 2006. *Clostridium difficile*-associated disease: New challenges from an established pathogen. *Cleveland Clinic Journal of Medicine* 23(2):187–196.

Thomson, K. S. 2001. Controversies about extended-spectrum and AmpC beta-lactameses. *Emerging Infectious Diseases* 7(2). http://www.cdc.gov/ncidod/eid/vol7no2/thomson.htm (accessed on June 14, 2007).

Ulrich, R. S., C. Zimring, A. Joseph, X. Quan, and R. Choudhary. 2004. *The role of the physical environment in the hospital of the 21st century: A once-in-a-lifetime opportunity.* Center for Health Design: Concord, CA.

Oncology Waiting Area | Rebecca and John Moores Cancer Center
UC San Diego Medical Center, La Jolla, CA. Zimmer Gunsul Frasca Partnership. Photography: © Robert Canfield

Incorporating Research into Design Features | 4

Although attention to infection control issues is the foundation of good hospital design, this should be something that patients can rely on and, perhaps one day, take for granted. The aesthetics of the environment, however, present an opportunity to comfort and nurture patients. While incredible views are an added bonus, the ambience of most hospitals is dependent on the building's architecture as well as lighting, ceiling design, use of color, artwork, and sound. Manipulating these items is what makes the difference between creating a lifeless environment versus one that builds an experience to be enjoyed and remembered. Wayfinding legibility is another important aspect of how visitors experience an environment. Navigational problems erode the sensory pleasures of beautiful design features.

LIGHTING

Lighting—both natural and electric—is the most important component of an interior environment. Adequate exposure to natural light is essential for biological health and entrainment of circadian rhythm. Research indicates that patients in rooms that receive more sunlight are less depressed and have reduced length of stay (Beauchemin and Hays as reported in Ulrich et al. 2004).

Likewise, staff members who have exposure to natural light may be less fatigued and more able to direct their attention (Tennessen and Cimprich 1995). Clearly, light affects humans psychologically and physiologically. There is a difference between sunlight (electromagnetic radiation in the wavelength range that can be absorbed by the photoreceptors of the eye) and electric light, which contains wavelengths of light concentrated in limited areas of the visible light spectrum (Joseph 2006).

Full-spectrum fluorescent lamps that approximate daylight can be purchased, but the cost is much higher than more commonly used lamps that have more limited spectral range such as red to orange or blue to green, and they provide less light per unit of electrical energy. Other research findings include:

- **Lighting levels can influence the performance of visual tasks:**
  Fewer dispensing errors were made in a pharmacy when light levels were quite high—1,500 lux (Buchanan et al. as reported in Joseph 2006). The aging eye requires significantly more light due to the reduced translucency of the lens. As the healthcare workforce ages, providing adequate light for high performance becomes an important consideration.

- **Light impacts biological functions:**
  When light hits the retina, it is transmitted to the hypothalamus, which regulates the body's circadian rhythm—the release of hormones and coordination of biological functions that are synchronized by the body's internal time clock. Changing time zones or the absence of a day-night cycle of light interrupts this function causing irritability, drowsiness, and a sense of disorientation. Charles Czeisler at Harvard is one of the leading researchers in this field. Keeping those who work night shifts alert while they perform critical tasks such as nursing requires exposure to intermittent bright light during the night shift. In one study, four 20-minute exposures to 5,000 lux bright light alleviated the nurses' distress associated with night-shift work (Leppamaki et al. as reported in Joseph 2006).

A more detailed explanation of the physiology of the body's circadian system and a discussion of the benefits of exposure to daylight, as well as a more general review of the impact of light on outcomes in healthcare settings can be found in the Joseph article (2006).

Focus on Natural Light

Huge, dense buildings that have historically been associated with large medical centers are now being more imaginatively designed to bring light into the core. In fact, several European countries require that every room occupied by humans must have natural light. This does pose a challenge for large buildings that spreads them out horizontally, but it can be done if this is a cultural or code-imposed imperative.

Practical Lighting Considerations

Good lighting design is an art in any building, no less so in hospitals. Indirect lighting should be used in any area where patients are lying on their backs, which means corridors, procedure rooms, and patient rooms. Indirect lighting comes in a variety of forms from a linear uplighted valance running along the perimeter of a corridor to a recessed cove light or a lay-in light fixture with a reflector that directs the light upward, as opposed to downward. These fixtures work well for ambient (general) illumination in emergency department treatment rooms, diagnostic imaging rooms, and patient rooms when complemented by examination lights. The standard 2 x 4-foot fluorescent fixture with prismatic acrylic lens that has been the hallmark of institutional lighting should be used only in back-of-the-house areas.

Here are a few tips for lighting:

- Make use of natural light by way of sidelights alongside doors, skylights, clerestories, and windows whenever possible.

- Use energy-efficient low-mercury content lamps by manufacturers committed to the Environmental Protection Agency's goals of reduce, reuse, and recycle. The newest lamps provide more lumen output per watt without sacrificing color or ambience.

- Use fluorescent lamps with 3500° Kelvin color temperature (this refers to the phosphors that coat the lamps) to render colors more realistically and to enhance skin tone. Another important dimension of lamp selection is the color rendering index (CRI), which should be a minimum of 86, regardless of color temperature. While it's true that general cool white lamps are less expensive, the gray-blue color they cast on skin tone and interiors makes them a poor investment. St. Joseph's Community Hospital of West Bend, Wisconsin (see Image 7.24), after working with General Electric's lighting laboratory in Nela Park, selected a high-performance fluorescent lamp with 4100° Kelvin color temperature and a high CRI so that one consistent lamp could be used throughout the facility, including procedure areas, which means the patient's skin tone will appear the same in any setting from a clinical perspective. The aesthetic ambience of this lamp is good due to the high CRI.

- Use a variety of light fixtures to add design interest.

CEILINGS

An array of prefabricated ceiling systems offers designers an opportunity to create unique design treatments at far less expense than a custom design. These include a variety of wood ceilings, undulating acrylic panels, aluminum grids, and more. Often these are combined with acoustical tile. A most important consideration is the noise reduction coefficient (NRC) rating of the tile. What most hospitals and commercial buildings use is .65 NRC, which is not adequate to reduce the noise and reverberation at nurses' stations, in corridors, and in patient rooms. The maximum NRC currently available in acoustical tile is .95, which means that it absorbs 95% of sound energy. Acoustical tile should be carefully selected for each functional area of the hospital as opposed to one general tile used throughout.

ACOUSTICS

Noise is the most deleterious of environmental stressors. It interrupts sleep, impacts speech intelligibility, increases heart rate, and creates a stressful work environment for staff. Noise is generated by equipment carts, paging systems, staff conversation (particularly annoying to patients at night), alarms, telephones, visitors, falling objects, ice machines, and HVAC systems.

In nursing units, studies have shown that reverberation time is a key factor (Berg 2001; Blomkvist et al. 2005). The nonsound-absorbing surfaces in a hospital enable the sound to linger, echo, and overlap, especially within a patient room. Reverberation is the persistence of sound in an enclosed space, resulting from multiple reflections after the source of the sound has stopped (Joseph 2007). Many studies document that staff conversation is a major source of loud noise on inpatient units (Ulrich et al. 2004; Joseph 2007).

Neonates are especially impacted by loud noise levels, which decrease oxygen saturation (increasing the need for oxygen support therapy), elevate blood pressure, increase heart and respiration rates, and interrupt sleep (Joseph 2007). The rate of wound healing can be negatively impacted by noise and result in a longer hospital stay, and noise can increase the perception of pain, requiring more pain medication.

Working in a noisy environment takes its toll on staff members who have to raise their voices to be heard; staff suffer noise-induced stress, emotional exhaustion, and burnout (Joseph 2007).

Measurement of Noise

Hospitals are noisy places. The World Health Organization (WHO) guidelines for continuous background noise in hospital patient rooms are 35 dB(A) during the day and 30 dB(A) at night, with nighttime peaks not to exceed 40 dB(A). Current background noise levels in hospitals are commonly 72 dB(A) during daytime hours and 60 dB(A) during the nighttime (Joseph 2007). A decibel is a unit for quantifying sound pressure intensities or loudness levels based on a *logarithmic* scale, which means that a *doubling* of sound intensity would result from a 3 dB(A) increase in sound-pressure levels for diffuse sound fields; but, to human ears, a 10 dB(A) increase would be perceived as a doubling of loudness. This means that a 60 dB(A) sound is perceived as approximately four times as loud as a 40 dB(A), despite having a pressure level 100 times higher (Joseph 2007). The human ear responds to certain frequency ranges, which explains the (A) or (a) after the decibel (dB) reading; this is a weighted decibel reading that can also be written "dBA." The essentials of recording decibel levels in a hospital and a process for documentation and analysis are explained by Mazer (2005).

Noise levels in hospitals, according to Joseph (2007), often peak at decibel levels equivalent to jackhammers or walking next to a busy highway when a truck passes. A portable X-ray machine can exceed 90 dB(A), which is more than 100,000 times higher in sound pressure than the recommended daytime level of 35 dB(A). It would be prudent for hospital purchasing agents to request technical data on the noise generated by medical devices and equipment that they are considering for purchase. If enough focus is put on this issue as a criterion for procurement, manufacturers will pay more attention to it in research and development.

Strategies for Reducing Noise

Strategies for reducing noise levels include the use of high-performance ceiling tile (high NRC rating) in nurses' stations and patient rooms, changing the type of food service carts used to a type that rattles less or has an insulated enclosure to muffle the sound, walls that extend above the finished ceiling to the deck above, single patient rooms, and the use of wireless communication devices that eliminate overhead paging.

The presence of another patient in a room with the concomitant conversation of visitors, caregivers, the snapping of bed rails, coughing, cries of pain, and snoring create tremendous stress for the other patient in the room. The advantages of single bed rooms is discussed in detail in Chapter 7, but this is the most effective strategy to reduce noise, and it also leads to higher patient satisfaction, according to Press Ganey and other surveys (research cited in Chapter 5). Although environmental interventions are important, staff-education programs are another component of noise-reduction strategy. Staff should not call to each other from a distance and should be aware of the need to speak quietly, especially at night.

The strategies employed in the design of St. Joseph's Hospital of West Bend (see Image pages 4.23 to 4.28) to reduce noise were numerous and so successful that the total absence of noise in a patient room is almost eerie.

Seven fixes to reduce noise at Mayo (Sykes 2004)

These seven strategies were employed by Mayo Health System in Rochester, Minnesota, to reduce noise in patient units:

1. Move shift-change staff report to enclosed room away from nurses' desk.
2. Place foam rubber padding in chart holders outside patient rooms and in pneumatic-tube document delivery system.
3. Replace roll-type paper towel dispensers with folded-towel dispensers.

4. Routinely close the doors to patient rooms.
5. Modify cardiac monitor setting to allow lower volumes in patient rooms, add alarms that sound at nurses' station.
6. Use flashlights instead of overhead lights when entering patient rooms.
7. Educate staff about the issue and share noise-control measures.

The Mayo outcome, according to Sykes (2004), is that "two-thirds of the patients commenting in a satisfaction survey about noise and sleep issues gave positive feedback to the closed door, general unit quietness, and the willingness of staff to ensure a quiet night of sleep."

Six fixes to reduce noise at Rhode Island Hospital (based on research by Richard Millman, director of the Sleep Disorders Center of Lifespan Hospitals, Providence, Rhode Island) (Sykes 2004)

1. Arrange patients in individual rooms.
2. Move equipment alarms away from patients.
3. Relocate nurses' stations away from rooms.
4. Switch beepers to vibrating mode.
5. Train doctors and nurses to speak softly.
6. An alternative: Determine if ear plugs or noise cancellation equipment yield better sleep quality.

These are the three methods designers can use to deal with noise (Sykes 2004):

1. Absorb sound by using high NRC-rated ceiling tile (minimum 0.85 and above) and wallcoverings.
2. Block sound by using NRC and sound transmission class-rated panels, partitions, doors, and ceiling tiles.
3. Cover (mask) sound by using electro-acoustic privacy systems.

In addition, patients can be offered noise-cancellation headphones or noise-isolation headphones for a CD or DVD player. Managing this in a hospital can be a challenge due to theft and infection control issues associated with something that touches the ear and hair.

Sound-masking systems can be problematic in healthcare environments because the ability to hear and respond to many types of auditory stimuli such as monitor alarms, oral communication, and speech-recognition dictation systems can be compromised by something that renders speech less intelligible and may lead to errors (Joseph 2007).

A study to assess noise and flooring applications in patient care units
A study undertaken by an architectural firm describes how two aspects of the physical setting—noise and flooring materials—impact each other (Geboy, Keller and Schnuck 2005). This type of on-site research also

reveals how the competing influences of principal stakeholders (the infection-control and environmental services teams) affect the final decision. In this case, the former rejected carpet over sheet vinyl flooring and the latter preferred carpet.

Field measurements of noise levels revealed that conversation and human interactions (walking, noisy shoes, jangling keys) were the most frequent sources of noise, followed by environmental (telephones, televisions, rolling carts, and equipment) and architectural (sources of noise penetrating the building from outdoors). Fixed features such as the opening and closing of doors and panic hardware ranked fairly high.

There were four strategic recommendations for sound control: material selection and installation, proximal location of support spaces and equipment on the unit, operational and behavioral change, and equipment maintenance. In the end, the design team recommended sheet vinyl for inpatient nursing unit corridors due largely to practical considerations of ease of maintenance, durability, and infection control. Recommendations included that a sound-control committee be formed to focus on controlling noise in nursing units in addition to a sound-control protocol to address behavioral interactions and equipment noise. Furthermore, sound-awareness signage was proposed as well as a committee to explore strategies to introduce positive auditory interventions such as music.

Speech privacy and patient confidentiality

Anyone who works in any capacity in healthcare is aware of HIPAA, the Health Information Portability and Accountability Act of 1996, which mandates that oral communications with patients be kept private—not overheard by unintended listeners. This has become the standard of care, and breaches of privacy can result in litigation and fines.

Here are some examples from case law: Upon learning someone had metastatic cancer, a banker called a mortgage due for that individual. The disclosure by a pharmacist, to a family member, that the customer had HIV led to a custody suit being filed by the man's ex-wife. Revealing drug-abuse information about an individual caused her to lose her job.

The level of speech privacy achieved in a space is expressed as a privacy index (PI) as presented in an Armstrong Ceiling Systems (2003) document in Exhibit 4.1.

The *Interim Sound and Vibration Guidelines for Hospitals and Healthcare Facilities* recommend that normal speech privacy be provided between enclosed rooms, and confidential speech privacy be provided in admitting areas, any place where patients discuss personal health issues, exam rooms, blood labs, etc. (Joseph 2007).

Exhibit 4.1 Levels of Speech Privacy

- **Confidential:** PI rating 95% to 100%

  Conversations within a space may be partially overheard but not understood.

- **Normal:** PI rating 80% to 95%

  Conversations may be overheard but are only partially intelligible.

- **Marginal or poor:** PI rating 60% to 80%

  Most conversations will be overheard and intelligible to unintended listeners.

- **No privacy:** PI rating less than 60%

  All conversations can be fully overheard and understood.

Another organization working on issues of oral privacy is the Workgroup for Electronic Data interchange (http://www.wedi.org/).

VIEWS: CONNECTING PATIENTS TO NATURE

There is no doubt that a great view enhances the pleasure of our experience. Whether it is distant mountains (Image page 5.4), a restorative garden (Image page 5.14) accessed from a chemotherapy setting, or a view of water from a patient room (Image page 7.40), humans respond positively to natural light and views of nature.

The patient's experience can be enhanced by the placement of images of nature in the ceiling in procedure rooms such as radiation therapy, diagnostic imaging, endoscopy, and in preparation and recovery rooms as well as corridors with gurney traffic. These are realistic images printed on film transparencies that are applied to a rigid translucent lens that replaces the standard light-fixture lens.

Another opportunity for enabling patients to connect with nature in the patient room is by way of a large flat-screen television and programs such as the Continuous Ambient Relaxation Environment (CARE) channel (www.healinghealth.com). A disk with 60 hours of nonrepetitive nature images accompanied by specially composed music based on research as to what is soothing or healing is provided on a closed-circuit channel through the hospital network. This channel can be set as the default whenever someone turns on the television. As an option, a patient may select a specific nature image that will personally be most healing and actually keep it on the screen as a piece of artwork as long as desired, or allow the images to sequence. This system was developed for hospitals to provide an alternative to the noise of monitors and conversations overheard from the nurses' station. Built into it is a 24-hour clock that adjusts the tempo of the music for nighttime vigils in the intensive care unit, for example, when television with its annoying advertisements can be quite stressful for families.

ARTWORK

Works of art are a positive diversion in healthcare settings, enabling patients who are in pain or who are experiencing anxiety to momentarily take their mind off their problems. In the hospital setting, however, the specific subject matter of the art is important. Ulrich has noted in his research that a person who is ill interprets a piece of art in a very different way than a person who is well. This is known as the emotional congruence theory—the notion that a person's emotional state can bias the perception of environmental stimuli to match his or her feelings (Bower 1981; Singer and Salovey 1988; Niedenthal, Setterlund, and Jones 1994).

This means that images that are ambiguous can be frightening, stimulating patients to see hands about to grab them or a sky opening up to swallow them. A scene with an empty chair or a boat dock with an empty boat may cause a healthy person to recall pleasant memories of a vacation escape, but to a person whose spouse is critically ill, the empty chair can symbolize death or abandonment. Similarly, artful photographs of women who have had mastectomies may be cathartic for the women who posed for the photos, or for the photographer, who might have grappled with recovery from cancer. However, for women about to undergo cancer treatment, exposure to such images can be painful, unless they are introduced in a one-on-one session by a therapist who can assess the readiness of the patient.

Evolutionary theory indicates that images of nature are the most successful in being restorative—relieving stress—for diverse groups of people, provided the subject matter realistically depicts nature, whether it is a view of gardens, calming water features, mountains, or sand dunes. Compositions that have a depth of perspective and an element of mystery (for example, a path that winds back into the image leading the eye to imagine something that is just around the bend) are especially effective as are those that are spatially open and savannah-like.

The research also shows that abstract art can be almost pathological for patients in a treatment or patient care setting; however, this type of art could be considered for lobbies (Ulrich, Lundén, and Eltinge 1993; Wypijewski 1997). Images that are provocative or designed to make a statement are not suitable for healthcare facilities. (Author's note: For a thorough, research-based discussion of art in the healthcare setting, see Chapter 7, "Healing Arts," by Ulrich and Gilpin in Frampton and Gilpin 2003).

Although not in the conventional sense a work of art, the Phillips Lighting ambient experience is designed to allow patients to customize a diagnostic imaging room, or even a patient room, by waving a radio-frequency card over a reader to trigger specific lighting effects and animations projected onto the walls and ceiling to create a more personalized experience. This type of technology can also be used to change the color of a wall to suit a patient's preference.

Color

Color is an elixir; it can stimulate, soothe, excite, and add dramatic impact to a space. For too many years, hospitals were characterized by white walls and floors (or that pale green color) and corridors that seemed to run to infinity with no accent walls to break the monotony. This ambience is synonymous with institutional environments. It's what would come to mind when one pictured a hospital. In recent years, however, architects and designers have embraced color and texture in healthcare settings and used innovative lighting techniques to highlight those features. Children's hospitals today are wonderful examples of design that lift the spirit, harnessing technology, color, and artwork to delight and educate children. For a thorough discussion of color research, specifically for healthcare, see Malkin (2002) and Tofle et al. (2004). The photos in various chapters of this book provide an opportunity to evaluate the use of color to enhance and define spaces.

Music

A preponderance of research indicates many positive benefits to employing music in patient care settings. This body of research is quite large; a few examples follow.

Routhieaux and Tansik (1997) examined the benefits of music in hospital waiting rooms and found that it reduced self-reported stress levels, which were, in turn, inversely related to perceptions of customer service. Chlan and Tracy (1999) found that music therapy is an effective intervention for anxiety reduction and stress management in critical care patients. Coughlan (1994) provides an overview of the physiological and psychological benefits of using music therapy in intensive care. Updike (1990) explores the physiological and psychological impacts of music therapy simultaneously, as opposed to considering them individually. He concludes that music therapy is a necessary nursing intervention in a holistic model of care.

Snyder and Chlan (1999) looked at research on music therapy between the years 1980 to 1997 and, although great variation existed in the type of music selected, the populations studied, and the methodologies used, overall, music was found to be effective in producing positive outcomes. These included the reduction of pain and decreases in anxiety and aggressive behaviors as well as enhancement of well-being.

Standley (1986) conducted a comprehensive review of the literature between the years 1929 to 1984 on the topic of music and medicine. Using meta-analysis to integrate diverse findings, she discusses the clinical use of music, the physiological and psychological benefits (which had been recorded as early as 1880 in France), and the translation of this research to clinical applications of music-therapy techniques and program development in a general hospital setting.

Music, noise, and the human voice

Occasionally one comes across a journal article that touches on a number of related topics and integrates them in a profoundly interesting way, pulling in references as diverse as Florence Nightingale and what is referred to as "women's talk" among nurses as they care for patients. Many research studies are brought into the discussion as the author (Pope 1995), a nurse, examines music, noise, and the human voice in the nurse-patient environment and how these significantly alter people's perception of their experience. We learn that hearing is the first sense fully attained by a human fetus at 135 days' gestation and that an infant, less than two hours after birth, can identify its own mother's voice. We also learn that some people are more sensitive to noise than others, and this may be influenced by past experience and the familiarity of a sound and the necessity of a noise.

Pope reviews numerous studies about the impact of verbal communication among nurses and patients as well as the physiological responses to music on subjects as varied as ventilated neonates (simulated intrauterine sounds mixed with synthesized female vocals led to improved oxygenation and weight gain) and oncology patients (required less pain medication than those who did not listen to music). Overall, subjects who listen to music they like exhibit significant positive immune responses.

Cultural interpretations of sound

Choice is an important component of any complementary therapy, such as music. What is music to one person may be noise to another. Certainly gender, age, and ethnicity influence this. What we hear is filtered through a cultural context. Sound is actually neutral, but our perception of it determines the physiologic and psychological effects (Pope 1995).

An amusing example of the discord between type of music and listener is illustrated by the trend in which classical music is used to disperse teenage loiterers at 7-Eleven stores in Victoria, British Columbia (Wallis 1999). Bombarding the parking lot with classical music kept teens from congregating. The owner of a commercial building in downtown Denver, Colorado, found that broadcasting operatic arias was highly successful in irritating sidewalk preachers and religious fanatics who would go on late into the night (Wallis 1999). And a judge in Colorado punishes offenders arrested for blaring music from their cars by forcing them to listen to a special playlist starting with Beethoven's *Fifth Symphony* to Wayne Newton and the theme song from "Barney."

Biomedical foundations of music as therapy

Music therapy, the intentional use of music to enhance well-being or to reduce pain and anxiety, has been used in every patient setting. Manipulation of the rhythm, beat, pitch, or harmony can cause the music to be more therapeutic in inducing relaxation and positive responses in the neuroendocrine and sympathetic nervous systems, resulting in decreased anxiety, heart and respiratory rates and increased temperature (Joseph 2007).

The biomedical foundations of music therapy are well documented in a book by that title (Taylor 1997), in which the theoretical basis for the observed clinical effects of music is explained. This book is technical enough to appeal to scientists, but it is enriched with anecdotes and applications to specific patient populations. A vast number of interesting facts, reports of conference proceedings, and case studies are interwoven into the text. An appealing aspect of the writer's style for readers who lack medical training is the careful description or explanation of medical disorders or procedures, such as hemodialysis or the panoply of changes to virtually all organ functions in response to a severe burn injury. This type of information is difficult for design professionals to obtain, but it is basic to being able to design optimal environments for specific patient populations.

"Shaping" the environment with music

A system to improve the typical hospital soundscape (developed by Don Campbell, author of *The Mozart Effect*) offers a vast library of world music tailored to the unique function of each area of the hospital, from the chapel to the emergency department. Campbell's strategy separates the hospital into harmonic zones, each with music that beats to a different tempo and rhythm depending upon function and time of day. Campbell, in his high-profile public appearances and popular books on the benefits of music, has introduced this topic to a wide audience (Campbell 1997). His reference citations are a mix of new-age spirituality sources and research journals. It's interesting reading, but for someone trying to relate the stories to the research, it's cumbersome as the notation method is idiosyncratic: references are listed by chapter, at the end of the book, not by name, but by page number in the form of endnotes. Nevertheless, Campbell's passion for collecting stories about music and healing from diverse cultures and his travels to many countries bring a unique perspective.

Wayfinding Design

Space planning should be a collaborative effort between architect and interior designer. Since wayfinding legibility is basically a function of good space planning, it is essential to step back and look at the building form and schematic layout to see if architectural landmarks are present (a view of a garden, courtyard, perhaps another building on the campus that has a memorable presence) that can serve as visual cues. A clear strategy should be developed for moving patients from each point of entry to all major destinations. For example, maintaining contact with the outdoors is desirable for all main artery corridors if site planning allows for this. Architectural features such as skylights, atriums, a ceremonial stair, unique public art, and sufficient reinforcements to let people know that they are on the right path become a network of wayfinding aids. These are complemented by artwork and signage and a careful application of color that enhances, but does not compete with, visual wayfinding cues (Malkin 1992).

If space planning is well-executed, one should not have to rely on a lot of signage. Exquisite attention should be paid to wayfinding issues in parking structures, especially with respect to calling attention to building entries. It is shocking to note how many medical centers fall short in this regard and cause enormous stress for patients and visitors. Likewise, building entries should be obvious and architecturally attention-getting for anyone entering the suite.

Getting lost is merely annoying and aggravating when one is well, but in a healthcare setting, it is far more serious. When not feeling well, anxiety about being late for an appointment, cardiac insufficiency, and ambulation problems can combine to make wayfinding problems a big stressor that taxes patients in many ways.

Hospitals sometimes regard signage as a wayfinding system. In fact, it is only one component. An integrated system includes, in main artery circulation corridors, easily understood signs and numbers coordinated with lighting and interior finishes that highlight and support—not compete with—the signage. Interior design features can be used to call attention to important directional signage. For example, at a critical decision point, a soffit, background wall color, or a photograph of an easily remembered image can focus attention on the signage to visually create a memorable landmark.

Other components of a wayfinding system are clear and consistent verbal directions, printed materials, and mailers with maps and travel directions sent to patients in advance of their visits. Website directions should also be consistent with verbal and printed directions.

Much has been written about wayfinding design in recent years, but the research by Carpman, Grant, and Simmons (1984) laid the foundation by providing many practical guidelines and graphic illustrations. Among other things, they discuss the necessity of using easily understood nomenclature for departments. *X-ray* is better than *diagnostic imaging* and *blood draw* better than *phlebotomy* if the goal is to communicate effectively.

Because people use different strategies to find their way through a complex building, it is important to layer multiple orientation aids. Some may prefer to follow a handheld map, while others may use signage; still others will continually ask staff for directions as they move through the building. To be effective, "you-are-here" maps should always be oriented in the direction of travel (Carpman, Grant, and Simmons 1984). Several studies have demonstrated that there are gender differences in wayfinding strategies: women tend to rely on landmarks and relative directions while men rely more on cardinal direction and distances (Choi et al. 2006).

CONCLUDING REMARKS

Understanding how to use research to create interior environments that comfort and nurture patients as well as enhance the well-being of staff is both an art and a science. While studies can document noise on patient units and its negative effects on patients as well as staff, it's the designer or architect's skillful manipulation of solutions to the problem that becomes an art. The importance of views of nature is well established in research literature, but it is the skill of the design team that determines how successfully interior spaces are suffused with natural light and how accessible views of gardens and water features are to patient care areas.

Lighting is another issue of great importance. Need it be said that one can meet functional illumination levels, use indirect lighting as appropriate, and still lack the magic that good lighting design can bring to the ambience of an interior environment? Both science and art, good lighting design enhances color and texture to create spaces that are memorable.

This chapter has presented a number of environmental features that can be manipulated by design professionals who wish to improve the patient's experience. Research specific to patient unit design and related design concepts is presented in Chapter 7.

References

Armstrong Ceiling Systems. 2003. *Rx for healthcare speech privacy: A balanced acoustical design.* Lancaster, PA: Armstrong Ceiling Systems.

Berg, S. 2001. Impact of reduced reverberation time on sound-induced arousals during sleep. *Sleep* 24(3):289–292.

Blomkvist, V., C. A. Eriksen, T. Theorell, R. S. Ulrich, and G. Rasmanis. 2005. Acoustics and psychosocial environment in coronary intensive care. *Occupational and Environmental Medicine* 62:1–8.

Bower, G. 1981. Mood and memory. *American Psychologist* 36:129–148.

Campbell, D. 1997. *The Mozart effect.* New York: Avon Books.

Carpman, J. R., M. A. Grant, and D. Simmons. 1984. *No more mazes: Research about design for wayfinding in hospitals.* Ann Arbor, MI: University of Michigan Hospitals.

Chlan, L., and M. F. Tracy. 1999. Music therapy in critical care: Indications and guidelines for intervention. *Critical Care Nurse* 19(3):35–41.

Choi, J., E. McKillop, M. Ward, and N. L'Hirondelle. 2006. Route strategy differences in men and women. *Environment and Behavior* 38(6):791–801.

Coughlan, A. 1994. Music therapy in ICU. *Nursing Times* 90(17):35.

Geboy, L., A. B. Keller, and K. Schnuck. 2005. Assessing a hospital sound environment: Findings and evidence-based recommendations for architectural design and behavior. Paper presented at the annual meeting of the Environmental Design Research Association, Atlanta, GA.

Joseph, A. 2006. The impact of light on outcomes in healthcare settings. Issue paper, Center for Health Design.

Joseph, A. 2007. Sound control for improved outcomes in healthcare settings. Issue paper, Center for Health Design.

Malkin, J. 1992. Wayfinding design: A new look at an old problem. In *Hospital interior architecture.* New York: John Wiley and Sons Inc.

Malkin, J. 2002. Impact of color on the medical environment. In *Medical and dental space planning: A comprehensive guide to design, equipment, and clinical procedures,* 3rd ed. New York: John Wiley and Sons Inc.

Mazer, S. E. 2005. Hear, hear: Assessing and resolving hospital noise issues. *Health Facilities Management,* April.

Niedenthal, P. M., M. B. Setterlund, and D. E. Jones. 1994. Emotional organization of perceptual memory. In *The heart's eye: Emotional influences in perception and attention*, eds. P. M. Niedenthal and S. Kitayama. Orlando, FL: Academic Press.

Pope, D. S. 1995. Music, noise, and the human voice in the nurse-patient environment. *IMAGE: Journal of Nursing Scholarship* 27(4):291–296.

Reiling, J. 2007. *Safe by design.* Oakbrook Terrace, IL: Joint Commission Resources.

Routhieaux. R. L., and D. A. Tansik. 1997. The benefits of music in hospital waiting rooms. *Health Care Supervision* 16(2):31–40.

Singer, J. A., and P. Salovey. 1988. Mood and memory: Evaluating the network theory of affect. *Clinical Psychology Review* 8:211–251.

Snyder, M., and L. Chlan. 1999. Music therapy. *Annual Review of Nursing Research* 17:3–25.

Standley, J. 1986. Music research in medical/dental treatment: Meta-analysis and clinical applications. *Journal of Music Therapy* 23(2):58–122.

Sykes, D. M. 2004. Noise, privacy, and sound: Impacts on healthcare [A primer]. Lecture presented at HealthcareDesign '04, Houston, TX.

Taylor, D. B. 1997. *Biomedical foundations of music as therapy.* St. Louis, MO: MMB Music Inc.

Tennessen, C. M., and B. Cimprich. 1995. Views to nature: Effects on attention. *Journal of Environmental Psychology* 15:77–85.

Tofle, R. B., B. Schwarz, S. Y. Yoon, and A. Max-Royale. 2004. *Color in healthcare environments.* Concord, CA: Coalition for Health Environments Research/Center for Health Design.

Ulrich, R. S., O. Lundén, and J. L. Eltinge. 1993. Effects of exposure to nature and abstract pictures on patients recovering from heart surgery. Paper presented at the 33rd Meeting for the Society of Psychophysiological Research, Rottach-Egern, Germany. (Abstract published in *Psychophysiology*, 30.)

Ulrich, R. and L. Gilpin. 2003. "Healing Arts," in *Putting patients first: Designing and practicing patient-centered care. Eds., S. B. Frampton, L. Gilpin, and P.A. Charmel.* New York: Jossey-Bass.

Ulrich, R. S., C. Zimring, A. Joseph, X. Quan, and R. Choudary. 2004. *The role of the physical environment in the hospital of the 21st century: A once-in-a-lifetime opportunity.* Center for Health Design: Concord, CA.

Updike, P. 1990. Music therapy results for ICU patients. *Dimensions of Critical Care Nursing* 9(1):39–45.

Wallis, D. 1999. Eine Kleine bus-terminal-clearing music. *The New York Times*, August 8.

Workgroup for Electronic Data Interchange. 2004. Oral communications: Myths and facts. White paper, Security and Privacy Workgroup.

Wypijewski, J., ed. 1997. *Painting by the numbers: Komar and Melamid's scientific guide to art.* New York: Farrar Straus and Giroux.

Restorative Garden | Good Samaritan Cancer Center
Puyallup, WA. KMD Architects. Michael O'Callahan Photography

Designing the Experience: Choreographing the Patient/Process Interface

5

Clearly one of the factors influencing hospital design is competition among providers. The response is to provide the best possible experience for patients and their families. Marketing experts tell us that Baby Boomers, in particular, are interested in services that are packaged to create a memorable experience, and that they will quickly shift their loyalty to a provider who meets these expectations.

Starbucks tapped into this by figuring out how to orchestrate an experience around a basic commodity—a cup of coffee—and charged three times the norm for the product. Starbucks, and the coffeehouse experience in general, has become so ubiquitous that it's hard to remember there was a time when coffee was just a basic drink made with beans of unknown origin that were pre-ground in a factory. One either drank it at home (and some even used instant coffee) or at a restaurant or donut shop.

Starbucks and the romanticizing of the coffee bean has spawned a sociological phenomenon of the coffeehouse having become a locus of neighborhood socializing, a place where one can "hang" for hours writing a book, answering e-mails, or reading—with no pressure to buy anything.

The lesson from this? The coffeehouse has created social value beyond the product itself.

CREATING MEMORABLE EXPERIENCES

There is any number of other successful retail and entertainment establishments such as Nike Superstores or Disney that do a superb job of creating a memorable experience that goes beyond the purchase of a product. And it's not just the built environment that's a factor. In the hospital setting, it's a script for how patients are greeted, how recovery is made when service falls short of promise, and it replaces individual improvisation with consistently appropriate messages that help communicate an institution's culture.

Experiences can be *designed*. It starts with a patient's first impression—whether it's stress associated with finding parking and the correct door to enter or the view of the emergency department waiting room (Image pages 9.5 and 9.7). The goal is to manage the clues or evidence coming through all of the senses so that they tell a story consistent with the mission, values, and culture of the organization (Berry, Wall, and Carbone 2006).

Every Business Is a Stage

Orchestrating the consumer's experience is the subject of a book by Pine and Gilmore (1999) called *The Experience Economy* that proclaims every business is a stage, and the healthcare setting is but another opportunity to manage details in a way that bonds the patient to the brand. This is an even more powerful concept when applied to healthcare because patients are at a great knowledge disadvantage with the provider; to dispel fear, they look hard for clues they *can* understand—interactions with staff and the design or comfort of the environment. Because healthcare service is intangible and complex, patients can neither see nor understand it (Berry 2002).

Leonard Berry posits that the environment is a surrogate for this—it provides a torrent of clues about the healthcare services. It helps tell a story that the service itself cannot. The experience includes views of nature in the treatment setting, a harpist playing at patients' bedsides, staff who ask patients how they would like to be addressed, and notifying patients in advance via their television screens of scheduled procedures so that a transport gurney doesn't suddenly arrive to take them away for an MRI or CT scan.

Three Types of Clues Create Impressions

Services are performances. There is no tangible product to try on or demonstrate. And certainly there is no more intimate service experience than healthcare. During these experiences, customers consciously and unconsciously filter clues and organize them into sets of impressions—this includes whatever can be perceived by its presence or absence. If you can see, hear, taste, or smell it, it's a clue. Anyone wishing to manage these factors in designing the patient's experience would do well to read an outstanding article by Berry, Wall, and Carbone (2006) that goes into considerable detail. The following is based on that article.

Functional Clues

Functional clues reveal the reliability and competence or the technical quality of the service. Is the room-service order correct? Were the medications given on time?

Mechanic Clues

Mechanic clues involve the sensory presentation of the service—anything from a signature color to the sounds of equipment to the tangibles associated with the temperature of the oatmeal.

Humanic Clues

Humanic clues are associated with the behavior and appearance of the service providers—choice of words, body language, smile, level of enthusiasm, and dress. The guest-relations programs undertaken by hospitals fall into this category.

According to Berry, Wall, and Carbone (2006), "Clues create the service experience by influencing customers' thoughts, feelings, and behavior." The uniqueness of the medical-service encounter is that patients are rarely able to fully evaluate the technical competence of the clinical care, nevertheless they make a judgment based on interactions with staff and their sensory perceptions of the setting or built environment.

During surgery, for example, there are numerous opportunities for error in the administration of anesthesia, in surgical technique, or protocols for preventing blood clots from forming, but the patient will be unaware of these occurrences certainly at the time they are happening and, possibly, will only become aware of malfeasance by having suffered ill effects. So it seems there is another dimension unique to healthcare services. Whereas functional, mechanic, and humanic clues deal with what is directly experienced and within the realm of the senses, much of what happens in a hospital—some of which can have catastrophic consequences—cannot be seen, but can cause anxiety and worry. How can one not be concerned about errors made in the pharmacy, illegible physician handwriting, medications given at the wrong time or dosage, allergic drug reactions not heeded, or room furnishings not adequately disinfected? The built environment can be part of a strategy to relieve this anxiety in that, if properly designed, it becomes a surrogate for what people can't directly observe; it can reassure and inspire confidence.

A Complex Cluster of Value Satisfactions

According to 1980s marketing guru Ted Levitt, even the most generic products, or in this case, basic healthcare services such as drawing blood, are to the potential "buyer" what Levitt calls "a complex cluster of value satisfactions." Differentiation among products or services is not limited to giving customers what is expected. The expected service may be augmented by things they never thought about (Levitt 1980). As an example, for years renting a video or DVD meant walking into a store for the transaction. Netflix came along and enhanced the convenience and customer satisfaction (order by Internet, ability to preview a film before ordering, set up a personal queue, two-day delivery, free shipping) and seriously damaged Blockbuster's business.

First Impressions Matter

Psychologists say that the human tendency to form impressions quickly is an evolutionary adaptation. In order for the species to survive, humans were forced to develop a keen sensitivity to quickly identify nurturing or threatening environments. This may account for the immediate physiological changes that often occur when an individual encounters the typical healthcare setting: an environment that is cluttered and noisy and has hard, shiny surfaces, unfamiliar equipment, and frightening views of patients on gurneys with numerous IV lines and tubes. Confronting our own mortality—*this could happen to me*—realizing that your life may be changed forever by what occurs in this environment may be a subconscious but real fear.

To help create better experiences, hospitals have occasionally turned to the hospitality industry for guidance on guest relations and for appealing visual images that connote comfort. The fundamental flaw in this thinking is that patients come to hospitals to experience what are often life-changing events of great emotional significance, such as the birth or death of a child, the death of a parent, the trauma of a serious accident. There is simply no parallel in the hospitality industry. For this reason, hospital experiences are seared into their memories. The life-and-death nature of these encounters elevates them to a sacred status, yet the stage on which this drama unfolds is often unworthy of such holiness.

The Impact of Baby Boomers

Planning new hospitals requires a look at the demographics of the population, and this shows it is clearly biased toward that huge group of individuals called Baby Boomers. Born between 1946 and 1964, this generation of 76 million people currently represents 25% of the population, and they will present a challenge for which hospitals are unprepared. Today, one in eight Americans is age 65 or older (Coile 2003). Baby Boomers are well-informed, harder to please, and have greater expectations than any previous generation. Conditioned by years of have-it-your-way retail marketing, Baby Boomers expect an array of amenity options offered in a healing environment setting by staff who are responsive, kind, and attentive. They expect convenience, comfort, and are motivated by the power of choice. A recent cartoon featured a patient, seated on an examination table, saying to the physician: "Well, www.what'swrongwithme.com says it's just a virus, but I came to you for a second opinion."

Remember that it was this group of women, who, in their childbearing years, demanded changes in the birthing experience, which led to LDRs (labor/delivery/recovery) and LDRPs (labor/delivery/recovery/post-partum). They refused to have their babies delivered in an operating room. Imagine what changes they will demand as they approach the age of 65 and start needing lots of healthcare. For example, one of the things they expect is allopathic care interwoven with complementary therapies, which has led hospitals to introduce integrative medicine programs and spa services to meet those needs. The focus on wellness, the desire to remain healthy until the end of life (in fact, it has humorously been said that Californians consider death as optional) and the significant lifestyle changes some individuals are willing to make to live to the age of 100, mean that the healthcare system will be overwhelmed by the sheer number of persons in this age demographic.

The literacy problem

Oddly, the many articles written on the tastes and sociological habits of Baby Boomers often fail to recognize that they, like any age cohort, are not a homogeneous group. Along with those who are well educated and seek the latest health information on the Internet, there is an equal number who score in the below-basic or basic levels of literacy in the three levels of literacy: prose (reading), document (understanding instructions), and quantitative (performing simple computation, such as addition) (National Adult Literacy Survey 2003).

This isn't limited to Baby Boomers. According to the same survey, nearly half of the U.S. adult population (90 million people) have low functional health literacy (National Adult Literacy Survey 2003), and 61 percent of seniors (age 65-plus) read at or below the fifth-grade level (DeBuono 2007). Most health-related material is written at the tenth-grade reading level or higher (Institute of Medicine quoted in DeBuono 2007), and literacy skills are a stronger predictor of health status than age, income, employment status, education level, or racial/ethnic group (DeBuono 2007).

Literacy is a major problem in healthcare today. Many individuals cannot find basic information on a prescription label and are likely to interpret "take a pill four times a day" as "take all four at once." Forty-two percent of patients had trouble understanding the instruction to take medication on an empty stomach (Baker et al. 1996).

The implications for design are numerous. For example, the way signage and wayfinding orientation systems are designed and our expectations that patients will be able to use electronic wayfinding kiosks may have to be re-examined. Think about this: The literacy test for basic level includes tasks such as using a television guide to find out what programs are on and comparing the ticket prices for two events. Intermediate level includes tasks such as identifying a specific location on a map or calculating the total cost of ordering office supplies from a catalog (DeBuono 2007). Hospitals increasingly use websites to provide instructions to patients and offer health information. Perhaps a low-literacy version should be available. The many educational brochures handed out in hospital lobbies and in specialty departments and the admissions forms that patients must sign do not address the literacy problem. And, when speaking of designing the patient's experience, we must consider the tastes and needs of less-educated people as well as the many immigrant populations served by hospitals across the nation, people who may have very different customs and may not speak any English.

The ramifications of health literacy for hospitals and the risks they assume when treating these patients is underscored in a fact sheet published by the Center for Health Care Strategies Inc. (2007). In one study, 67% of patients who admitted low literacy said that they had not even disclosed it to their spouses, and 85% had not disclosed it to co-workers. Imagine what this means for healthcare workers treating patients. One of the strategies offered (and this may apply to the aforementioned signage and wayfinding issues) is the use of cartoon figures to help patients visualize instructions. Other strategies are discussed by Villaire and Mayer (2007).

Health status of Boomers

A 2007 study published by the nonprofit National Bureau of Economic Research presents a very different picture of the health status of aging Boomers than that portrayed in popular magazines and newspapers. The sample was drawn from more than 20,000 Americans over age 50, with tracking starting in 1992. The lead author of the report, Beth Soldo, a sociologist and director of the Population Aging Research Center at the University of Pennsylvania, noted "Our findings certainly run counter to the prevailing expectations of generally good health in old age, the idea that we'll be running marathons when we're 100 and drop dead unexpectedly" (Bowman 2007).

The differences between the youngest group and the oldest was most notable in reporting problems of chronic illness, pain, drinking, and psychiatric problems. Men in the early Boomer group were three times more likely to report psychiatric problems than the oldest group, and women were more than twice as likely to report these types of problems. Oddly, the youngest group had more problems with activities such as walking, climbing stairs, or getting up from a chair. Participants in the study led by Soldo were not asked their weight, but the reports of disability in early Boomers led the researchers to wonder if obesity was the cause, noting that this also contributes to heart disease and diabetes. According to Soldo, researchers in aging are closely watching this group as an indicator of what lies ahead for the huge group that follows as they enter retirement. A Scripps Howard analysis undertaken in early 2007 looking at causes of death among Boomers in 2003 found that deaths due to suicide and drug-related causes were higher than the rate in the preceding generation (Bowman 2007).

Children of Boomers are referred to as Gen-X, born between 1965 and 1976. In 2007, persons 31 to 42 years of age represented approximately 21% of the population. Having grown up with computers, they are very comfortable with technology: they want to be connected to the world. Considered the best-educated generation, they are entrepreneurial and tend to be overachievers. This is not generally the age group that hospitals need to consider, however, when designing an optimal inpatient experience as they are too young to need much healthcare themselves, but they do need to be considered in the design of children's hospitals. It's Baby Boomers and their parents who are the focus of adult healthcare facilities including long-term care.

Patients as Consumers

There is another force at work influencing strategic planning. In the millennium, the patient is the consumer, not the health plan. And quality is the primary purchasing criterion, not price. Consumerism represents a fundamental realignment of strategy for healthcare providers, from wholesale bargaining with managed-care plans to retail marketing directly to consumers to attract their business. Market share can be won or lost based on consumer perceptions. This means marketing is directed primarily to women because women make most of the healthcare choices for their spouses, children, aging parents, friends, and colleagues.

WHAT DO PATIENTS REALLY WANT?

As Gervais points out (1993), what patients care about most are not the things that health professionals often think they care about. Patients in the Picker/Commonwealth project focus groups, for example, spoke little of hotel-type amenities so dear to marketers (Gerteis et al. 1993). Instead, foremost in their minds was the sense of vulnerability and helplessness imposed by hospitalization and having to be dependent on others for the most basic of daily activities. Until those needs were met, patients couldn't focus on anything else. If call lights were not answered promptly or patients could not get help with bathing or toileting, they were four times more likely to say they would not return to that hospital and nine times as likely to not recommend it to a friend. Yet these tasks may not even be monitored as part of a caregiver's performance evaluation. Although improving the process of care and the way in which services are delivered lies outside the purview of architects and designers, it's important to realize the broader context of what matters to patients. Designing the patient's experience is always a multidisciplinary endeavor that starts with how care will be delivered; planning the built environment is a response to the care model and redesign of the delivery process to make it safer and more efficient. At best, process redesign and the physical design of the building are a tightly woven tapestry.

The largest patient satisfaction survey ever conducted (Press Ganey Associates 2006) involving 1,576 hospitals and more than 2 million patients, highlighted the 10 issues most highly correlated with the likelihood of recommending the hospital (ranked in order of priority).

1. Response to concerns/complaints made during your stay
2. Staff effort to include you in decisions about your treatment
3. Staff sensitivity to the inconvenience that health problems and hospitalization can cause
4. Degree to which hospital staff addressed your emotional/spiritual needs
5. How well the nurses kept you informed
6. Promptness in responding to the call button
7. Room cleanliness
8. Waiting time for tests or treatments

9. Accommodations and comfort for visitors

10. Amount of attention paid to your special or personal needs

11. Pleasantness of room decor

Further analysis of the data indicated that, right across the board, patients who had a roommate (semiprivate room) rated every aspect of the experience lower. Moreover, 3 of the top 10 issues concern the facility.

Rating the Hospital Experience

In a survey in which patients rated their experiences of hospitalization, the five items with the highest and the lowest rankings are shown in Table 5.1.

Highest and Lowest Ratings of Hospitalization Experience	Table 5.1
Items with Highest Ratings	**Average Rating**
Skill of physician	91.46
Friendliness/courtesy of the nurses	89.84
Friendliness/courtesy of physician	88.89
Skill of nurses	88.70
Courtesy of person who admitted you	87.76
Items with Lowest Ratings	
Quality of the food	71.15
If you were placed on a special/restricted diet	72.34
Noise level in and around room	73.47
Temperature of food	75.26
Room temperature	76.18
Source: The Press Ganey Satisfaction Report, Vol. VII, August 2003	

In the same report, gender differences in ratings of hospital care seem idiosyncratic, as shown in Table 5.2.

Gender Differences in Ratings of Hospital Care	Table 5.2
Rated Higher by Men	**Rated Higher by Women**
Skill of person starting IV	Pleasantness of room decor
Amount of attention paid to special/personal needs	Rating of pre-admission process
Promptness in response to call button	How well physician kept you informed
Nurses' attitude toward your requests	Noise level in and around room
Quality of the food	Speed of admission process
Source: The Press Ganey Satisfaction Report, Vol. VII, August 2003	

IMPORTANCE OF THE BUILT ENVIRONMENT

The physical environment has a substantial impact on patients' and family members' hospital experiences, their ability to function, their comfort, and their overall well-being according to a study done for the Center for Health Design by the Picker Institute (1999a). This research included both focus groups and in-depth interviews that occurred over a two-year period; through it, the elements of the built environment that mattered most to people can be summarized in the following eight themes.

1. **Promotes connections to staff:** visual access to caregivers, quick access in emergencies, and an effective communication system

2. **Is conducive to well-being:** focus on noise reduction; patient control of room temperature, TV, lighting; accommodation for family; adequate space for grooming and daily tasks; Internet access; negative distractions minimized (sharps container, hazardous waste containers, strange equipment); adequate lighting; storage for personal belongings; adequate electrical outlets

3. **Is convenient and accessible:** clarity of wayfinding on the campus, parking close to hospital, clearly marked entrance and drop-off areas, emergency department entry clearly identified, privacy at admitting and registration, visible wayfinding directories and visitor information near entry, an easy-to-navigate internal signage and wayfinding system, elevators clearly marked, short travel distances between destinations

4. **Is confidential and private:** quiet areas where patients can be alone, privacy for bathing and dressing, privacy when treatment options and financial issues are discussed

5. **Shows caring for family:** access to telephones, visiting areas for family with seating in privacy groupings, play space for children, variation in seating to accommodate a wide range of users, overnight accommodations, private grieving space, family amenities (shower, kitchen, vending machines)

6. **Is considerate of impairments:** consideration for persons using assistive devices, wheelchair access at information desks and elsewhere, adequate space to move around patient room using wheelchair, bathrooms large enough for use of assistive devices, signage easy enough to read for someone with a visual impairment, benches or chairs placed in strategic locations to enable ambulating patients to rest

7. **Facility's connection to the outside world:** exterior gardens and opportunities to connect with nature, views from the bed, keeping in touch via Internet, television

8. **Is safe and secure:** well-lit parking lot, safe path from public transportation, adequate handrails within facility, clearly-marked fire exits, slip-proof bathrooms

Attempts to Improve the Patient Environment

The first attempt to challenge the status quo in the delivery of care occurred in the early 1980s. Prior to that, hospitals were run on a military timetable—everything focused on convenience for the caregivers, not the patients. Then came the 13-bed Planetree Model Hospital project in San Francisco, California, that challenged the very essence of what it means to deliver care in a way that honors and respects the patient. Many articles have been written about Planetree over the years, as well as *Putting Patients First*, a book that should be required reading (Frampton, Gilpin, and Charmel 2003). Even though Planetree principles should be familiar to design professionals and caregivers, this is often not the case. What everyone *is* familiar with is patient-centered care, but they may not know that this concept is the legacy of Planetree. Planetree has had an epic influence on hospitals culminating in the patient-centered care movement—the first real change in the way care was delivered since 1900. And to think that just a handful of passionate contrarians could kick off a revolution in an industry as large as healthcare.

Patient-centered care is not patient-focused care

Although the terms *patient-centered care* and *patient-focused care* are often used interchangeably, they are quite different. Patient-centered care is based on evaluating all ideas in terms of what is most convenient and comfortable for patients. Patient-focused care, on the other hand, is an approach to re-engineering hospital operations to achieve higher performance (Lathrop 1993). In something akin to time and motion studies, all aspects of hospital operations were studied by the consulting firm Booz Allen Hamilton (Lathrop's firm) looking for wasted effort and inefficiency. Some of this does, of course, benefit patients, but that is not the focus, as it is for patient-centered care.

The nine elements of Planetree patient-centered care

The nine elements of Planetree patient-centered care are (Frampton, Gilpin, and Charmel 2003):

1. The importance of human interaction
2. Informing and empowering diverse populations (consumer health libraries and patient education)
3. Healing partnerships (the importance of including family and friends)
4. Nutrition (the nurturing aspects of food)
5. Spirituality (inner resources for healing)
6. Human touch (the essentials of communicating caring through massage)
7. Healing arts (nutrition for the soul)
8. Integrating complementary and alternative practices into conventional care
9. Healing environments (architecture and design conducive to health)

Family-Centered Care

According to the Institute for Family-Centered Care, family-centered care is an approach to the planning, delivery, and evaluation of healthcare that is grounded in mutually beneficial partnerships among patients, families, and healthcare professionals. Families are understood to be anyone whom patients regard as significant in their lives. Family-centered care focuses on individuals' and families' strengths instead of their limitations, with appreciation for diversity across racial, geographic, age, and economic lines. Family-centered care is an expression of patient-centered care, both respect collaboration between families, patients, and healthcare professionals. The Institute for Family-Centered Care is a terrific resource for designers, architects, and healthcare professionals who wish to design positive patient experiences. Many of the institute's publications deal with specific patient populations such as children or cancer patients. Very detailed strategies for implementing family-centered care are offered in the form of guides and action plans.

Families: Visitors or partners in care?

Family members used to be considered visitors as opposed to partners in care (*Advances in Family-Centered Care* 2002). Access to the patient was often limited. The most powerful messages about the roles of families are conveyed by staff communication and body language. The Planetree movement in the early 1980s boldly asserted that family should participate in care because it provides emotional support for the patient and makes the transition to home care more successful. Designated family members can be educated about wound care, timing of medications, and gain other skills while under the watchful eye of nurses prior to having to execute care when patients return home. It gives them confidence that they can do it. Family members can provide much-needed information that will help in clinical decision making. After all, they know the patient much better than the staff does.

Family-centered care is well-accepted by children's hospitals for obvious reasons, but it has been a hard sell for many other hospitals. As recently as 2002, the Institute for Family-Centered Care made this the theme of an issue of its journal, *Advances in Family-Centered Care* (2002). The articles present the viewpoints of a number of national and regional organizations on this topic. The ability for a family member to sleep overnight in the room on a sofa designed for this purpose has become familiar, if not widespread, in recent years, and most hospitals currently being planned embrace this as a given. Acceptance of this has been most difficult for those who work in critical care. It is a hurdle a number of courageous nursing leaders have successfully surmounted in new inpatient units (Image pages 7.17 and 7.21). Now that all new hospitals will have private rooms, it will be easier to have a family member sleep in the room and, as acuity-adaptable rooms become more common, integration of family as part of the care team will be firmly established for all levels of acuity.

DESIGNING THE EXPERIENCE

The process of developing a new model of care delivery has many steps and is approached in different ways by different organizations. The foundation must be based on understanding the community's perceptions of the hospital, its strengths and weaknesses. Hospitals sometimes undertake the task of "designing the experience" when they are building a new campus on a greenfield site or they may be embarking upon a patient tower on an existing campus. An individual department or service, such as a cancer center or the emergency department, may want to improve its patient satisfaction scores and thus begin an audit to uncover problems.

Branding and Experience Engineering

Branding is a concept from retail marketing in which a set of messages and images are created to associate a company and its products with emotional values. Experience engineering, on the other hand, focuses on creating a business that delivers the brand as an experience incorporating these values (Haeckel, Carbone, and Berry 2003). Consistency in graphics, logo, and messages makes sense, and these are aspects of branding, but it seems the term is being overused of late as a quick fix instead of doing the hard work of engineering positive experiences for patients and families.

Mayo Clinic is known for extraordinary service and an unwavering commitment to the well-being of its customers. Berry and Seltman (2007) discuss the services branding model responsible for Mayo's success and how it turns customers into marketers by virtue of word-of-mouth communications. They explain that a *services brand* is essentially a promise about the nature of a future experience with an organization or individual service provider; the *presented brand* is the organization-controlled communication of a desired brand image (this includes uniforms, logo, website, advertising, all of which directly impact brand awareness); *external brand* communication is the organization-influenced communication about the brand by the consumer or publicity, and it is often conveyed via the Internet.

Doing an Experience Audit

The process for doing an experience audit is discussed by Berry, Carbone, and Haeckel (2002) and illustrated by an example of a university hospital emergency department that undertook this task. The audit revealed minimal recognition of the emotional needs of patients and even less for the needs of their families. In a careful analysis and documentation of the entire patient experience, the study team task force created more than 100 positive experiential clues that started with positioning signs saying "Hospital 3 Miles" to reassure people as they approached the facility and creating a less confusing entrance for drive-up patients. The security guard became a greeter and roving ambassador, helping people navigate the registration process. The hospital even improved the morgue experience. Overall, the hospital eliminated many negatives that had previously gone unnoticed and added many emotionally positive clues.

Listening with the heart, not the head

Developing empathy for what patients experience is very different from gathering information and trying to fix problems. Leebov (2007) points out that, too often, leaders focus on solutions and improvements, but they lack the emotional intelligence about what patients are really feeling. She proposes an action plan of empathy fitness exercises, such as

- putting on a patient gown and being taken by a transporter on a gurney ride from the emergency room to an inpatient unit;
- shadowing a patient fully through one service experience and, afterward, asking the patient what helped reduce anxiety and build confidence;
- eavesdropping in an area where staff make follow-up calls to patients;
- identifying a high-traffic point where patients come for service and sitting inconspicuously reading a magazine—listening to and noticing what patients are experiencing;
- putting on a uniform and having a transporter train you to do this job;
- walking around with a camera and taking photographs, looking through the patient's eyes;
- identifying 10 visible indications that patients are not front and center.

Leebov (2007) offers many additional examples of how leaders and staff can respond to patients with compassion and empathy. Data derived in this manner are going to be very different from what is gleaned from patient satisfaction surveys.

Walk a Mile in My Shoes

Patients are on a journey—whether it is to prevent disease and maintain wellness or to deal with a life-threatening illness. The journey the patient takes from sickness to health is sometimes more like a rollercoaster than a well-planned sequence of events. "Patients and their family members are constantly torn between assertiveness and compliance, bargaining and demanding. They cannot afford to alienate the caregivers on whom they must depend" (Beckham 1993). If ever there was a sentiment that deserved to be tattooed on the minds and hearts of all who serve patients, it is what ethicist Emily Friedman says: "Treat patients as if your life depends on the outcome of your care; as if your fate is tied up with theirs. An airline pilot has a vested interest in getting you safely to your destination."

Tell patients what measures are in place to ensure their safety. St. Joseph's Hospital of West Bend, Wisconsin (Image pages 7.23 to 7.28) hands out a lexicon for diagnostic imaging equipment, explaining in common language what these machines do. The booklet also explains the names of different hospital departments to demystify them. Patients are encouraged, in writing, to watch for caregivers washing their hands, and it empowers them to request this if such protocols are not followed.

Functional Silos: Specialty Myopia

Those who seek to redesign the processes by which care is delivered often refer to hospital departments as specialty silos, each functioning independent of the others, each concerned about its own welfare and share of the pie. Carried to the microlevel—that of direct patient care—there is often a tendency for each specialist to focus on one body part or disease process without regard for the patient as a whole being. An apt analogy is offered by Beckham (1993): "The patient passes from specialist to specialist who, like horses with blinders, can lack the benefits of peripheral vision…we've set up a delivery organism with inadequate neural pathways, unable to conduct the spark of communication across its ever-widening synapses. Human beings…come as complete packages. They are holistic. The care they receive is too often fragmented. The specialists go about their business as if the organs of their concern exist in splendid isolation."

Commenting on this from another perspective, futurist Ian Morrison described one of his personal hospital experiences as "islands of clinical excellence surrounded by the Department of Motor Vehicles" (Morrison 2006).

Here and there efforts to enhance teamwork and communication are occurring. Paul Uhlig, MD, and colleagues instituted multidisciplinary collaborative rounds at the patient bedside in a cardiac surgery program in Concord, New Hampshire, in 1999 (McCarthy and Blumenthal as reported in Joseph 2006). The team reviews the patient's care plan, discusses medication and treatment and, with full transparency, addresses errors in a blame-free environment (Joseph 2006). Mortality rates declined, and both provider and patient satisfaction increased significantly (Uhlig et al. 2002).

Putting It All Together

A culture that is seamlessly integrated with the design of the new building creates a positive experience for patients. Clarian North Medical Center in Indianapolis, Indiana (Image pages 5.2, 5.3, 5.10, 5.11, and 5.20) is a good example. Collaboration among hospital staff, physicians, and patients leads to lasting impressions of compassionate care and impeccable service. Five principles or core maxims were developed to guide expectations of behavior and express the organization's mission, vision, and values. Every employee/associate takes a pledge to uphold the core maxims to ensure that patients always have an extraordinary experience (Finkam 2006).

1. **Show kindness:** Demonstrate that I care.
2. **Connect fully:** Listen, make eye contact, and make each person feel appreciated.
3. **Take ownership:** Be responsible for my actions, attitudes, and decisions.
4. **Create joy:** Be positive and lift the spirits of those around me.
5. **Do more:** Look for ways to surprise my customers, to exceed their expectations.

Clarian is also dedicated to family-focused care, which is expressed in the following four principles.

1. **Dignity and respect:** Incorporate patient/family culture, beliefs, and values in care delivery.
2. **Information sharing:** Patients receive timely, complete, and accurate information to enable them to participate in decision making.
3. **Participation**: Patients and families are encouraged to participate in decision making at whatever level they choose.
4. **Collaboration**: Teamwork between physicians, nurses, and other healthcare providers is encouraged.

Outcomes of the Process					Figure 5.5
Diagnostic (Including Imaging) Study Team					
Challenge with Current Process	**Suggested Improvement**	**Design Issue**		**Process Improvement Issue**	
		Implement Now	Future Opportunity	Implement Now	Future Opportunity
There are many duplications in the outpatient registration process	Pre-register patients and ask for patient information only at one time in the process		Provide cabling for electronic integration Provide space for registration in the physician's office	Conduct "trial" registration process in Physician Offices Simplify the process/require less information	Electronic pre-registration

Source: Lehman et al. 2000. "Translating Function into Form: Redesigning the New White Memorial." Education Forum, Symposium on Healthcare Design, Anaheim, CA, December 1, 2000.

Lean design

Breaking down the processes for delivery of care is a complex task. The director of planning and architecture for a large health system counted 47 individual steps required for a patient to get an X-ray (Stinson, Chambers, and Radovanovich 2003). After considerable study, the team was able to reduce it to 17 steps, but department boundaries blocked going below that, as did the inadequate flow of information—certain data were never there in time. There was a disconnect between the building and the strategic plan: the building was holding hostage an optimized process and flow. Interestingly, there is often disagreement among clinical staff as to what the current process is. Clinical-services process mapping can be used to understand current practices.

An example of process redesign for pre-admit testing (PAT) underscores the value of this type of analysis for both improving the patient's experience and the organization's financial performance. The team noted the average cycle time was 43.2 minutes for PAT for each modality times an average of three modalities for a total of two-and-a-half hours. By centralizing these activities (laboratory, electrocardiogram, consult, and admitting questionnaire) in the exam room, the total time can be reduced to 27 minutes (exclusive of the chest X-ray) with much lower cost (Stinson, Chambers, and Radovanovich 2003). From the patient's perspective, it involves only one wait and one stop. However, the financial analysis can be complex: cutting five FTEs (full-time equivalents) in specimen collection, for example, may add an FTE to another department, which makes its bottom line look bad. Therefore, an analysis of the entire organization is required to see the overall impact.

Beware of recreating the familiar

Here's where culture eats strategy for lunch. Changing the process of delivering care is mighty hard. This is especially true when the new building is on an existing campus as opposed to building a new hospital on a greenfield site. It takes strong leadership to help nursing teams envision something other than "this is the way we've always done it." And yet this is so understandable. Nurses do not get rewarded for taking risks. Following protocols is what they are expected to do, and they are expected to adapt to all kinds of poorly planned work environments in which they find themselves. They are experts at making do when supplies do not arrive on time or the desired piece of equipment cannot be found. Nurses are the flexible joint in the hospital according to Beckham (1993): "When the wrong medication arrives and a nurse adjusts, a physician is unavailable and a nurse compensates, the unexpected occurs and a nurse explains…hospitals would cease to function without nursing's blessed capacity to compensate for systemic inadequacies."

Culture: The Success Factor

On a parallel track with redesign of the care delivery process and the design of the building is the choreographing of the experience—the elements that make the customer feel respected, nurtured, and valued. Some of these were discussed previously. Much of this work is an expression of the organization's culture—what values are held dear, what types of behaviors are rewarded, the unwritten social etiquette of the place. As an example, an organization may have a culture of safety that includes total transparency about reporting errors and near misses, always striving to improve quality of care.

One of the great success stories in cultural transformation is that of Baptist Health Care in Pensacola, Florida. In 1995, patient and staff satisfaction had reached an all-time low. Its journey to becoming a national benchmark for performance excellence and being awarded the Malcolm Baldrige National Quality Award in 2003 is documented in a book that will be inspiring to any organization attempting major change (Stubblefield 2005). Baptist also runs a Leadership Institute that offers consulting and training for other organizations outside its system. *Fortune* magazine has recognized Baptist for being one of the nation's 100 Best Places to Work. This might be due in some measure to the lightheartedness and fun the leadership team has put in place to reinforce the culture. For example, the "Baptist Shuffle" is a floor cleaner, a dance move, and a state of mind (Solovy 2006). A sheet was published with dance steps to show how staff can erase scuffmarks on the floor while having fun. Over the years, many such antics have been highlighted in healthcare magazines, giving the impression that this is indeed a creative and imaginative group.

Staff training is so important to reinforcing the culture. It's probably expressed in every hospital's customer service training manual that the staff is there to serve the patient; but does the meaning of this filter down to the transporters, to the technicians and aides, to the housekeepers? As an example, from the author's recent personal experience with a specific hospital on several occasions, virtually every staff member smiled and greeted patients as they passed; during two-person transports of a patient on a gurney or when two techs were setting up a procedure, the expected personal chit-chat or worse, griping about the hospital or a supervisor (talk about undermining a patient's confidence in the clinical care!) never occurred. They always engaged the patient in conversation and gave the impression that there was no place they would rather be at that moment. This happened with such consistency that it had to be an expression of the culture, not happenstance. No wonder this has been designated a magnet hospital for excellence in nursing care.

Undertaking Consumer Research

There are various methods of collecting consumer perceptions and impressions of the provider's service (Table 5.3). Focus groups are often used to look at a variety of issues. The group dynamic provides insight into why opinions are held and can help reveal the degree or lack of consensus. It also works for populations with low levels of literacy. An excellent resource is a *Focus Group Manual and Moderator's Guide*, a Healthcare Design Action Kit developed for the CHD by the Picker Institute (1999b). Surveys are another method of gathering data but not as successful as focus groups for examining complex issues.

Comparison of Data Collection Methods			Table 5.3
More detail, less generalizability / Method	Pros	Cons	
Casual Observation	No cost	Observer may misinterpret events; observations may not be representative	
Systematic Observation	Low cost; unobtrusive; can be done quickly	Observer may misinterpret events; observations may not be representative	
In-depth or Cognitive Interviews	Provides patient's perspective on meaning of events and ways of describing experiences; flexible	Labor intensive; answers may be difficult to compare	
Focus Groups	Provides patients' perspective; allows explanation of complex issues; takes advantage of synergy among patients; elicits different perspectives efficiently; can provide insight into why opinions are held; can help reveal degree or lack of consensus; flexible; appropriate for populations with low levels of literacy	May not be generalizable; more expensive than less formal methods	
Less detail, more generalizability / Surveys	Samples are more representative; questions can be standardized; easy to replicate and compare	More expensive; not good for complex issues or exploration of meaning; assumes knowledge of problem and patients' discourse; not appropriate for populations with low levels of literacy	
Source: Health Care Design Action Kit, Picker Institute, Boston ©1999			

A number of consulting firms provide the insights of social scientists and cultural anthropologists to help hospitals understand the current culture of the organization or, for a new hospital not attached to an existing campus, to help frame the culture. One such firm was engaged by OhioHealth to study consumer expectations and help the organization create a vision for a new culture (Image pages 7.29 to 7.34).

IDEO is another firm that has, in the past few years, expanded its reach to healthcare. This multidisciplinary firm employs engineers of various kinds, social scientists, anthropologists, industrial designers, and technology experts. It is often involved in new product design and in system re-engineering. IDEO staff members are respected for their creativity and their ability to bring fresh solutions to old problems. Olson Zaltman offers market research based on a research technique that unites thought and emotion. The Zaltman Metaphor Elicitation Technique, ZMET, uses metaphor to delve into consumers' thoughts and feelings on specific research topics. Subjects cut photos out of magazines and assemble them into a collage—a visual metaphor—that is assumed to represent a type of nonverbal communication based on sensory impressions (Zaltman 1996, 2003).

The CHD also offers educational consulting to help get some of these ideas in front of decision makers.

Visioning Events

A healthcare organization may stage a multiday event that begins with a number of speakers on topics of interest and proceeds to facilitated exercises and workshops to enable key staff and stakeholders to do out-of-the-box thinking. Consulting firms that do this type of facilitation use a variety of tools. For example, people may be encouraged to use other senses to see a problem from a different perspective. Drawing a picture as one person explains to someone else why it's a problem can help both of them see the issue more externally (Plsek 1997).

Breaking through cultural filters

Cognitive science tells us that we see what is not there. We have perceptual patterns and cultural filters that color what we see or how we interpret it. Most of the boxes that trap us are of our own design—we recall a regulation as being much more restrictive than it actually is. Rereading it may give us more flexibility than imagined (Plsek 1997).

Creativity expert Edward De Bono (Plsek 1997) suggests that the mind is like a rugged landscape. If someone says "hospital," people develop a visual pattern in their mind of what that is. Without these valleys and patterns, a lot of description would be required. If someone says "design a hospital," the mind does vertical, analytical thinking that tells us what to do, but it has passed through our cultural filters. For example, if a manager of Hertz was dropped into a hospital, he is likely to hand patients a map and maybe have their names appear on a monitor along with a "welcome" remark as they enter their rooms. When Enterprise came up with the idea of delivering the car to the customer, that was out out-of-the-box thinking.

To steer the mind away from conventional solutions, creativity consultant Paul Plsek suggests taking the opposite of the problem, then turn it around again. For example, nurses sometimes forget to give patients their medications at the appropriate time. Turn it around: How can we assure that nurses will fail to give meds on time? Hospitals sometimes lose patients' dentures and eyeglasses. Turn it around: How can we make sure we lose patients' dentures and eyeglasses?

If the goal is to speed up laboratory results, look at UPS or Federal Express and see if there is something in their processes that is applicable to hospitals in trying to envision new ways of doing things.

Surgeons at London's Great Ormond Street Hospital for Children recognized the analogy between race car activities and patient procedures. They asked a team of mechanics from Ferrari's Formula 1 racing group to critique their procedures for moving patients from the operating room to intensive care units. The Ferrari team devised a protocol that improved the process and minimized chances that a needed piece of equipment or a vital message would be overlooked. The protocol includes changes such as banning nonessential chatter and disconnecting lines in a specific order, both of which have achieved better patient outcomes. It's hard to break out of old paradigms: there's got to be a waiting room, the patient is passive and heals in bed, the patient moves from place to place, and each time waits. What if the patient were glued in place and could not move? What implications would this have for care delivery and for facility design? A good example of creative visioning is illustrated on Image pages 7.29 to 7.34. The president of Dublin Methodist Hospital in Dublin, Ohio, told her team to "run until apprehended" with new ideas for the hospital to be built on a greenfield site.

Rolling out a Plan for Success

In redesigning an intensive care unit (ICU), Exempla Lutheran Medical Center in Wheat Ridge, Colorado, tracked patient outcome statistics prior to remodeling and later compared these data with outcomes in the new units (Buenning and Shepler 2007). They employed evidence-based design and also developed a new care model as part of a Veterans Health Administration-sponsored quality initiative called Transformation of the ICU. Two significant changes were the implementation of clinical bundles and collaborative care rounds. *Bundles* are evidence-based order sets for patients. These include: sedation and pain control, oral care, bed positioning (to prevent ventilator-associated pneumonia), glucose management, and sepsis prevention. Collaborative care rounds involve a multidisciplinary team with up to 12 members who visit patients and jointly collaborate on assessment and treatment plans. The team may include a pulmonologist, cardiologist, nurse, dietician, respiratory therapist, speech therapist, occupational and rehabilitation therapist, case manager, infection control specialist, and an ethics and pastoral-care representative. The team's charge is to ensure that evidence-based care is implemented. Collaborative care is the opposite of specialty silos, in which physicians focus narrowly on their own specialties and no one looks at the whole person.

Unit design features

The new ICU rooms at Exempla Lutheran range from 265 to 315 square feet and have decentralized caregiver stations (Image page 7.89). Lighting was enhanced, both ambient and examination light. Carpeted corridors reduced noise and contributed to a less institutional ambience. Aesthetic details such as rounded walls, decorative columns, raised ceilings, and a warm color palette were employed.

Move Therapy support for staff

Although staff members were involved in the design process, the completed project represented significant changes from the old model of care, and there was some resistance about the change (Buenning and Shepler 2007). To address this, the critical care and cardiovascular services director initiated the Living and Working in the Intensive Care Unit or *Move Therapy* support group sessions three months prior to the move to help prepare and adapt to the new model of care and physical environment. The use of effective change-management strategies facilitated by a consultant with experience in workforce development helped the staff to deal with turf wars, cross-training, coordination of services, creating a respectful work environment, team building, and patient-centered care (Buenning and Shepler 2007). Tools included Elisabeth Kubler-Ross's five stages of grief and loss, change and mastery tools, and constructive feedback. One of the issues focused on the dynamics of moving from a centralized workstation versus being more independent in a decentralized caregiver station.

Improved outcomes

In the new unit, changes in the design, in patient safety protocols, and the new care model resulted in improved patient outcomes.

- Incidence of infection for patients on ventilators with ventilator-associated pneumonia decreased from 8% to 0% initially and leveled off at 2.3%.
- The mortality rate for patients on ventilators decreased from 16% to 6%.
- Patient satisfaction scores increased from 80% to 91% positive. There was 0% voluntary staff turnover in the first three months.

The Last Word

It's hard to top this comment by Leonard Berry, a renowned scholar in the field of service marketing (2002): "Being a patient is just about the least amount of fun a consumer can buy. What is more stressful, frightening, and emotionally draining than being a patient?"

References

Advances in Family-Centered Care. 2002. 8(1):1–37.

Baker, D. W., R. M. Parker, M. V. Williams, K. Pitkin, N. S. Parikh, W. Coates, and M. Imara. 1996. The health care experience of patients with low literacy. *Archives of Family Medicine* 5:329–34.

Beckham, J. D. 1993. Andrew's not-so-excellent adventure. *Healthcare Forum Journal* 36(2): 90–98.

Berry, L. L. 2002. Communicating without words. *Healthcare Design* 2(7).

Berry, L. L., L. P. Carbone, and S. H. Haeckel. 2002. Managing the total customer experience. *MIT Sloan Management Review* 43(3):85–89.

Berry, L. L., E. Wall, and L. P. Carbone. 2006. Service clues and customer assessment of the service experience: Lessons from marketing. *Academy of Management Perspectives* 20(2):43–57.

Berry, L. L., and K. D. Seltman. 2007. Building a strong services brand: Lessons from Mayo Clinic. *Business Horizons* 50:199–209.

Bowman, L. 2007. Study: Aging boomers report more health woes. *Scripps Howard News Service.* http://www.centredaily.com/220/story/32496.html (accessed March 5, 2007).

Buenning, F., and M. Shepler. 2007. Research that supports evidence based design and effects positive patient outcomes and staff satisfaction: Exempla Lutheran Medical Center. Conference proceedings AIA/ASHE International Conference and Exhibition on Planning, Design and Construction, San Antonio, TX.

Buggy, J., and J. Nelson. 2006. A lean and green community healthcare asset: Park Nicollet's new Heart and Vascular Center, St. Louis Park, MN. Presentation at *HealthcareDesign 06*, Chicago.

Center for Health Care Strategies Inc. Health literacy fact sheet. http://www.chcs.org (accessed April 26, 2007).

Coile, R. 2003. *Russ Coile's Health Trends* 15(9):1.

DeBuono. 2007. What is health literacy? Partnership for Clear Health Communication. http://www.p4chc.org/health-literacy.aspx (accessed April 26, 2007).

Devenney, N. 2006. In appreciation of lean processes. *Healthcare Design* 6(7):74–76.

Finkam, S., ed. 2006. *Best of health.* Indianapolis: Clarian North Medical Center.

Frampton, S. B., L. Gilpin, and P. A. Charmel. 2003. *Putting patients first: Designing and practicing patient-centered care.* New York: Jossey-Bass (John Wiley imprint).

Gerteis, M., S. Edgman-Levitan, J. Daley, and T. L. Delbanco, eds. 1993. *Through the patient's eyes.* San Francisco: Jossey-Bass Publishers.

Gervais, M. 1993. What patients really want. *HMQ* Third Quarter:2–6.

Haeckel, S. H., L. P. Carbone, and L. L. Berry. 2003. How to lead the customer experience. *Marketing Management,* January/February.

Joseph, A. 2006. The role of the physical and social environment in promoting health, safety, and effectiveness in the healthcare workplace. Issue paper, Center for Health Design. http://www.healthdesign.org/research/reports/workplace.php.

Lathrop, P. 1993. *Restructuring health care: The patient focused paradigm.* San Francisco: Jossey-Bass Inc.

Leebov, W. 2007. Empathy fitness for leaders. *Hospitals & Health Networks,* April 17, 2007. http://www.hhnmag.com/hhnmag_app/jsp/articledisplay.jsp?dcrpath=HHNMAG/Article/data/04APR2007/070417HHN_Online_Leebov&domain=HHNMAG.

Lehman, M., and F. Casey, S. Goe, C. Mabus, and D. Chambers, 2000. Translating function into form: Redesigning the new White Memorial. Educational Forum, Symposium on Healthcare Design, Anaheim, CA.

Levitt, T. 1980. Marketing success through differentiation—of anything. *Harvard Business Review* 58(1):83–91.

Morrison, I. 2006. The future of the healthcare marketplace: The quest for value. Keynote address at Healthcare Design '06, Chicago.

National Adult Literacy Survey. 2003. Literacy in everyday life: Results from the 2003 National Assessment of Adult Literacy. National Center for Educational Statistics. http://nces.ed.gov/pubsearch/pubsinfo.asp?pubid=2007480 (accessed April 26, 2007).

Picker Institute. 1999a. *Assessing the built environment from the patient and family perspective.* Boston: Picker Institute.

Picker Institute. 1999b. *Patient-centered environmental checklist.* Boston: Picker Institute.

Pine, J., and J. Gilmore. 1999. *The experience economy.* Boston: Harvard Business School Press.

Plsek, P. 1997. *Creativity, innovation and quality.* Milwaukee, WI: ASQ Quality Press.

Press Ganey Associates. 2006. *Satisfaction report.* South Bend, IN: Press Ganey Associates.

Reiling, J. G., B. Knutzen, T. Wallen, S. McCullough, R. Miller, and S. Chernos. 2004. Enhancing the traditional hospital design process: A focus on patient safety. *Journal on Quality and Safety* 30:115–120.

San Diego Union-Tribune. 2007. Stories for the waiting room. May 1.

Solovy, A. 2006. The Baptist Shuffle. *Hospital & Health Networks,* April.

Stinson, M., D. Chambers, and B. Radovanovich. 2003. Extending patient-centered care to the caregivers: Enabled caring. Lecture presented at the *International Conference & Exhibition on Health Facility Planning, Design and Construction,* Phoenix.

Strategos. 2007. Kaizen—what does it mean? www.strategosinc.com/kaizen.htm (accessed June 2, 2007).

Stubblefield, A. 2005. *The Baptist Health Care journey to excellence.* Hoboken, NJ: John Wiley & Sons Inc.

Uhlig, P., J. Brown, A. Nason, A. Camelio, and E. Kendall. 2002. System innovation: Concord Hospital. *Joint Commission Journal on Quality Improvement* 28(12):666–672.

Value-Based Management. 2007. Kaizen philosophy and Kaizen method. www.valuebasedmanagement.net/methods_kaizen.html (accessed June 2, 2007).

Villaire, M., and G. Mayer. 2007. The price of poor literacy. Hospital & Health Networks. http://www.hhnmag.com/hhnmag_app/jsp/articledisplay.jsp?dcrpath=HHNMAG/Article/data/05MAY2007/070501HHN_Online_Villaire&domain=HHNMAG (accessed on May 1, 2007).

Zaltman, G. 1996. Metaphorically speaking. *Marketing Research* 8(2):13–20.

Zaltman, G. 2003. *How customers think: Essential insights into the minds of the market.* Boston: Harvard Business School Press.

Hospital entry/donor wall.
Cabell Huntington Hospital, Huntington, West VA
Perkins+Will (architecture and interior design)

Photographer: Chris Little

Photographer: Chris Little

Lobby and donor wall. Edwards Comprehensive Cancer Center,
Cabell Huntington Hospital, Huntington, West VA
Perkins+Will (architecture and interior design)

Photographer: Dana Wheelock

Lobby, TRIA Orthopaedic Center, Bloomington, MN
A joint venture of U. of Minnesota, the Orthopaedic Center,
and Park Nicollet Health Services
Perkins+Will (architecture and interior design)

Commentary

Monitors (top left photo) can be used to announce upcoming events, fund-raiser results, or for welcoming messages to visitors. Each monitor operates individually and is 30 × 48 inches in size. Welcome wall has acrylic panels for donor recognition. The entry to the Cancer Center (top right photo) has a donor wall with water running down glass terminating in river rock at the bottom. The project benefactor wanted blooming plants (orchids) as an uplifting element. TRIA (lower right photo) is a technologically advanced orthopedic center (outpatient) with a focus on physician learning and teaching by way of observation rooms and video recording of procedures. The reverse side of the fountain is a two-story fireplace, tying together the feng shui elements of water, fire, and stone.

Photographer: Jain Malkin (all photos)

Clarian North Medical Center, Indianapolis, IN
HKS Architects, Maregatti Interiors (all photos)

Reception/greeter   Coffee bar

Commentary

continued on next page

Opened in 2006, this is the Clarian flagship. The lobby is a grand space full of natural light, greenery, and the spirit of well-being. Interior finish materials are highly durable and easy to maintain as well as colorful. Some have criticized the lavish appearance of the space but it's to the credit of the skilled design team who were able to turn out such a stunning design and stay within budget. Looking at the patient population served, it seems right on target.

Photographer: Jain Malkin (all photos)

Clarian North Medical Center, Indianapolis, IN (all photos)
HKS Architects, Maregatti Interiors

Outpatient department.

Commentary

Although this is a multi-story atrium, seating clusters create a comfortable scale at ground level. Floor lamps, securely attached and hard-wired, help to organize the space as well as provide light needed at lounge chairs in the evening. This type of space is always hard to light for intimacy, but this seems to be a good solution. Signage is well coordinated. Outpatient departments coming off the lobby have an attractive sandblasted glass pattern to provide privacy screening. An alcove off the lobby offers an ecumenical and tasteful tribute to world religions.

Photographer: ©Vance Fox

Openings in walls dramatically frame the view. Carson Tahoe Regional Medical Center, Carson City, NV
Moon Mayoras Architects, Inc., Brandt Design Group (interiors)

Photographer: Ed LaCasse Photography

Family lounge area on each nursing unit. Parker Adventist Hospital, Parker, CO
HKS Architects (architecture and interior design)

Commentary

Two different approaches to a setting of great natural beauty. In the top photo, the architecture captures the majesty of the mountains and the room is wide open to the outdoors with a lobby as spacious as the view. In the lower photo, the focus is on coziness: fireplace, armchairs, rough-cut stone — a great place to curl up and read. A 15" deep soffit over seating surrounds a wood grid ceiling element with fluorescent downlights above. This is a repetitive element that starts in the main lobby and is varied in different locations to establish scale.

Renderings courtesy RTKL Associates, Inc.

Gallery/main lobby. Community Hospital North, Indianapolis, IN
RTKL Associates, Inc. (architecture and interior design)

Main circulation spine from lobby to outpatient services. Community Hospital North, Indianapolis, IN
RTKL Associates, Inc. (architecture and interior design)

Commentary

The new lobby (upper photo) expresses, stylistically, the transformation from a suburban hospital to a full-service urban hospital with 60 LDRP maternity suites, 36 Level 3 NICU suites, totaling 296 beds (with capacity to add 48 more beds later). Lower photo is a first floor primary circulation corridor. The arc in the ceiling and the floor lead the eye, in terms of wayfinding, as the corridor turns. The photos of nature, accent wall, and "sky" combine to make this a highly memorable path.

Photographer: Fred Charles

Waiting room set up for a lecture (note podium).
Jay Monahan Center for Gastrointestinal Health, Weill Cornell Medical Center, New York City
Guenther 5 Architects (architecture and interior design)

Photographer: Adrian Wilson

Same as above.

Commentary   *continued on next page*

Named in honor of Jay Monahan, Katie Couric's late husband who died of colon cancer, the 3,500 SF center is located at street level at York Avenue and 70th Street. Large window walls emphasize transparency as a metaphor for addressing a disease that is often hidden – hard to see and uncomfortable to discuss. Therefore a focus on providing information and education to patients as well as making available the resources of a large academic medical center were central goals. Multiple monitors show videos of colonoscopy procedures and other educational programming. An interesting footnote is that a sufficient number of patients did not want to see images of the colon and this was discontinued. The waiting room can be set up for lectures (top photo), supporting the idea that cancer prevention and early detection require self-education.

Jay Monahan Center, Weill Cornell Medical Center, New York City (all photos)
Guenther 5 Architects (architecture and interior design)

Research

Principles of green design were employed. Natural light reduces the use of electricity. The uplifting design has sustainable interior materials such as bamboo flooring, domestic woods, glass, and ceramic tile. This clinic is part of a Weill Cornell Medical Center research study entitled "The Ecology of the Patient Experience," in which the research hypothesis is that the design of the environment impacts the perceived time spent waiting in a doctor's office and the preceived quality of care provided. The study found that the more attractive the environment (the Monahan Center was the most attractive of the sites studied), the higher the perceived quality of the medical care and the lower the anxiety. Patients underestimated the longer actual wait times and overestimated the short wait times. In the attractive environment, with many diversions, wait time seemed less and staff interaction was perceived as more positive. Patients' perceptions of staff interaction were more strongly correlated with feeling cared for as a person. In summary, patients' perceived waiting time was significantly related to perceived quality and staff interaction (Franklin Becker, Ph.D., College of Human Ecology, Cornell University).

Photographer: Nick Merrick © Hedrich Blessing

Waiting lounge. Rebecca and John Moores Cancer Center at UC San Diego Medical Center, La Jolla, CA
Zimmer Gunsul Frasca Partnership

Entry features water wall.
Abbott Northwestern Heart Hospital, Minneapolis, MN
HKS, Inc. (architecture and interior design)

Photographer: Ed LaCasse Photography (both photos)

Lobby with seating arranged in privacy groupings. Adjacent amenities:
resource library, business center, cafe.
Abbott Northwestern Heart Hospital, Minneapolis, MN
HKS, Inc. (architecture and interior design)

Commentary

Both of these waiting rooms have the ambience of a living room in that there is variety in the types of seating; it can be repositioned by the occupants; the fireplace is the focus of the room – a symbol of comfort deeply embedded in the human psyche. Photo lower right is called the Family Care Center which serves as the admitting and waiting area for all ambulatory services of the Heart Hospital. Photo lower left, in contrast, has a more formal ambience and features a 15-foot-high granite water wall which, with the fireplace, wood, and metal elements comprise the five-element theory that underpins the project. The COO set a goal for a design that engaged the mind, body, and spirit of the patient.

Photographer: Chris Little Photography

Pediatric waiting area.
Edwards Comprehensive Cancer Center, Cabell Huntington Hospital, Huntington, West Virginia
Perkins + Will (architecture and interior design)

Commentary

This is an interesting way to provide privacy for families and still maintain openness and visibility. The built-in banquette helps to "anchor" the seating grouping in contrast to a room with all individual chairs.

Photographer: Jain Malkin (all photos)

Clarian North Medical Center, Indianapolis, IN (all photos)
HKS Architects, Maregatti Interiors

Commentary

Throughout the hospital, cast glass walls incorporating inspirational messages as well as images of grasses, flowers, and nature are used to convey the provider's culture of healing. Quotations celebrating humor, hope, and courage enrich the experience of patients and families and reinforce that they are in a caring and healing environment. These also encourage one to find the placebo within oneself.

Photographer: Jain Malkin (all photos)

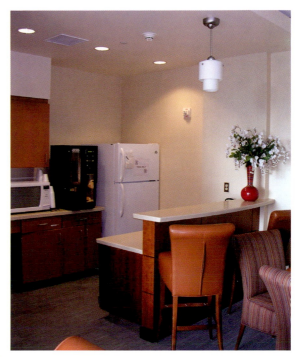

Family lounge med/surg unit. Clarian North Medical Center, Indianapolis, IN (all photos)
HKS Architects, Maregatti Interiors

Attractive residential-type accessories create a
"home away from home" ambience.

Commentary

This large family lounge on each med/surg floor is a welcome departure from the standard family waiting room. Numerous seating areas with variety in seating types offers many options, different views, and privacy clusters. The blue ceramic glass-tiled room divider with two-sided fireplace has shelves supported by cables and colorful accessories (glued in place for security). The variety of textures, finishes, lighting, and the soothing blue-green color palette make this room an oasis for families needing a dose of stress relief.

Photographer: © 2006 Douglas A. Salin

Family Resource Center. Alta Bates Summit Medical Center — Merritt Pavilion, Oakland, CA
Ratcliff Architects (architecture and interior design)

Planview. Courtesy Ratcliff Architects

Commentary

The family resource center (2,000 SF) supports patients and families of the inpatient cardiovascular unit with a variety of amenities available 24 hours per day. It offers an educational library, kitchenette, lounge, children's play room, business center, and family consulation rooms. Cut-away walls with openings aesthetically frame spaces beyond and also provide visibility in a clever way. Soffits also have cut-outs and light coves. The blue-green palette is relaxing, yet vibrant.

Features:

1) Refrigerator
2) Multi-purpose table
3) Sleep sofa
4) Ample storage for family
5) Refrigerator
6) Tackable surface

Photographer: © Paul Warchol

LDRP Room. Pomona Valley Medical Center, Pomona, CA
NBBJ Architects

Photographer: Dan Francis, Mardan Photography

Acuity-adaptable room. Cardiac Comprehensive Critical Care Unit
Clarian Health, Methodist Hospital, Indianapolis, IN
BSA LifeStructures; Maregatti Interiors

Photographer: Gary Knight

Family lounge on nursing unit. Oklahoma Heart Hospital, Oklahoma City, OK
WHR Architects, Inc. (architecture and interior design)

Photographer: Michael O'Callahan Photography

Restorative garden. Good Samaritan Cancer Center, Puyallup, WA
KMD Architects

Commentary

The family lounge with wooden-grille openings enables families to relax and still be able to see corridor activity, the arrival of friends, or a physician. In the lower photo, patients in radiation therapy have a view of the healing garden.

Courtesy: Nemschoff

Flop Sofa™ enables a family to sleep in the patient's room on a standard-size twin "mattress."

Commentary

Sleep sofas designed for patient rooms should have mechanisms that are intuitive, not requiring instruction. There are numerous good examples available that function as easily as the unit depicted above. Noteworthy are the clean lines, the simplicity of operation, storage in the hinged arms, and overall comfort both as a sofa and a bed.

Photographer: Geoff Lyon

Photographer: Geoff Lyon

M.D. Anderson Cancer Center, Houston, TX
KMD Architects, FKP Architects (interior architecture)

Photographer: Jain Malkin

Throughout this facility interesting works of art have been "framed" into the walls. The integration with the interior architecture of the building makes the statement that art was not an afterthought. The Birthplace at Gaston Memorial Hospital, Gastonia, NC
KMD Architects, American Art Resources, Dawson Design and Healthcare Interiors

Commentary

Positive distractions like the fountain in the top photos at the M.D. Anderson Cancer Center offer an antidote to the stress of undergoing cancer treatment or supporting a friend or family member who is. It is multi-sensory: one can touch it, hear it, see it, and even smell it. Water never ceases to fascinate and delight us.

Photographer: Gene Pollux, Pollux Photography

3 Tesla MRI. Morton Plant Hospital, Clearwater, FL
TRO/The Ritchie Organization
TESS (Therapeutic Environmental Solutions) USA, Inc.

Photographer: Lois Gervais

St. Joseph's Medical Center, Stockton, CA
Anshen+Allen Architects

Photographer: Jain Malkin

M.D. Anderson Cancer Center, Houston, TX
KMD Architects, FKP Architects (interior architecture)

Features:

1) The virtual skylight, using integrated mirrors, creates an infinity view with TESS patented non-ferrous MRI lighting system and art panels
2) Stained glass art
3) Skylight – natural light
4) Fountain – water element is soothing and tactile
5) Columns of bubbling water, internally illuminated

Photographer: Jain Malkin

Lobby garden. Bronson Methodist Hospital, Kalamazoo, MI
Shepley Bulfinch Richardson Abbott, Architects

Courtesy: Robin Orr

Photographer: Jain Malkin

Whimsical sculpture main lobby circulation spine.
University Medical Center, Groningen, The Netherlands

Salt-water aquarium in
emergency department waiting room.
Kettering Medical Center, Dayton, OH
Jain Malkin Inc. (interior design)

Photographer: Jain Malkin

Commentary

Music, art, watching the wonders of nature (the colorful fish) tap into the spirit and are a momentary distraction from pain, worry, or grief.

Gurney elevator lobby. Doernbecker Children's Hospital, Portland, OR
Zimmer Gunsul Frasca Partnership

Photographer: Eckert & Eckert

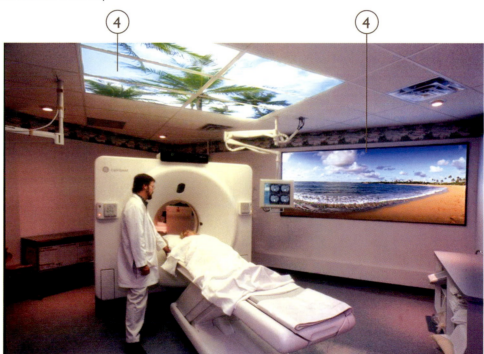

Photographer: Joey Fischer
Art Research Institute

Features:

1) Indirect lighting does not "blind" gurney patients
2) Internally illuminated art panel provides interest during transport
3) Etched metal panel and butterfly relate well to flooring pattern and further enhance ambience of space
4) Nature views, even when simulated, reduce anxiety in a treatment setting

Photographer: Ed LaCasse

Cafeteria. Parker Adventist Hospital, Parker, CO
HKS Architects (architecture and interior design)

Photographer: Jain Malkin

Dining room/cafeteria. Clarian North Medical Center, Indianapolis, IN
HKS Architects, Maregatti Interiors

Commentary

A good meal in an attractive environment nurtures staff, visitors, and families. It also conveys a provider's caring and culture. It's part of the total experience of care.

Photographer: Matthew Millman

Visitor elevator design, orthopedic unit.
UC Davis Medical Center, Davis, CA
Anshen + Allen in collaboration with Fougeron Architecture

Internally illuminated sandblasted glass is a highly visible wayfinding device. Stone panels around the base add durability. Below, bright blue tile calls attention to visitor elevators.

Photographer: Jain Malkin

Visitor elevator design.
The Birthplace at Gaston Memorial Hospital, Charlotte, NC
KMD Architects

Photographer: Jain Malkin

Visitor elevator design.
Clarian North Medical Center
HKS Architects, Maregatti Interiors

Physicians' Lounge | Kettering Medical Center
Kettering, OH. Jain Malkin Inc. in collaboration with Lorenz + Williams Architects. Photography: Andy Snow

Staff Spaces: Nurturing the Healers | 6

In recent years, there has been widespread acknowledgement that caregivers also need to be cared for. Spaces for relaxation, restoration, and nurturing are now recognized as important. It may not be politically correct to say, but prior to the nursing shortage, nurses were sometimes taken for granted, not appreciated for the precious resource they are. And if they had a lounge or relaxation space, it rarely had windows or natural light, was frequently a very small room, was makeshift in terms of amenities, and often served multiple purposes as a lounge, staff report or meeting room, or an education room.

For a particularly extreme—although not necessarily atypical—example, consider the nurses' lounge at a community hospital in the Midwest. It is a room no larger than 100 feet square, has a bathroom that opens right into the room with no vestibule, and this door, when opened, exposes the toilet just inches away from where nurses eat. Food preparation amenities consist of a toaster oven placed on an upholstered chair (fire hazard), because there is no other place for it. There is a three-foot cabinet with a tiny sink in one corner. Four persons can sit in this room at one time eating lunch with their food placed in their laps.

Nurses are often expected to make do and live with less than optimal situations with grace and good humor, and they do. Fortunately, new facilities designed in recent years have, for the most part, addressed the needs of nurses by providing lounges with natural light and views, sometimes even a rooftop garden with access limited to staff. It is clearly understood that nurses experience tremendous stress in the course of their workday. Creating opportunities for nurses to relax together builds relationships and provides psychological support when nurses are feeling particularly stressed, such as after caring for a very ill patient or dealing with a difficult family member.

Another new trend is the development of staff respite areas that are designed to be meditative spaces with a quiet environment, subdued lighting, and comfortable lounge chairs (Image page 6.1). Staff can use these spaces to meditate, collect their thoughts, and re-charge before going back into the stressful patient care area. Staff respite rooms provide a place of solace and comfort and are meant to be different than the lounge, where the staff may engage in conversation or eat their meals. Staff respite rooms are often designed in high-stress areas such as critical care environments or emergency departments.

WHAT IS A RESTORATIVE ENVIRONMENT?

One can apply the same principles for designing a healing environment to the design of restorative spaces for nurses and other caregivers:

- connection to nature (views, gardens)
- choices (privacy vs. socialization, options for seating, dedicated areas for food preparation and dining, private space to make a phone call)
- positive distraction (aquarium, massage chair, headphones/DVD of nature images with calming music)
- social support (access to team members in an informal setting "off stage")
- elimination of environmental stressors (use of indirect lighting, ability to dim lights in specific areas of the room, use of acoustic ceiling to absorb sound)

The Soft Side

The ambience of the room (colors, finishes, style of furnishings) varies based on functional directives and the interior designer's inclination. It is difficult to obtain photos of staff lounges because architects don't typically photograph these spaces. However, they often look more like a large break room with hard-surface flooring, dining tables, a few not-terribly-comfortable lounge chairs and a food preparation area. Some have lockers for personal belongings.

Why not provide really comfortable lounge seating, massage chairs, recliners, or a foot massager that can be pulled up to a lounge chair? The relaxation area of the room can have carpet. The color palette should be calming, not stimulating, if relaxation and restoration are the goals.

Making a design statement

Now and then one sees, in a design magazine, a nurses' lounge that is touted as a restorative space. Although the designers seem to have put considerable thought into the design to make a refined design statement, the spaces are "hard" architecture, sometimes with wooden bench seating and a highly stimulating red-orange color palette. Monastic in ambience, one wonders where a nurse with tired feet and aching knees would find respite. One would never find a recliner chair interrupting this highly designed environment.

A Holistic Approach to Restorative Spaces

Patricia Novick, PhD, executive director of Alive Ltd. (2007), is a senior fellow at Harvard's Center for the Study of World Religions. She founded the first degree-granting program for holistic health in the United States according to her website, which is a resource for the design of restorative spaces for nurses. As an example, she cites two studies about the value of music.

> When healthy adults listened to 15 minutes of music they liked, their blood tests revealed higher levels of interlukin-1, a polypeptide hormone necessary for immunological reactions, and lower levels of the stress hormone cortisol, both signs of stronger immunity (Bartlett, Kaufman, and Smeltekop 1993).

> Regular music and relaxation sessions have been shown to match up body temperature, electrolytes, corticosteroids (hormones), and neurotransmitters—circadian rhythms—with daily patterns and activities (Rider, Floyd, and Kirkpatrick 1985).

Music is one of the activities of brief duration that has deeply restorative effects, according to many studies.

HUMAN FACTORS AND ERGONOMIC DESIGN

Creating safe work environments for nurses and other healthcare workers is very important. Occupational injuries and illnesses cost tens of billions of dollars in employee medical care, lost time, workers' compensation, and indirect costs incurred by the healthcare industry annually. In 2003 the National Safety Council reported these costs to be $156.2 billion or $35,500 per case (Chaff 2006). The kinds of injuries expected only in manufacturing and construction occur with regularity, and at significant rates, in healthcare facilities (Chaff 2006). Many of these injuries occur when attempting to lift patients and, for that reason, a number of newer hospitals have installed ceiling lifts (Image pages 7.23 and 7.24).

A study done by Peace Health as part of the Center for Health Design's (CHD) Pebble Project research initiative found that the annual cost of patient-handling injuries at the hospital in which the research was carried out was 83% lower than before the installation of ceiling lifts.

In the end, commitment by hospital leadership to a staff safety and health program is essential. However, design professionals can also play a role in designing nurse work areas, for example, that accommodate persons of different stature. Upper cabinets should be within reach of an average-sized woman (about five feet four) without having to stand on something to access supplies. Countertops and task seating should offer sit-down and stand-up options. Unnecessary twisting of the upper body should be avoided in order to reach things.

The CHD published an excellent paper that discussed environmental issues impacting healthcare workers' effectiveness and safety (Joseph 2006). It has a wealth of evidence-based design reference citations for topics ranging from multidisciplinary collaborative rounds at the patient bedside to the cost and prevalence of patient transfers and strategies for improving the circadian rhythms of night-shift workers.

A good resource for standards on human factors and ergonomics is the Human Factors and Ergonomics Society (www.hfes.org), the publisher of *Guidelines for Using Anthropometric Data in Product Design.* This is also an ANSI (American National Standards Institute) standard.

While there is some overlap between human-factors design and ergonomics, human-factors engineering covers a broad range of activity from product manufacturing to human performance and the way humans interact with technology. According to the dictionary definition, ergonomics is an approach to design that entails the scientific study of the relationship between users and their environment. Human-factors analysis may apply to a physical facility, equipment, furnishings, and fixtures and the way people use and operate them. A visit to the aforementioned website shows the array of human factors endeavors from spaceship design to automobiles.

PHYSICIAN LOUNGES

Physician lounges are often located within or adjacent to the hospital's administrative offices to promote dialogue between C-suite leadership and physicians. Usually furnished with comfortable sofas and lounge chairs, the dining component may consist of drinks and snacks or a more elaborate temperature-controlled buffet table for meals catered by food service. Taking this to new heights, the chief executive officer of Kettering Medical Center in Dayton, Ohio (Image pages 6.2 and 6.3) created a physicians' lounge that ensures physicians will arrive early to do rounds because of the tempting breakfasts offered. This lounge creates the type of nurturing experience for physicians that is usually reserved just for patients. The cost of doing this is offset by patients being discharged earlier in the day, making the rooms available for new patients. The lounge is adjacent to the hospital boardroom, the medical library, and chart completion. The benefits of this lounge have made it a wise business decision.

The physicians' library, located on the penthouse floor of the medical center (Image page 6.4) is suffused with natural light and has attractive design features and furniture.

References

Alive Ltd. Restorative spaces. http://aliveltd.org/rspace (accessed April 22, 2007).

Bartlett, D., D. Kaufman, and R. Smeltekop. 1993. The effects of music listening and perceived sensory experiences on the immune system as measured by interluken-1 and cortisol. *Journal of Music Therapy* 30(4):194–209.

Chaff, L. 2006. Safety for the healers. *Hospitals & Health Networks,* August 8. http://www.hhnmag.com/hhnmag_app/jsp/articledisplay.jsp?dcrpath=HHNMAG/PubsNewsArticle/data/2006August/060808HHN_Online_chaff&domain=HHNMAG

Joseph, A. 2006. The role of the physical and social environment in promoting health, safety, and effectiveness in the healthcare workplace. Issue paper, Center for Health Design. http://www.healthdesign.org/research/reports/workplace.php

Rider, M.S., J. W. Floyd, and J. Kirkpatrick. 1985. The effects of music, imagery, and relaxation on adrenal corticosterioids and the re-entrainment of circadian rhythms. *Journal of Music Therapy* 22:46–58.

Reception. The Renfield Center for Nurses,
Beth Israel Medical Center, New York, NY
Guenther 5 Architects (architecture and interior design)

Photographer: Dub Rogers (all photos)

Classroom.

Meditation room.

Commentary

A healing place for healers — this was the goal for Beatrice Renfield, the benefactor. Her strong sense of style and personal collection of folk art and textiles gathered worldwide (some of which were used in the project) set the design direction. The 5,000 SF facility has spaces for relaxation, classrooms, offices, meeting rooms and computer work stations. Principles of sustainable design were employed: bamboo on floors and walls, operable windows, non-toxic materials. A feng shui consultant guided the space plan in order to assure that positive energy would flow. The small meditation room is for quiet contemplation. Historical artifacts associated with nursing are displayed in the Center.

Photographer: Andy Snow

Physicians' lounge seating encourages impromptu collegial conversations. Kettering Medical Center, Dayton, OH
Jain Malkin Inc. in collaboration with Lorenz+Williams

Buffet table.

Staircase to chart completion.

Commentary

continued on next page

Hot pecan rolls, custom omelettes, and waffles ensure that physicians will arrive early to do rounds, and that means patients can be discharged sooner and beds made available for others. Tempting lunches and high tea pastries keep physicians in close contact with executive leadership whose offices (CEO/CFO) are a few steps away. Physicians have commented that opportunities for impromptu collegial conversations have been invaluable. A concierge is always available to assist physicians and a steward works out of a kitchen to coordinate the presentation of food. The lounge is also used by board members when on site.

Library with fireplace. Kettering Medical Center, Dayton, OH
Jain Malkin Inc. in collaboration with Lorenz+Williams Associates

Restrooms.

Commentary

A library with fireplace, daily newspapers, and journals provides a quiet place for reading while the lounge (previous page) has a large plasma TV to keep doctors current on news and sports. A monitor tied into the diagnostic imaging department enables physicians to review digital radiographs and reports. A final amenity are restrooms like those in a five-star hotel with all private cubicles and full-height walls. Floors and walls are marble tile.

Photographer: © Charles Davis Smith (both photos)

Physicians' library. The Heart Hospital Baylor Plano, Plano, TX
RTKL Associates, Inc. (architecture and interior design)

Physicians' library.

Commentary

Located on the fifth floor of the building, the "penthouse" physicians' library/lounge benefits from natural light.

Acuity-Adaptable Patient Room | The Heart Hospital at Baylor Plano
Plano, TX. RTKL Associates, Inc. Photography: Charles Davis Smith

Patient Units: Planning Considerations 7

The years 2006 and 2007 will be remembered as seminal years for research and analysis of patient room planning options. In a fairly brief period, enough research was gathered on the subject of single versus semiprivate rooms to culminate in the American Institute of Architects (AIA) *Guidelines for Design and Construction of Health Care Facilities* (2006) standard of one bed per room unless the functional program demonstrates the necessity of a two-bed arrangement.

BENEFITS OF SINGLE OCCUPANCY ROOMS

This is a victory for patients and families on all fronts. Research shows that single bed rooms reduce nosocomial (hospital-acquired) infections, are quieter, enable the patient to sleep better, have more space for family, enable more private conversations with physicians and nurses, and reduce medication errors. In addition, there are fewer patient transfers, which reduces errors and improves satisfaction with the overall quality of care (Chaudhury, Mahmood, and Valente 2004; Ulrich et al 2004). A survey of more than two million patients in 1,500 hospitals by Press Ganey Associates in 2004 revealed that patients in single bed rooms were much more satisfied. Findings from several studies indicated that the presence of a roommate is usually a source of stress, not social support (Ulrich et al 2004). In fact, patients often ask to be moved due to lack of compatibility with a roommate or concerns about privacy.

Imagine checking into a hotel and being told that the other guest in your room—a total stranger—had already checked in and you were sharing beds three feet apart and sharing a bathroom. It is surprising that the psychological discomfort of being in this intimate environment with a total stranger has not before now been the demise of multibed occupancies.

Something that is rarely discussed in the single versus double bed discussion is sharing a toilet. Often toilet seat covers are not provided. Flushing a toilet creates a fine aerosol that can spread fecal particles to the other patient, and aerosols spread by typical bedpan rinsing is even worse. Diarrhea is not uncommon among hospitalized patients due to the effects of medications and other factors. Imagine how easy it is to spread any number of enterococcal pathogens in this manner. And consider how many persons touch the door pull entering and leaving the toilet room—patients, family members, and nurses emptying bedpans.

Looking at the Research

The study sponsored by what used to be the Coalition for Health Environments Research (CHER), now a part of the Center for Health Design (CHD), (Chaudhury, Mahmood, and Valente 2004) examined several aspects of single versus multiple occupancy room design such as construction and operating costs, management issues, staff efficiency, infection control, and patient outcomes. Researchers also looked at issues of patient fall prevention and sociobehavioral issues of patient privacy, social interaction, and daily functioning.

A synopsis of the executive summary, which is available at http://www.aia.org/siteobjects/files/03_executive_summary.pdf, may be seen in Exhibit 7.1.

Exhibit 7.1 Review and Analysis of the Literature

First costs and operating costs

1. Even with higher first costs of construction, single occupancy can match the per diem cost of multibed rooms due to higher occupancy rates.
2. Operating costs are reduced in single patient rooms due to reduction in transfer costs, higher bed occupancy rates, and reduction in labor costs.
3. Patients' length of stay is shorter in private rooms, which reduces costs. Shorter length of stay can potentially reduce the risk of hospital-acquired infections.
4. Medication errors are reduced in single occupancy rooms, which reduces costs.

Infection control and falls prevention

1. Nosocomial infection rates are lower in private rooms with proper design and ventilation systems. Compliance with handwashing is reported to be higher in private rooms.

2. Private rooms make it easier to isolate infected patients or those susceptible to infections.
3. Falls usually occur in patient rooms when patients are alone trying to get to the bathroom. Private rooms enable family members to be accommodated more easily. Their assistance helps to reduce falls.
4. Patients requiring constant supervision may do better in a multioccupancy room due to increased surveillance.

Therapeutic Impacts

1. Influence of pain medication type or usage is mixed with some research studies indicating patients in private rooms are more likely to use narcotics than were similar patients in multiple occupancy rooms; other research shows that patients in private rooms use less pain medication.
2. More private conversations with healthcare professionals can occur in private rooms.
3. A majority of patients prefer single bed rooms because of greater privacy, less noise, reduced embarrassment, better sleep, and not having to be concerned about disturbing the other patient.
4. Patient stressors in the hospital include perceived lack of control, lack of privacy, noise, and crowding. Excess noise can cause increased anxiety and pain perception. Also, crowding can contribute to higher blood pressure.

Comparative assessment of first costs:
Single versus double occupancy

Ten nursing units with varying configurations were analyzed. Some had all single rooms and some had a mix of single and double rooms. The gross area per bed was used as the indicator of cost per patient for building construction. The grossing factor was calculated for all single patient room floors and for mixed floors. A construction cost of $285 per square foot (2003) was used for both types of floor plans. Using this cost model, the costs per patient, based on 10 different nursing unit configurations follows:

- $182,400 per patient, single patient room floor plans
- $122,550 per patient, mixed room floor plans

Comparative Assessment of Operational Costs and
Patient Care Issues in Single and Multioccupancy Rooms

Structured interviews with administrators and frontline staff in four large hospitals in the Pacific Northwest were conducted. The findings represent the respondents' experiences as reported on questionnaires.

1. Nurses thought single bed rooms were more flexible, had more space, were more suitable for patient examination and history taking, had better bathing facilities, and were better-suited for different ethnocultural groups.

2. Double occupancy rooms were thought to result in shorter walking distances from the nurses' station.

3. The most common reason for transfer requests is privacy, followed by patient behavior issues and infection control.

4. Nurses felt staff efficiency was greater in single rooms and that patients use less pain medication.

5. The issues of patient falls was considered moderate in both types of rooms, but 57 % of nurses emphasized that the rate of acquiring a nosocomial infection is low or very low in single occupancy rooms.

Limitations of the study

The limitations of the study include sample size and limited actual data on operating costs. The complex relationship between patient care issues, operating cost variables, patient outcomes, staff efficiency, and subjective evaluations by patients and their families extend beyond the limits of this pilot study.

ATTEMPTS TO RETHINK CARE AT THE BEDSIDE

Significant landmarks in attempts to rethink care at the bedside involving the physical layout and design of the room start with the Kern Critical Care Unit at Legacy Health System in Portland, Oregon, designed in the mid-1990s by Tom Sagerser.

Innovation at Kern Critical Care, Legacy Health System

This was among the first uses of a rotating boom for medical gases and services in a patient room, and it permitted the bed to be rotated 360 degrees (Image page 7.83). In this case, the patient bed can face the nurses' station when the patient needs more observation but, as health status improves, the bed can be rotated to enable the patient to look out at the garden. Formerly beds were tethered to the headwall in intensive care units (ICUs). Another notable aspect of the room is the wide floor-to-ceiling window looking out onto a patio/deck.

The architect based the design on Roger Ulrich's work and other research about the importance of natural light and views of nature. At that time (and even now), critical care patients were often characterized as comatose and, therefore, unable to benefit from or be aware of views. It is disturbing to note that, today, critical care rooms are still being designed with a narrow window behind the patient or the orientation of the bed is such that the patient cannot see out the window.

Access to natural light matters because an individual's circadian rhythm is entrained through the change of light from day to night. Circadian rhythm (24-hour cycle) enables the production and release of numerous hormones that control metabolic processes, endocrine functions, and the sleep cycle. According to several directors of nursing, when patients have window views, their vital signs improve and their outward orientation returns more quickly. Patients were reported to be overall more alert, but this is subject to patient type, acuity level, and severity of illness.

Innovation at the Cardiac Comprehensive Critical Care Unit, Clarian Health, Methodist Hospital

Another landmark attempt to rethink the work environment of the caregiver and its relationship to the patient occurred in a critical care unit. Opened in 1999, the Cardiac Comprehensive Critical Care Unit (CCCCU) at Clarian Health, Methodist Hospital in Indianapolis, Indiana, is a 56-bed unit with design that was based on 1,000 hours of video capture that included the patient room, corridor, and nursing station. The intent was to understand how caregivers spent their time. According to Ann Hendrich, RN, MS, FAAN, the project investigator, the least amount of nursing time was spent with the patient. Details of this project and room design are presented on Image pages 7.17 to 7.22. This is generally considered to be the origin of the acuity-adaptable patient room, which has influenced the design of many projects undertaken by other organizations.

Learning from the Clarian CCCCU

The evolution of the Clarian experiment will be of interest to many. Significant performance improvement resulted from the new design as measured two years after occupancy of the new unit (Image page 7.22) compared to those measures in the old unit. Although one of the most important aspects of the room was not having to transport patients when their acuity levels changed, today, seven years after opening, the patient mix has changed, which has redefined how the rooms function.

In personal communication with the author on December 19, 2006, Director of Nursing Joy Fay said that staffing these rooms according to the original intent (all levels of care in any room) has become a challenge. High-acuity nurses do not want to care for med/surg patients. Considerable competition from heart hospitals has siphoned off the less-complex cases, while the older patients with more co-morbidities find their way to Clarian, an academic medical center. They also treat many medical (nonsurgical) patients and use the acuity-adaptable rooms for two levels of care: medical and progressive. They have designated a group of contiguous rooms as "critical," which makes it easier to mentor new nurses. It's an advantage, according to the director of nursing, that these rooms can be accessed without walking through a door to a discreet critical care unit. Also, since the rooms are all identical, they have the flexibility to reassign them at will. There are two levels of rooms for purposes of billing: progressive and critical care.

The Clarian rooms are mirror image and, because this unit was built in existing space, a number of existing conditions has created some variation among the rooms that the director of nursing finds frustrating. She points out that a nurse needs to walk from toe to head in observing the patient, and that approaching the patient from the side is not optimal from the patient's perspective. From this standpoint, it would seem that the room layout at St. Joseph's Hospital of West Bend, Wisconsin, (Image page 7.23) would be desirable.

One often hears and reads the comment that patients today are sicker when they enter the hospital. The director of nursing at Clarian countered that idea by explaining that the issue is actually that people are living longer and they are older with more co-morbidities. Heart bypass grafts (CABG procedures) are being done on 90-year-old individuals. Because this project has influenced so many others, it is informative to discuss what worked and what was not as successful as planned. Refer to Image page 7.18 for planview reference. In personal communications with the author, Fay listed some of the problems and challenges:

- variability in layout among rooms
- walking distances too great between rooms—a corridor running across the unit side to side would have helped this situation
- although there is an equipment room on each side, the equipment doesn't get put back in the correct room causing staff to look in both rooms
- although the hinges on the headwall casework break, the drop-down-door compartment (Image page 7.17) is useful for storing a variety of items
- too many drawers that collect junk, too much storage in room
- too much glass in nurses' conference room
- the central nurses' station used by unit clerks could be smaller
- the variable acuity room is a staffing issue
- need more conference rooms
- the electronic window screening is not used—windows are typically left in open (vision) position

What Works

- decentralized nursing is a success, but the workstations could be improved by having two options for countertop height
- the universal room concept is good but difficult to staff; however, it allows patients to be moved on the same floor to a critical care room when acuity changes
- high-acuity patients are stepped down to a med/surg room from which they are discharged
- accommodation for family has worked well as the unit gets more end-of-life patients now
- desk work area and laptop connection mean a lot to families
- the nurse server is used for linens, but storage on shelves has not been ideal; a mobile cart would be preferable
- they encourage families to get involved in the care process

Clarian Health System

Clarian Health System has had a unique opportunity to apply the learning from the 56-bed CCCCU at an academic medical center to a new suburban community hospital (Clarian West) that opened in 2004 and a new larger, more urban hospital (Clarian North) that opened in December 2005.

Clarian West has 64 beds, all acuity-adaptable rooms, and a 16-bed maternity center. In personal communication with the author on December 12, 2006, Chief Executive Officer Alfonso Gatmaitan offered these comments: The inpatient units care for patients with all types of med/surg conditions (not a single service line like orthopedics or cardiovascular disease), which made it impossible, from a staffing standpoint, to serve a patient transitioning from ICU to progressive to general med/surg in the same room. Because the rooms are identical, the ability to reassign them has been highly successful.

A six-bed designated critical care unit with hard-wired electronic monitoring is observed by an intensivist from a remote location. Data from the physiological monitor go to the intensivist. According to the hospital chief executive officer, this works very well. He also noted that being able to move critical care beds to another floor or to expand them with no construction other than rewiring for telemonitoring has been terrific. As well, the acuity-adaptable room allowed the hospital to avoid having to comply with state board of health requirements that ICUs be restricted with doors and designated at a fixed location. The board accepted the premise that the entire floor was ICU-ready, with all rooms having met the size and medical gas requirements for ICU.

Clarian North Medical Center

Clarian North is a 170-bed, 440,000 square-foot hospital that includes 12 labor, delivery, and recovery (LDR) rooms, 24 postpartum rooms, 11 high-risk obstetrics rooms, a Level III neonatal ICU, and 14 bariatric rooms. According to personal communication with the author on December 13, 2006, Chief Nurse Executive Kathy Mathena, the hospital was originally primarily dedicated to women and children, plus various subspecialties, but when it opened, its patient mix was quite different. The hospital has many patients with very specific needs—the types of patients for whom a large urban hospital would have dedicated specialty units, such as radical head and neck, mixed into a general nursing unit.

At the same time, pediatric hematology/oncology, orthopedics, cardiovascular services, and spine were growing quickly. The challenge became how to manage the patient flow process that supported dedicated patient types when separate units could not be realized. In addition, all types of medical patients were being admitted through the emergency department (diabetes, pneumonia, chronic obstructive pulmonary disease). It seemed as if the hospital was a victim of its own success. The extraordinary effort that went into the crafting of the patient's experience and the architecture and interior design have made it the hospital of choice (see "Putting It All Together" in Chapter 5).

Bed management—a frantic activity

Surgery quickly outstripped projections, according to Mathena. Twelve operating rooms were built, but only six were equipped at the time of opening. Within four months, they needed all twelve. At times the census is such that the hospital loses flexibility. A team meets twice a day to assess placement of patients. Some patients, like those having radical head and neck surgery, may require 16 days of hospitalization. Clarian North didn't build an ICU because it didn't think it would have that type of patient, anticipating instead progressive care and general med/surg. It now has six dedicated ICU beds with a hard-wired e-ICU, as does Clarian West, although it also has an intensivist in house and 24-hour hospitalist coverage.

Staffing

It has been hard to recruit cardiovascular and ICU nurses to work in a nondedicated unit. The hospital employs the 60/40 rule: 60% of the time nurses care for patients within their specialty and 40% of the time care for general and miscellaneous patients. The chief nurse executive observes that ICU nurses have a different skill set than med/surg nurses, and they organize their time differently. Working side by side on a team can be difficult.

> Staffing ratios:
> med/surg 1:4 or 1:5
> progressive care 1:3
> ICU 1:1 or 1:2

Billing

Another aspect of acuity-adaptable rooms is how to clearly delineate for purposes of billing when the patient has changed acuity because he or she is not physically moved. The line blurs. Dedicated e-ICU beds are easier to define. At the Clarian CCCCU, there are two levels of care for billing—progressive and critical, relying on industry standard assessment criteria and DRG codes.

Transforming Care at the Bedside

In 2003, the Institute for Healthcare Improvement (IHI), a not-for-profit organization based in Cambridge, Massachusetts, in partnership with the Robert Wood Johnson Foundation, launched an innovative project called Transforming Care at Bedside (TCAB). The goal of the project is to transform the delivery of care in med/surg units in accordance with the following themes:

- safe and reliable care
- patient- and family-centered care
- vitality, teamwork, and a safe environment for all staff
- value-added care processes and elimination of waste

The TCAB design team utilized IHI's Idealized Design model (Moen 2002) to generate new ideas, test changes on the med/surg units, and implement and spread successful changes. An initial retreat conducted in conjunction with IDEO (a San Francisco-based design innovation consultancy) included direct in-the-field observation on all shifts by observers with cameras, using creative thinking, patient interviews, and staff interviews. These methods and tools allowed the design team to develop an innovation transformational framework (Institute for Healthcare Improvement 2007). The 13 hospitals selected as prototype sites have been guided in a collaborative process designed to achieve improved clinical outcomes (e.g., reduced infections, reduced complications, and reduced errors and delays) and restore joy in work (e.g., reduced nursing turnover, fewer staff injuries). The teams continue with this work today and are achieving impressive results, yet, to date, no team has achieved the complete transformation of care across all units.

Within TCAB, there are several examples of redesigned processes intersecting with the built environment. All units are operating in existing nursing units, so total redesign has not been possible, but the teams have focused on process changes and other innovations, including:

- multidisciplinary rounds including family members and the patient at the bedside
- use of white boards in patients' rooms to communicate daily goals, care plans, and questions
- organization of the unit using the 5-S (sort, simplify, sweep, standardize, self-discipline) process from lean design
- redesign of existing facilities by utilizing an alcove to store linen and creating mini-nursing stations that are closer to patient rooms to decrease walking time
- locating handwashing sinks/dispensers in proximity to patients to increase compliance with handwashing protocols
- decreasing noise on units through scheduled peace-and-quiet periods during each shift

It is not known whether, at the end of the study, there will be significant built-environment issues that will be identified as having contributed to safer or more effective care, as this is not among the measures being studied. The CHD's work and the evidence-based design body of knowledge seems like the ideal corollary to the TCAB initiative. Patient-centered care defined as "care that honors the whole person and family, respects individual values and choices, and ensures continuity of care" is one of the key design themes of the TCAB project. As an example, one of the most cost-effective and immediate changes hospitals can make to better meet the needs of the patients follows.

(Recall, when reading this example, the research mentioned in Chapter 5 about what patients really want and how important the discharge activity is to patients.)

Imagine this: during a hospital stay for a routine procedure or surgery you see pictures of your nurse, physician, physical therapist, nurses' aides—everyone on your care team—on a white board across the room. And on your bedside table you find a small notebook called *Questions about My Care* that suggests good questions to ask your doctor when she visits. And on the day you leave the hospital, the nurse gives you a write-up about your hospital visit—what they did to you while you were there and why, what the tests found, what comes next, and what it all means about your health status. It's nothing technical; more of a story about your stay in the hospital that's simple enough to explain to your family and friends. Source: http://www.IHI.org

This is one of many patient-centered improvements TCAB study participants are implementing.

Time and Motion Study by Ascension Health and Kaiser Permanente

Commonly referred to as the Time and Motion Study, the full name is A Multi-Site Study of How Medical Surgical Nurses Spend Their Time: A Baseline Study in Preparation for an Electronic Health Record and an Evidence-Based Nursing Unit Design. Principal investigators are Ann Hendrich, RN, MS, FAAN, now vice president, clinical excellence operations for Ascension Health, and Marilyn Chow, DNSc, RN, FAAN, vice president patient care services, Kaiser Permanente. It is funded by grants from the Robert Wood Johnson Foundation, the Gordon and Betty Moore Foundation, Ascension Health, and Kaiser Permanente. The study began in 2005.

This is the largest study of its type, with 22,000 hours of nursing work and patterns having been gathered and submitted from 36 clinically diverse hospitals within 17 healthcare systems that are dispersed across 15 states. The healthcare systems operate a total of 274 hospitals with more than 63,000 beds. More than 200 variables of the acute care med/surg environment were documented for analysis to determine correlation and significance of environmental variables that impact direct nursing care time and, ultimately, patient care quality and safety.

Data were collected for seven consecutive days, 24 hours per day, on the randomly selected med/surg units, with 827 nurses completing the study, during a total of 2,200 workshifts.

The research provides detailed information about the amount of time nurses spend in identified activity categories, their movement throughout the nursing unit over the course of a typical nursing shift, and the physical/physiological impact of nursing workload and stress. The early study findings were disseminated and recommendations were made during the Nurse Work Environment Innovation Summit held in January 2007 at Kaiser's Sidney R. Garfield Health Innovation Center in Oakland, California.

The massive amount of data collected will enable the investigators to analyze and publish papers on many aspects of this study. At a recent conference (Hendrich and Chow 2007) a few findings were discussed:

- Nurses spend 20% of their time (120 minutes in 10 hours) in direct care (median time for day shift is 28%). Regardless of the staff-to-patient ratio, nurses do not spend any more time with patients.
- Nurses' activities generally fall into four categories: documentation, medication administration, locating supplies and equipment, and communication (with the care team, physicians, the patient, and locating people).
- Documentation required the same amount of time whether paper-based or electronic medical record. An average of 180 minutes was spent on this activity.
- There is a huge amount of indirect time, away from the patient, with no value added. Mostly, it involves hunting and gathering items needed for patient care.
- Nurses spend approximately 16% of their time on administration of medication.
- The median distance traveled by nurses in a 10-hour shift is three miles.

Variation among nurses on the same unit was greater than the difference between units, which indicates this is a matter of how individual nurses organize their work.

Table 7.1 summarizes how nurses spend their time.

Summary of Nursing Time	Table 7.1
Indirect care	48%
Direct care	28%
Waste	8%
Other	16%

There are implications of this study that involve the built environment. According to one of the principal investigators, variables of the physical setting may impact patient safety by indirectly impacting the time nurses can spend assessing, observing, and providing direct care. Center core nurses' station design is driving the inefficiency. In this study, nurses averaged 1.5 hours at shift change in the nurse station before going into a patient room. A new solution is needed to put caregivers closer to patients but also give them ready access to the equipment, devices, and supplies they need. Bar coding of equipment is a possible solution that requires a few hours each morning to scan everything, but then it can all be easily located. Nurse servers in rooms lead to too much contamination; too many supplies and medications have to be discarded.

The study investigators emphasize that nurses need to be innovators in their own work systems and work with vendors and architects to find new solutions. Technology is a major problem in that equipment and devices fail in being able to interface with each other.

A Bifurcation of Research

It is clear that a bifurcation—or split—exists in ongoing research. Organizations such as IHI and the Robert Wood Johnson Foundation as well as the major study undertaken by Ascension and Kaiser, are focusing their research on the complexity of the work environment, physical space, and technology, which is, of course, essential. Effects of the built environment are not being measured, which is not to say they think it's unimportant and has no impact, as all of these organizations have worked with the CHD and are sensitive to the synergistic relationship between care and environment. Healthcare cannot be separated from the settings in which it is delivered. The point is that the built environment is not a variable in any of their ongoing research. These are the most comprehensive studies being carried out to date, and the impact will be enormous. It is likely that once the reports are published, it will be possible to see how the built environment ties into it.

On the other side of the aisle, CHD and AIA have been sponsoring research based on the impact of the built environment on patient safety, patient clinical outcomes, and a variety of other issues, but there is no integration between this research and the various studies of clinical care at the bedside. Parties on both sides are well-intentioned and respectful of each other, but it isn't clear how and when the respective findings will be knit together to provide a holistic approach to the design of inpatient units.

Acuity-Adaptable versus Universal Room

Consensus about the meaning of these terms—acuity-adaptable and universal—does not exist. A number of seasoned healthcare architects have differing opinions regarding these terms, while others use them interchangeably.

A common definition of acuity-adaptable rooms is "rooms that are identically sized and designed for the full spectrum of inpatient care." The distinction between that and a definition of universal as "individualization of care so that every patient may be nursed at either critical care or acute care levels" is fuzzy. Some say the architectural standards for a universal room exceed that of acuity-adaptable and that, at one time, the universal room was defined as being large enough to serve as an LDR or labor, delivery, recovery, postpartum (LDRP) room with space for a portable computed tomography (CT) or magnetic resonance imaging (MRI) so that more invasive procedures could be performed at the bedside.

Others define acuity-adaptable as patient rooms within a single service line, sized and equipped to handle critical and step-down (progressive) levels of care. This definition excludes med/surg acute care. There is consensus that the former universal room concept is dead, and that the acuity-adaptable model is what most organizations are building. Whether it can be staffed as such is the challenge. Despite this, the flexibility of identical rooms that can be reassigned easily with no structural modifications has appeal to most organizations.

The bathroom redefined

Inherent in the acuity-adaptable room model is a change in the type of bathroom provided in critical care rooms. It used to be common for ICU rooms not to have a bathroom, as patients are often unable to get out of bed to use a bathroom. Sometimes a workroom with a clinical service sink used for washing bedpans was placed between two patient rooms. Other rooms had a swivel-out toilet in the patient room that is reminiscent of what one might find in a recreational vehicle. Occasionally two ICU rooms will share a toilet (Image page 7.84).

In the design of the Clarian CCCCU, it was very important for patients to be able to use the bathroom instead of a commode chair (Image pages 7.18 and 7.65), and this seems to have set a new benchmark. Acuity-adaptable rooms will, by definition, have a full toilet.

Excruciating Decisions

Throughout the nation, healthcare organizations are facing excruciating decisions about patient care unit design as they plan new hospitals that will be in use for at least the next 50 years. The experiences of two such organizations as they methodically explored numerous scenarios provide insight into this thought process.

Palomar Medical Center West

In planning a large replacement hospital (454 beds) on a greenfield site, the director of performance excellence for Palomar Medical Center West in Escondido, California, assembled four champion teams:

1. quality
2. customer service
3. financial strength
4. workforce and workplace development

These teams studied issues within their purview and made recommendations for design. The organization also did a lifecycle analysis, and anything with a five-year payback was considered worth doing; with more than a five-year payback they would consider it if it gave the patient more control. The architectural/engineering teams looked at energy and waste strategies, building commissioning (verification that all building systems are designed, constructed, and calibrated to operate as intended), and applied the Green Guide for Health Care throughout the project. They modeled energy and water consumption, looking at a 10-year payback for energy-saving measures. Site design using xeriscaping to reduce water use and construction will be managed tightly to control negative impacts on the surrounding area. Leadership in Energy and Environmental Design (LEED) gold award is their target.

In thinking about the goal of having all acuity-adaptable rooms and how to manage the staffing challenge, these considerations emerged.

1. Cohort by patient type. They had enough volume for specialized cardiovascular and neuroscience units. Then they looked at putting surgical and medical diagnoses on separate floors thinking that, if nurses are expected to handle multiple skill levels, they should be more successful if focusing on a narrower diagnostic range.

2. Don't expect any nurse to handle all levels of acuity. Critical care can flex down to intermediate and med/surg can flex up to intermediate. This makes the middle patient group the one that provides flexibility for staffing.

3. Charge nurses/supervisors should be ICU competent in order to handle emergencies.

4. After piloting the model prior to move in, the worst-case scenario will be that the units are acuity-assignable, although that won't achieve the patient safety benefits from reduced handoffs and continuity of patient and family education that were the goals.

5. Remote monitoring is being considered as, in theory, ICU patients may be on seven floors, and this would be a method by which to prioritize rounds for the intensivists and others.

6. The research teams recommended against having a dedicated ICU, but there was significant pushback on this leading to a decision to have a 24-bed super ICU for selected patients with the remaining rooms being acuity-adaptable.

7. All rooms will be same-handed, with space for family, and include an outboard bathroom on the headwall (Image pages 7.51 to 7.55). Decentralized care stations outside the rooms have a view into two rooms.

Florida Hospital

An opportunity to develop three expansion projects at different sites led Florida Hospital in Orlando to an intensive visioning and planning process, pooling the insights of several architectural firms and numerous consultants. As part of this effort, hospital leaders invited a number of contrarians to review the plans. One of the most significant recommendations was to reorient the building to take advantage of the lake views. Although costly ($25 million), it was soon realized that to not do this would be a mistake that they would be living with for the life of the building. In looking at patient room design, they built full-size mock-up rooms that were reviewed and analyzed by care teams as well as the contrarians.

In the end, although considering several options, they decided to build two types of rooms: critical care and an acuity-adaptable room that serves med/surg and progressive (midlevel monitored) care (Image pages 7.35 to 7.37). The contrarian process involved knowledgeable individuals from a variety of industries, such as hospitality and entertainment, architecture and interior design, and medical technology. The cost for this second opinion was $150,000 and was considered a good investment. Many patient and family focus groups were also conducted to get their perspectives. As a result of its role in the reorienting of the building on the site, CHD now provides "second opinion" educational consulting.

Room Size and Toilet Room Placement

The 2006 edition of the AIA *Guidelines for Design and Construction of Health Care Facilities* requires single occupancy rooms to have 120 square feet of clear floor space exclusive of toilet rooms, closets, lockers, wardrobes, alcoves, and vestibules with three feet clear at sides and foot of bed to any fixed obstruction. This refers to typical patient rooms.

Intermediate care units, per the *Guidelines*, allow for up to four patients per room with 120 square feet of clear floor space per bed or 150 square feet of clear space in a single bed room. There must be four feet clear at the sides and foot of each bed to another bed or any fixed obstruction.

Critical care, per the *Guidelines*, may be in multiple or single patient configuration. Each patient space must have 200 square feet of clear floor area or 150 square feet of clear space in a single bed room. The headwall must be 13 feet wide, and there needs to be five feet clear at the transfer and foot sides of the bed, four feet on the nontransfer side, and eight feet between beds.

Acuity-adaptable rooms are not mentioned in the *Guidelines*, therefore minimum sizes must, by definition, be based on critical care. Looking at the projects gathered for this book, 285 square feet (exclusive of bathroom) seems to be the average room size. There is a noticeable tendency to locate bathrooms on the headwall (Image pages 7.5, 7.6, 7.7, 7.8, 7.9, 7.11, 7.33, 7.35, 7.37, and 7.40), which is likely due to the influence of St. Joseph's Hospital of West Bend (Image page 7.23). This location is the shortest distance from the bed, and a handrail can be placed on the headwall to help patients reach it without falling.

Decentralized Nurses' Workstations

There is a strong tendency toward distributed or decentralized nurses' workstations (Image pages 7.9, 7.20, 7.38, 7.40, and 7.53), and some of these permit a view into two rooms (Image pages 7.15, 7.53, 7.54, 7.55, and 7.57). Still others provide observation from across the corridor (Image pages 7.6, 7.9, and 7.34), from more of a distributed central nurses' station. The nurse work alcove on the footwall offers several benefits discussed on Image page 7.23 and works especially well with same-handed rooms (Image page 7.24).

Mirror Image versus Same-Handed Room Orientation

Although the jury is still out on the level of evidence to make same-handed room orientation a must, theoretically it makes sense. The first major initiative to study this was St. Joseph's Hospital of West Bend (Image pages 7.23 to 7.28). Based on standardization common to other industries such as aviation, aerospace, and manufacturing, the supposition is that similar error reduction would occur by applying this strategy to healthcare and patient room design. The theory is that everything a care team needs should be in the same location in all rooms so that, in a crisis, staff can rely on long-term memory rather than short term. Staff can be on automatic pilot and know where to reach for something.

The rooms are usually oriented so that the patient's right side (and the nurse's access) is closest to the door, because that is the preferred side for addressing a patient during examination. An exception to this orientation is presented on Image page 7.33. Although it is often assumed that it costs more to build same-handed rooms over mirror image due to not being able to layout medical gases and plumbing lines back to back, at St. Joseph's of West Bend bids from three contractors ranged from same cost for both options to 10% less for same-handed due to savings derived from being able to produce more standardized units in a factory with few or no existing condition variations.

A study looking at costs of various patient room planning options (Black and Dorney 2006) indicated a difference of $63,000 per bed to ratchet up from a mirror-image acuity-adaptable room to one that is same-handed. Construction cost for this study was calculated at $230 per square foot. This does not support the actual experience at St. Joseph's, but allowing for geographic variability, the economics of the marketplace, and a credible attempt to look at all factors that must be considered, it represents a theoretical construct. It would be different to factor into this an actual bidding experience in which construction documents show large volumes of absolutely identical casework, for example, that can be produced in the shop without having to think about the number of left-facing and right-facing units. This follows for numerous items. The contingency that subcontractors build into their bids for having to correct errors due to variability among rooms is greatly reduced.

Discussion

The acuity-adaptable room seems to be what most organizations are building because of the flexibility it affords for easy reassignment of acuity, even if it is not initially used as intended to avoid transport of patients. However, this type of room may not be so adaptable depending on where the toilet room and nursing observation are located. An inboard toilet often reduces visibility into the room (Image page 7.4), but it can be placed to allow for a nurse observation station (Image pages 7.8, 7.14, and 7.35). Florida Hospital adapted its med/surg/progressive care room for ICU by modifying only the bathroom access and the width of the room entry (Image pages 7.35 and 7.37). A number of projects have distributed central nurses' stations across the corridor from patient rooms (Image pages 7.6 and 7.85), which seems unusual for critical care rooms. Other designs feature a group of acuity-adaptable rooms (Image pages 7.9 and 7.34) across from a nurses' station.

The AIA *Guidelines* offer a number of possibilities for patient observation, as follows: direct or remote visual observation between the administrative center, nurse station, or staffed charting stations and all patient beds in the critical care unit and a documentation space must be located within or adjacent to the patient bed with a countertop large enough for a computer monitor and a wide flow sheet. One sit-down documentation space per bed is required.

Although acuity-adaptable rooms are not addressed in the *Guidelines*, it would seem that a room could not be considered acuity-adaptable if it lacks a nurse observation station that would be required for a critical care patient (Image page 7.34) and may be desirable as well for progressive (step-down) care. Regulatory agencies and jurisdictions may interpret it that way or not. There exists considerable variation among states with respect to licensing requirements. Many nurses, however, feel there is no substitute for direct observation, and they want as much visibility of the patient as possible.

PATIENT ROOM DESIGN FEATURES

One of the premises of this book is that direct patient care areas deserve the same level of design as lobbies and public spaces. Too often they are plain vanilla, bland, and devoid of appealing aesthetic features. Finding projects that go beyond this for inclusion in the book was actually not easy. Patient rooms, bathrooms, and inpatient corridors all too often are institutional in design.

The prototype patient room developed by students at Clemson University (Image pages 7.11 to 7.16) gains some ground by challenging some of the notions held dear by more experienced design professionals. The room has been quite well thought out, and the placement of medical gases is worth considering. An oversight is the omission of a high-back patient chair and comfortable accommodation for family. What is metaphorically described as the "family hearth" is, in fact, a hard, very shallow, low bench that is unlikely to be anyone's first choice of seating for more than a 10-minute visit. The bathroom is too small to be functional. With the door open, the patient is exposed to passersby. Despite these considerations, which are fixable, the aesthetics of the room are attractive in a clear, organized way, not unlike contemporary Japanese design. It appears that surfaces would be easy to clean, although the extended soffit creates a dust shelf that would not be acceptable in some jurisdictions. The selection of image on the television monitor (Image page 7.13) is curious; an image of nature would have been more appropriate for the rendering. They probably intended to show that a patient's imaging studies could be viewed in the room.

Headwalls and Footwalls

Headwall and footwall designs do not need to be elaborate or expensive to satisfy the basic requirements of organizing the equipment and amenities in a manner that reduces clutter. The footwall designs on Image pages 7.7, 7.44 (upper left photo), and 7.72 are functional and attractive. Designs featuring more casework (Image pages 7.42 and 7.44 lower left photo) will be more expensive, but provide considerably more space for flowers, plants, and personal memorabilia.

Headwalls may completely conceal the medical gases and electrical outlets as on Image pages 7.42 and 7.43 (lower left photo) or leave them exposed. A successful example of this is shown on Image page 7.39, in which the gas outlets are neatly framed by a solid surface panel. A similar treatment can be seen on Image page 7.38. The lower photo on this page shows an internally illuminated translucent acrylic panel with wild grass embedded in it. Another example of this is depicted on Image page 7.80. An additional option for concealing medical gases, as well as the blood pressure cuff and suction canister, is a recessed unit with a door that slides up to provide access. This requires a slightly thicker wall. The door can also be a framed piece of art. Birthing rooms often have a more elaborate headwall (Image pages 7.71, 7.73, 7.74, 7.78, 7.80, and 7.81) that may house the infant warmer and the fetal monitor.

Sharps containers, glove boxes, and universal precaution gear can often be tucked into casework, where they are convenient to staff but out of view of patients (Image pages 7.13, 7.36, 7.60, and 7.75). Clinical handwash sinks are often in view of patients, which is good, but they can be attractive and functionally well-designed (Image page 7.44).

Ceiling Lifts

Back injuries account for 44% of lost workdays for nursing staff (Fragala and Bailey reported in Joseph and Fritz 2006). Performing manual lifting and transferring of patients is what causes most of these injuries. Mechanical patient-handling devices are increasingly being installed in ceilings of patient rooms. Ceiling lifts are preferred for their convenience and ease of use. As mentioned before, a Pebble Project research study conducted at PeaceHealth Sacred Heart Medical Center in Eugene, Oregon, (Joseph and Fritz 2006) documents the costs associated with these types of injuries and the savings after the lifts were installed and 100% compliance was achieved.

Patient Bathrooms

Often reminiscent of gas-station bathrooms in their pallor and utterly basic fixtures, stainless steel accessories, and white gloss ceramic tile (Image pages 7.62 and 7.63, upper right photo), bathrooms mean a lot to patients. Apart from specific safety features detailed elsewhere in this book, aesthetics really matter. Most people look at the bathroom when they first check into a hotel room. It's a benchmark of overall quality. Large size ceramic tile looks more elegant (Image page 7.62) but is also much easier to maintain due to fewer grout joints. The ubiquitous Bobrick mirror (Image page 7.63, upper right photo) can be replaced for the same cost with something less institutional (Image pages 7.62, 7.63, and 7.64).

Lighting on both sides of the mirror is desirable if possible (Image page 7.62) to make one look healthy. Lighting from a fixture above the mirror (Image page 7.63) often creates shadows on the face. An illuminated mirror (Image page 7.64) can be used to address this issue. Places for toiletries, towel bars, and a countertop for laying out makeup or toothbrushes (Image pages 7.62, 7.63, and 7.64) are appreciated amenities. Patient bathrooms are sometimes designed with two doors (Image pages 7.8, upper left photo; 7.11, and 7.65) to make access easier, and most have a shower with no curb (Image pages 7.7, 7.8, 7.60, 7.62, and 7.65).

Inpatient Corridors

Patients, visitors, and staff spend so much time in corridors within nursing units that they serve more than mere circulation. As such, they are deserving of excellent lighting, soffiting, artwork, and finishes all coordinated to create an ambience that is warm and welcoming. Whether they have resilient flooring (Image page 7.66) or carpet (Image page 7.67), an inset design will lead the eye through the space, as will a curved soffit (Image page 7.67). Wall sconces offer an option for ambient light at night (Image pages 7.67, 7.68, and 7.86). Wall and corner protection should be as unobtrusive as possible (Image pages 7.67 and 7.68). Indirect lighting is desirable wherever patients are on gurneys (Image pages 7.57, 7.66, 7.67, 7.68, 7.69, and 7.86).

Central nurses' stations should reflect the design theme and detailing (Image pages 7.68 and 7.69, top photo) predominant in the corridor, although occasionally they are somewhat bland in this regard (Image page 7.39, lower photo).

LDR/LDRP ROOMS

The mid-1980s heralded a dramatic shift in attitude toward the birth experience. Women entering a maternity unit to give birth often found it a terrifying experience; for many it was their first encounter with a hospital. The women's movement (women gaining confidence about making decisions and taking control), a more informed consumer, and the assertiveness of Baby Boomers together created a favorable climate for the germination of a new approach to birth. Much of the impetus for change resulted from the competitive environment hospitals found themselves in during the 1980s. The concept of the LDRP, all-in-one room had wide appeal, and it allowed the family to participate in a way that was unheard of previously except for home births. Now the focus is on family bonding, and the best birthing centers embed that in all of their protocols and practices. Some probably cannot imagine a time when hospitals had a waiting room for expectant fathers and after the birth someone would walk in and deliver the news. At that time, ultrasound was not available to image the fetus, and parents often didn't know the sex of the baby before the birth.

For operational reasons, some hospitals prefer LDR rooms, and, in this case, the patient is moved to a postpartum room after the birth. There is a pro and con to this from the patient's perspective. Some like the idea of moving to a clean room after birth, one that has no lingering reminders of painful labor. Others like the idea of remaining in that large room which generally has lots of space for family. The LDR and postpartum rooms on Image page 7.71 have similar design features, minimizing any negative feelings about moving to a new room. Since it is more expensive to build LDRPs and requires more space, high-volume birthing centers often prefer the LDR option. An exception to this is the 56-bed LDRP unit at Gaston Memorial Hospital in Gastonia, North Carolina, (Image page 7.75 and 7.76) and the 60-bed LDRP unit at Community Hospital North, Indianapolis, Indiana (Image page 7.78). Both of these projects have many interesting features that can be noted in the planviews (pages 7.76 and 7.79).

The layout and design of LDR and LDRP rooms have not changed dramatically in recent years. The infant warmer is always placed where emergency care teams have quick access to it without being too close to the bed. The infant warmer may be built-in (Image pages 7.71 and 7.81) or freestanding (Image pages 7.74 and 7.78, lower photo). Infants are often washed in the room immediately after birth in a sink designed for this purpose (Image page 7.77). A typical room and equipment layout can be seen in the planview on Image page 7.73.

The average size of LDRP rooms collected for this book is 350 to 380 square feet plus bathroom. One of the options that must be considered in planning these rooms is whether to equip each with such items as the case cart, which can be stored in the room's casework or in an attached equipment room (Image pages 7.73 and 7.79) or whether to store such items in a central equipment room. There are quite a number of requirements that go into the planning of these rooms, which will reflect specific preferences of the nurses at each institution.

CRITICAL CARE

Critical care may occur in an acuity-adaptable room or in a dedicated ICU, which may not have a single service line focus such as neuro-ICU or coronary care, or patients may be aggregated depending on patient type or patient acuity, such as medical or surgical. In ICUs, it is increasingly common to find a rotating boom for supply of medical gases (Image pages 7.83, 7.84, and 7.85), for support of monitors and other equipment to keep the floor unobstructed, and to reduce the tangle of cords one often sees with a more standard headwall. The boom rotates 360 degrees, providing greater flexibility of bed placement than is possible with medical gases mounted in a headwall (Image page 7.87).

In past years few questioned the large expanse of break-away glass that characterized ICU rooms. The resulting loss of privacy for the patient was accepted as the trade-off for constant observation by nurses. And, in numerous surveys when patients have been asked if they preferred privacy over knowing that they could easily be seen, most preferred being seen. Accomplishing both seems ideal, but staff at hospitals that have installed the glass that, with the flip of a switch, changes from clear to opaque (Image page 7.19), say they rarely use it in the privacy mode.

Now it seems that the amount of glazing is being reduced (Image page 7.37) because the break-away feature is so rarely used. The Clarian CCCCU has glazing that starts above the nurse server, and most of the acuity-adaptable rooms have glazing only at the nurse observation station (Image pages 7.40, 7.53, 7.55, 7.56, and 7.57). The new rooms planned for Hoag Memorial Hospital in Newport Beach, California, have the option of a hinged door with a fixed leaf or slider/break-away doors (Image page 7.60) for those designated as ICU. Some acuity-adaptable rooms being planned don't have any glazing except a panel in the door (Image page 7.34).

Various aspects of ICU room design such as the orientation of beds have been discussed earlier in this chapter. A few additional thoughts follow. The decentralized nurse workstation on Image page 7.88 is recessed enough to reduce the distraction of corridor traffic and has a larger than normal work surface that seems very functional. Windows into patient rooms have horizontal blinds for privacy. All too often, critical care units have a bland appearance as if color was bad medicine for people who are very ill. The application of color and the elegant finishes seen on Image page 7.86 are to be applauded. The large patient room is most likely appreciated by families.

Anyone planning an ICU may wish to read a comparative analysis of a group of ICUs built between 1993 and 2003 and recognized by the Society of Critical Care Medicine and the American Association of Critical Care Nurses as best-practice examples (Rashid 2006). The author of this journal article is an architect who has a doctorate. He discusses, in detail, various characteristics of these plans in a most thoughtful manner, looking at how the AIA *Guidelines* and the ICU design community have impacted the design of these projects.

References

American Institute of Architects. 2006. *Guidelines for design and construction of health care facilities.* Washington, DC: American Institute of Architects.

Black, S. A., and B. Dorney. 2006. The consequences of evidence-based design. Lecture presented at the International Conference & Exhibition on Health Facility Planning, Design and Construction: San Diego, CA.

Chaudhury, H., A. Mahmood, and M. Valente. 2004. Pilot study on comparative assessment of patient care issues in single and multiple occupancy rooms. Unpublished report. Concord, CA: Coalition for Health Environments Research/Center for Health Design.

Hendrich, A., and N. Lee. (2005). Intra-unit patient transports: Time, motion, and cost impact on hospital efficiency. *Nursing Economics* (23)1:157–164.

Hendrich, A., and M. Chow. 2007. How nurses spend their time and recommendations for change: Effects on quality, safety, and nurse retention in hospitals. Paper presented at American Hospital Association Health Forums, San Diego, CA.

Institute for Healthcare Improvement. 2007. Transforming care at the bedside. Cambridge, MA: Institute for Healthcare Improvement. http://www.ihi.org/NR/rdonlyres/37FDB5E8-52ED-4CC2-8E43-E2C22DA53AFE/0/TCABframework3807.pdf

Joseph, A., and L. Fritz. 2006. Ceiling lifts reduce patient-handling injuries. *Healthcare Design* (6)1:10–13.

Moen, R. 2002. *A guide to idealized design.* Cambridge, MA: Institute for Healthcare Improvement. http://www.ihi.org/IHI/Topics/Improvement/ImprovementMethods/Literature/AGuidetoIdealizedDesign.htm

Rashid, M. 2006. A decade of adult intensive care unit design: A study of the physical design features of the best-practice examples. *Critical Care Nursing Quarterly* 29(4):282–311.

Ulrich, R., C. Zimring, A. Joseph, X. Quan, and R. Choudary. 2004. *The role of the physical environment in the hospital of the 21st century: A once-in-a-lifetime opportunity.* Concord, CA: Center for Health Design.

Renderings by Earl Swensson Associates, Inc.

Corridors have been eliminated as patient rooms wrap around large clinical nursing worktable.
North Georgia Medical Center, Ellijay, GA
Earl Swensson Associates, Inc.

View from nurse station shows visibility into rooms while seated at workstation.
This is a "no hidden patient/no hidden caregiver" model.

Commentary

continued on next page

This design concept aims to increase patient safety by assuring there are no "hidden" patients. Outboard toilets achieve maximum visibility into the room and, unlike conventional nursing unit layouts, all patient rooms are equally close to the nurse station. The large worktable enhances team collaboration and care planning opportunities. The supposition is that much quicker response to a monitor alarm can be achieved in this layout. All rooms in the hospital will be designed similarly in recognition that patients are sicker today, more of them require a higher level of care, and because people are living longer, they have more co-morbidities. Each set of 6 med/surg rooms (12-bed units) will be staffed at 1:6 ratio nurse to patients. Rooms will be customized as required for specialized care. The first floor has a dedicated ICU with 6 rooms plus 4 med/surg and 2 observation rooms, all of which back-up to the ED. All rooms can be converted to ICU. This is a new 85,000 SF facility, a replacement hospital, with occupancy date end 2008. (See next page for unit layout.)

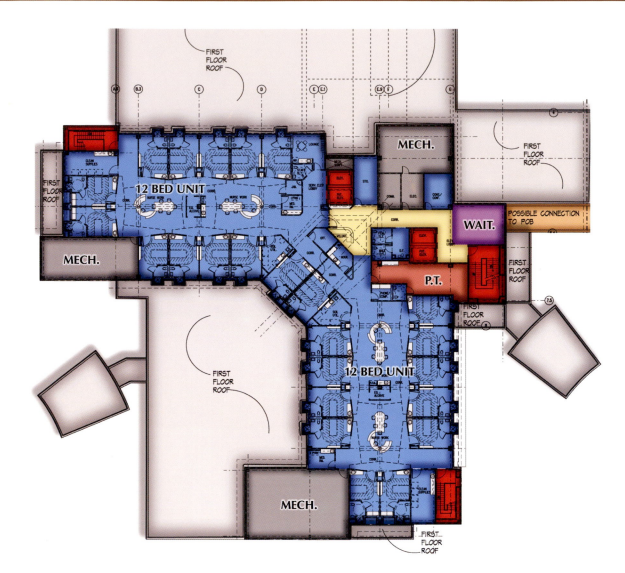

Second floor plan. Two 12-bed med/surg units. North Georgia Medical Center, Ellijay, GA
Earl Swensson Associates, Inc.

Commentary

continued on next page

Certain obvious questions occur upon looking at the perspective renderings on the previous page. Ancillary support rooms are not visible (clean, soiled, staff break room, equipment room, etc.) however these are visible in the unit floorplan on this page. Clean linen will be stored in patients' rooms; the red, bagged waste receptacle will be inside casework. Is there a trade-off here between immediate access to patients and enhanced visibility and patient privacy? Will light and noise from the nurse station keep patients from sleeping? The architect's response to this is integral blinds in windows and door, operable from the patient side. Coffered ceilings at the nurse station with acoustic attenuation, it is hoped, will deal with the noise issue. Will the inevitable clutter on the large worktable where everything is in view and nothing out of sight create a chaotic ambience? There are no walls for bulletin boards with emergency information and protocols. There is a private office away from the core area that nurses and physicians can use for private conversations. A wireless communication system like Vocera and EMR is anticipated.

Photo courtesy Glendale Memorial Hospital Public Relations Dept.
Photographer: Pam Pollock (both photos)

Views of the clinical nursing worktables in ICU setting.
Glendale Memorial Hospital, Glendale , CA

Commentary

The origin of the large nurse station worktable comes from Glendale Memorial Hospital where Valli Washburn, RN, Director of Emergency and Intensive Care Services, developed it as a response to the limitations of standard enclosed nurse stations: staff standing around it blocked the view for others; having to walk around the desk to exit on the sides in order to reach a patient; not enough seating for all involved in case management (respiratory therapist; pharmacist, social worker, dietician) to collaborate; nursing staff seated back-to-back as opposed to facing each other. The alcove between two patient rooms was considered but deemed a nurse-assignment challenge. Also, these spaces do not encourage collaboration of the team and workspace is often limited.

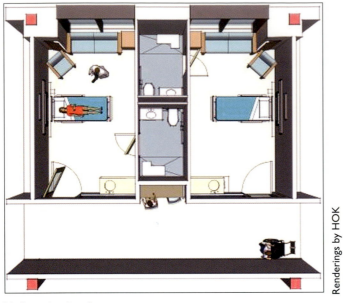

Renderings by HOK

Midboard toilet plan.

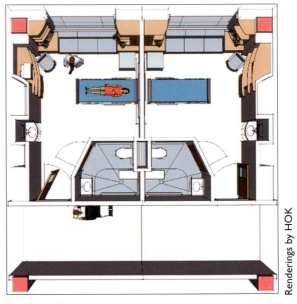

Renderings by HOK

Inboard toilet plan.

Features/Pro

- Enables rooms to be square or rectangular
- Full width wall at corridor provides maximum visibility
- Full width wall at window creates enough room for a sleep sofa
- Clinical handwash sink close to door upon entering
- Decentralized nurse station with view into two rooms

Features/Con

- Toilet is on footwall, which involves more steps to reach it and no possibility of a grab bar to enhance safety
- Toilet rooms large enough for wheelchair accessibility or ADA-compliant rooms with showers require 6 feet additional corridor length. This extends the building length and travel distance for nurses.
- Midboard toilet placement does not allow for same-handed patient rooms.

Features/Pro

- Bed is shielded from corridor noise by toilet room.
- Patient privacy is enhanced by toilet room placement.
- Toilet location convenient for patient assistance and housekeeping (close to door)
- Window wall full width to optimize views and size of family area

Features/Con

- Narrow entry to room pushes clinical handwash sink away from door
- Nurse work space, if located behind door, would be difficult to use
- Room cannot adapt to high level acuity care due to poor visibility

The content for the next six pages has been adapted from articles by Sheila Cahnman, published in *Healthcare Design*, April 2006, Vol. 6, No. 2, and May 2006, Vol. 6, No. 3.

Same-handed, acuity-adaptable patient room.
HealthEast St. Joseph's Hospital, St. Paul, MN
HOK Architects (architecture and interior design),
BWBR (architect of record)

Renderings by HOK

DIMENSIONS

325 SF w/bathroom
285 SF w/o bathroom
13'6" from headwall to footwall

Commentary
see next page for plan of inpatient unit

This city-center hospital is literally the oldest institution in St. Paul. As an ailing, very outdated infrastructure brought it close to closure, an outpouring of community support convinced the HealthEast system to move forward with a plan focusing on cardiovascular and neuroscience centers of excellence. Each specialty-dedicated 45-bed floor allows for a continuum of care from med/surg to critical care, which means that patients will not leave that floor and may even remain in one room throughout their stay. Patient rooms are sized to handle all levels of care, but one-third of beds have additional medical gas and power outlets and corridor view windows to meet ICU standards. All rooms have 12-foot-wide headwalls. The headwall aesthetically looks the same in all rooms, but is dual-tiered in ICU rooms. Therapy and rehab services related to each specialty are located, respectively, on each floor to decrease vertical transport of patients.

After debating issues of patient visibility vs. privacy, nursing staff requested outboard toilets to allow for maximum visibility from the corridor; however, the proximity of the bathroom door to the bed was another issue resolved by creating same-handed rooms. By canting the headwall, the family area was expanded and patients have greater window access to prime views of the State Capitol and the magnificent Cathedral of St. Paul.

There is minimal storage for supplies in the room due to a preference for centralized inventory control to reduce par stocking and waste. All toilets are floor-mounted and four rooms on each floor have bariatric ceiling lifts and structurally reinforced toilets and grab bars.

The hospital plans to employ decentralized charting using COWs (computers on wheels) or handheld computers. Numerous staff workstations enable nurses to be close to patient rooms. The dedicated critical care rooms are arranged around a large central nurse station.

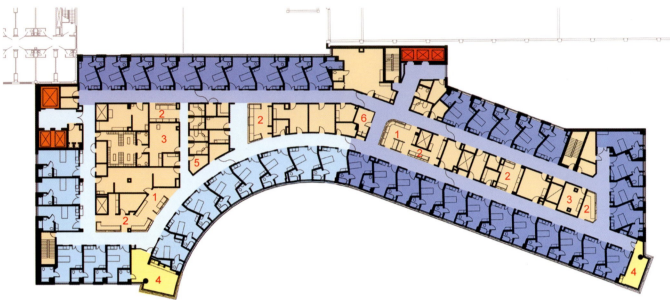

St. Joseph's Hospital – New Patient Tower
Typical Patient Floor – 45-Bed inpatient Unit

1. Head Unit Coordinator
2. Nurse/Work Station
3. Staff Conference/Lounge
4. Family Waiting/Lounge
5. Family Consult
6. Patient/Family Resource Center

Courtesy HOK Architects

Commentary

Rooms are all same-handed. The curved shape of the building is a response to site conditions and the desire to provide optional views of historic landmarks. The "thinner" area of the core will have med/surg/stepdown beds and the higher acuity critical care beds will have more core components by being located on the left side. Centralized nurse stations are dispersed throughout the floor. Therapy and rehab services related to each specialty are located, respectively, on each floor to decrease vertical transport of patients. Family waiting lounges have the benefit of corner views.

DIMENSIONS

327 SF w/bathroom
288 SF w/o bathroom
14 feet from headwall to footwall

Same-handed room with canted headwall to increase patient views.
The Miriam Hospital, Lifespan Health System, Providence, R.I. (all images)
Renderings courtesy HOK and the S/L/A/M Collaborative

Headwall design.

Footwall design.

Features:

1) The entry into the patient room widens to provide more clinical work space away from the door swing; note the cubicle drape that can be pulled for privacy

2) Nurse server pass-through for replenishment of linen and supplies and for removal of soiled linen

3) The headwall uses premanufactured, full-height millwork panels with a very "clean" layout of medical gases.

4) Clinical items (glove dispensers, sharps containers) stored out of patient's view; clinical handwash sink in optimal location, immediately inside room entry.

5) Considered acuity-adaptable, room size allows room to be upgraded to critical care. Currently designed for med/surg to step-up (progressive) care. Floorplan organizes 36 beds in linear groupings of six rooms across from a nurse station.

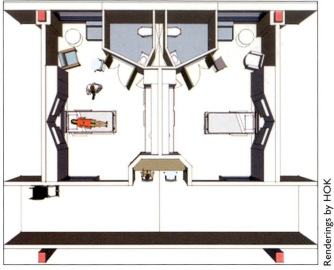

Renderings by HOK

Outboard toilet plan.

Renderings by HOK

Canted "same-handed" plan. Barnes Jewish Hospital, O'Fallon, MO

Features/Pro

- Outboard toilet provides maximum patient visibility from corridor and puts the bed closer to the door (corridor).
- Room configurations of this type are optimized by a 32-foot column grid to allow the window area and toilet adequate width, although this makes the building larger and increases costs.

Features/Con

- Window and family area are relatively small and distant from the patient, reducing both natural light and family interaction.
- Toilet is opposite the bed, which involves a few more steps to reach it and no possibility of a grab bar to enhance patient safety.
- Toilet location demands that housekeeping cross the room to reach it and it's farther for staff to assist patients into bathroom.

Features/Pro

- Canting the headwall toward the window expands the patient's view of the outdoors; canting it toward the corridor provides greater patient visibility.
- Same-handed rooms (as opposed to mirror image, which have medical gas headwalls back-to-back) are based on evidence from aviation and manufacturing industries indicating that standardization reduces error. These rooms can have either an inboard or outboard toilet.
- Sound transmission is reduced with separate headwalls (as opposed to back-to-back).
- Clinical handwash sink is in optimal location just inside room entry
- Access to toilet very close to bed
- Large footwall w/ amenities possible
- Decentralized viewing/nurse station gives room potential to convert to critical care. Easy for housekeeping and caregivers to reach toilet (when assisting patient).

Features/Con

- Toilets without a common plumbing wall cost more to build, however these costs are offset by the repetition of other items which cost less (casework, headwalls, med gas piping) due to standardization (fewer manufacturing errors and fewer adjustments at the job site due to varying existing conditions).

see next page for nursing unit layout

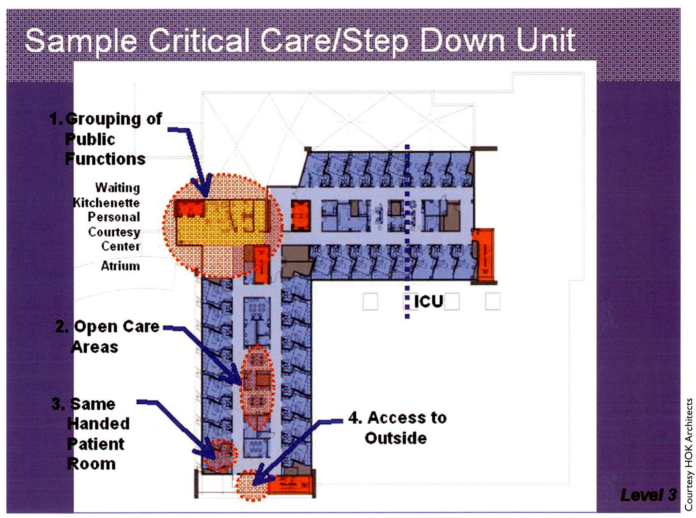

Sample Critical Care/Step Down Unit

1. Grouping of Public Functions

Waiting
Kitchenette
Personal
Courtesy
Center
Atrium

2. Open Care Areas

3. Same Handed Patient Room

4. Access to Outside

ICU

Level 3

Courtesy HOK Architects

Barnes Jewish Hospital, O'Fallon, MO
HOK Architects

Commentary

This is a new satellite hospital in a suburb of St. Louis. As a small community hospital, the number of critical care beds is low. All rooms are identical and those labelled "ICU" do not have the typical decentralized nurse observation stations outside the room. High acuity cases would no doubt be cared for at another Barnes location. The "public functions" area is centrally located and has the potential to be a very pleasant space with natural light and perhaps nice views. The double-loaded core with open nurse charting workstations should receive natural light flowing in from patient rooms. Refer to previous page for details of patient room design.

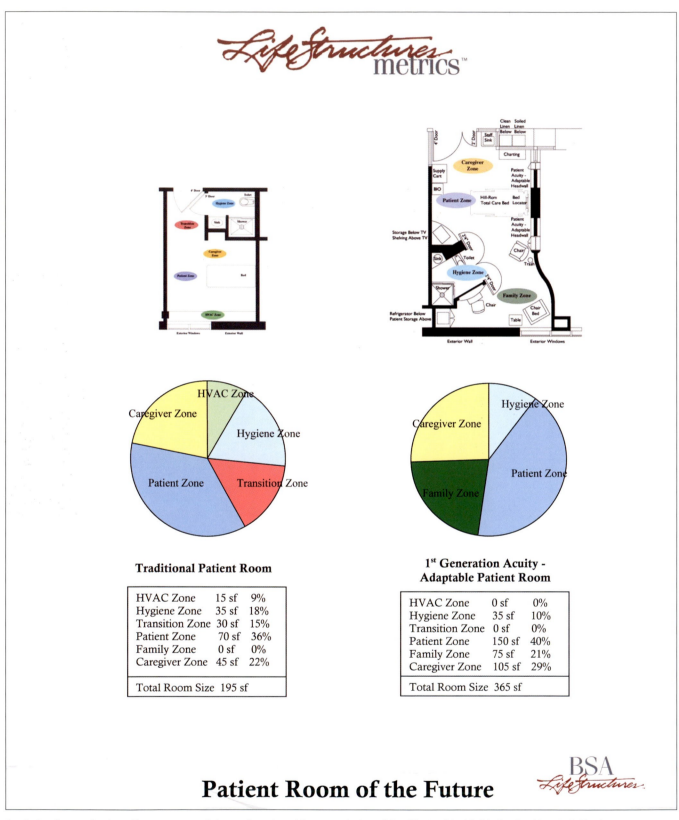

Traditional Patient Room

HVAC Zone	15 sf	9%
Hygiene Zone	35 sf	18%
Transition Zone	30 sf	15%
Patient Zone	70 sf	36%
Family Zone	0 sf	0%
Caregiver Zone	45 sf	22%
Total Room Size 195 sf		

1ˢᵗ Generation Acuity - Adaptable Patient Room

HVAC Zone	0 sf	0%
Hygiene Zone	35 sf	10%
Transition Zone	0 sf	0%
Patient Zone	150 sf	40%
Family Zone	75 sf	21%
Caregiver Zone	105 sf	29%
Total Room Size 365 sf		

Patient Room of the Future

Courtesy BSA LifeStructures

Analysis of a standard med/surg room and the acuity-adaptable room designed for Clarian Health Methodist Hospital, Cardiac Comprehensive Critical Care Unit, Indianapolis, IN (opened 1999).

Clemson University: Architecture + Health & The School of Industrial Design at Carleton University.
An interdisciplinary design research collaboration with the Spartanburg Regional Health Care System, South Carolina

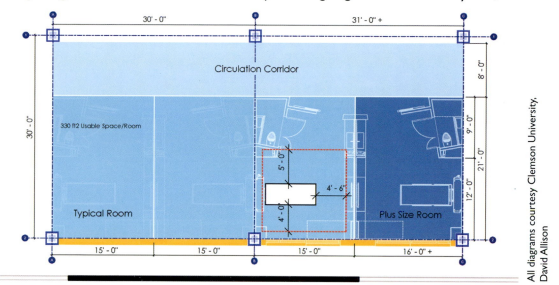

All diagrams courtesy Clemson University,
David Allison

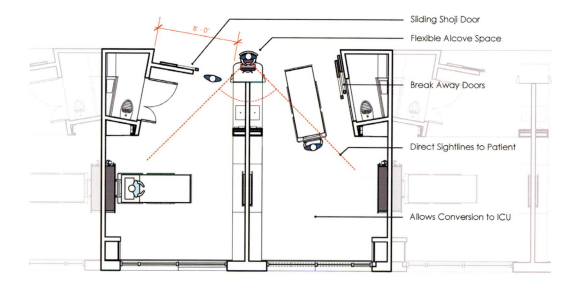

Commentary

continued on next page

This is a thoughtful and noteworthy attempt to rethink the layout and design of the patient room. It has many unique features and addresses technological issues, patient safety, and healing environments (lighting, visitor interaction/sleepover, natural light and views, patient interaction with colored light over bed). In addition, it's an aesthetically beautiful design. The prototype room will be the basic building block for the 48-bed Village Hospital at Pelham in Spartanburg, SC. Over time, the hospital is anticipated to grow to in excess of 150 beds. The prototype "chassis" is intended to adapt for all acute care and telemetry beds. The prototype is being built as a mock-up under simulated use conditions. After the refined version emerges, it will be built at an existing hospital and evaluated under standard operational conditions as planning for the new hospital moves forward. The design is based on a 30 x 30 foot structural bay; 15-foot headwall to footwall dimension; 22-foot-deep room from exterior face of exterior column to interior face of corridor wall.

Clemson University and Spartanburg Regional Health Care System Collaboration

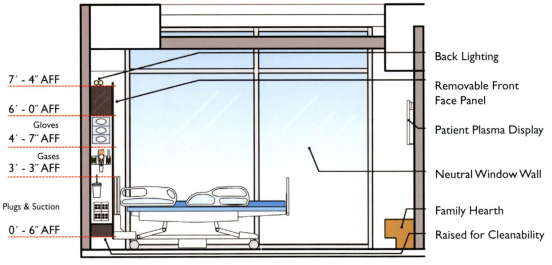

7' - 4" AFF
6' - 0" AFF
Gloves
4' - 7" AFF
Gases
3' - 3" AFF
Plugs & Suction
0' - 6" AFF

Back Lighting

Removable Front
Face Panel

Patient Plasma Display

Neutral Window Wall

Family Hearth

Raised for Cleanability

Ergonomic Zones

- Design locates all needed gas and power outlets in staff-determined ergonomic zones.
- Placement of headwall equipment determined by nurse testing.
- Objects are positioned to limit bending and reaching by nurses.
- Headwall can be preconfigured to meet the ergonomic standards for various staff demands.

Commentary

continued on next page

The concept of placing med gases, gloves, and electrical outlets on the side of the headwall breaks with tradition and is "outside the box" thinking. The problem is the vertical "column" forces some items to be too low. Plugs need to be at waist height to avoid bending. While these may work for plugging in some items, it would seem that additional outlets will be needed on the face of the headwall. The entire vertical panel has been designed to be a modular console to accommodate changing technologies.

Clemson University and Spartanburg Regional Health Care System Collaboration

Footwall.

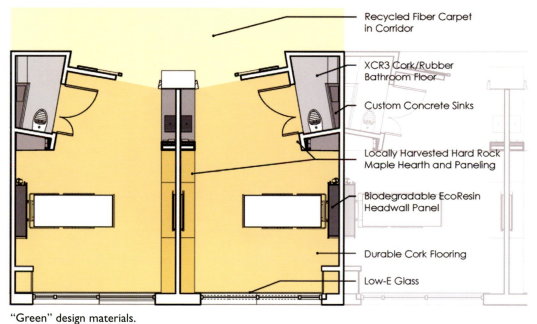

Recycled Fiber Carpet
in Corridor

XCR3 Cork/Rubber
Bathroom Floor

Custom Concrete Sinks

Locally Harvested Hard Rock
Maple Hearth and Paneling

Biodegradable EcoResin
Headwall Panel

Durable Cork Flooring

Low-E Glass

"Green" design materials.

Features:

1) Murphy bed hinges forward for family member sleepover.
2) Overbed light cove offers a "halo" of colored light selected by the patient.
3) Flat panel TV used for entertainment and education.
4) Bench seating minimizes loose furniture in the room that may have to be moved during patient care and it provides space for visitors directly in view of the patient. What appears to be missing is the required high-back patient chair at the side of the bed.
5) Clinical handwash sink with glove boxes, soap and gel dispensers are out of patient view, but the act of handwashing is done in full view of patient.

continued on next page

Clemson University and Spartanburg Regional Health Care System Collaboration

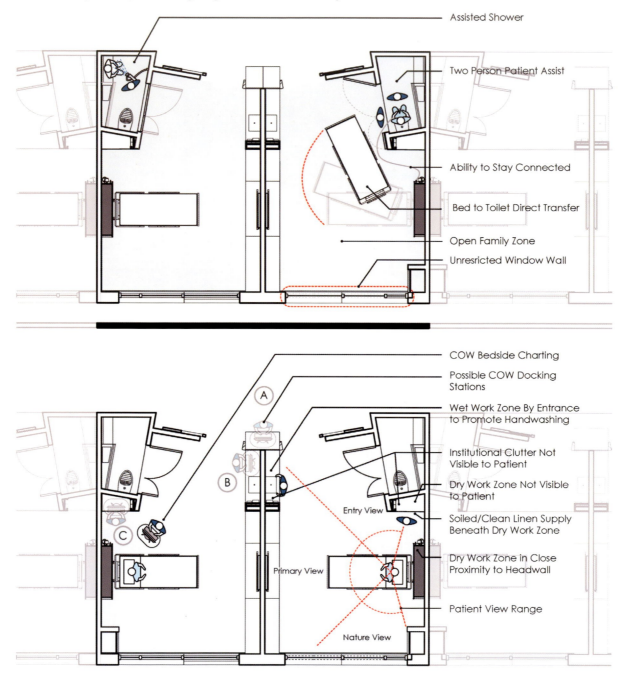

- Assisted Shower
- Two Person Patient Assist
- Ability to Stay Connected
- Bed to Toilet Direct Transfer
- Open Family Zone
- Unresricted Window Wall
- COW Bedside Charting
- Possible COW Docking Stations
- Wet Work Zone By Entrance to Promote Handwashing
- Institutional Clutter Not Visible to Patient
- Dry Work Zone Not Visible to Patient
- Soiled/Clean Linen Supply Beneath Dry Work Zone
- Dry Work Zone in Close Proximity to Headwall
- Patient View Range

A
B
C

Entry View
Primary View
Nature View

Commentary

continued on next page

The entry was designed to maximize visibility. The bathroom appears quite tight, apparently an attempt to widen the throat of the room. Multiple doorway options include a single four-foot-wide door, double-leaf 4 + 2 doors, Japanese shoji-style sliding door, and eight-foot-wide glass break-away door. Clinical handwash sink is in full view just inside room entry. A lowered ceiling (soffit) extends over entry to provide a transition into the room. The toilet has been positioned to create the shortest path for the patient; note (upper right diagram) that bed can be pivoted to get closer. The goal is to eliminate the use of a commode chair.

Clemson University and Spartanburg Regional Health Care System Collaboration

Courtesy Clemson University, David Allison

Rendering depicts one option for the entry workstation and opportunities for visibility into the room.

Commentary

continued on next page

The hospital has opted to use a mobile COW (computer on wheels) for charting in the typical med/surg room and use the alcove for decentralized linen/supply storage. They also wanted more privacy for patients. The design above was envisioned for higher acuity ICU and step-down units. In an acuity-adaptable setting, glazing that can be changed from vision to obscure by way of an electronic charge would be considered. This prototype room was developed as a "universally designed chassis" to allow for interchangeability of features.

Clemson University and Spartanburg Regional Health Care System Collaboration

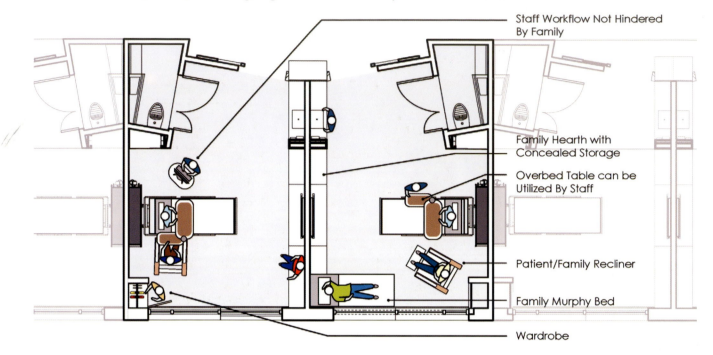

- Staff Workflow Not Hindered By Family
- Family Hearth with Concealed Storage
- Overbed Table can be Utilized By Staff
- Patient/Family Recliner
- Family Murphy Bed
- Wardrobe

PRODUCT DESIGN

OVER-BED TABLE

Attachable Storage   Integrated Light

Telescoping Neck

Table folds down into a patient walk assist.

Extra table pivots from below to accommodate guests, staff supplies

Removable Garbage

Commentary

The over-bed tray table is typically the only surface accessible to the patient. Too often, personal belongings have to be removed to accommodate the food tray. This clever design has a second swing-out surface, hangers for a trash bag and a washable cloth pocket for personal storage. The patient can even use it as an ambulation device although it is unlikely to replace a "walker" which, albeit ugly, enables even a fragile user to balance well and it provides bilateral support.

Clarian Health CCCCU, Indianapolis, IN

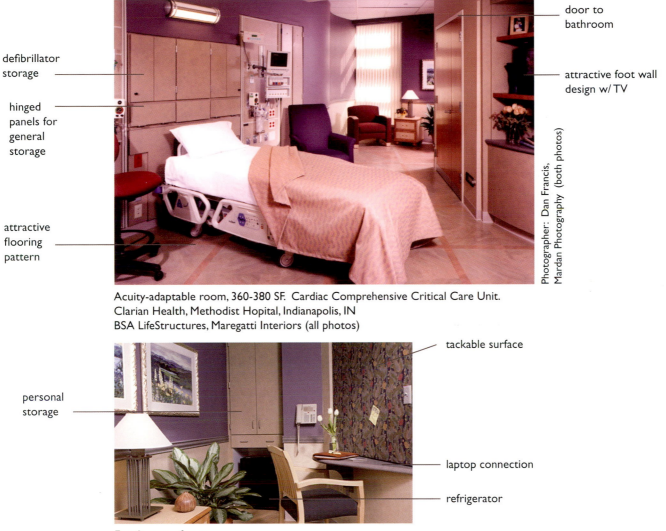

defibrillator storage

hinged panels for general storage

attractive flooring pattern

door to bathroom

attractive foot wall design w/ TV

Photographer: Dan Francis, Mardan Photography (both photos)

Acuity-adaptable room, 360-380 SF. Cardiac Comprehensive Critical Care Unit. Clarian Health, Methodist Hopital, Indianapolis, IN BSA LifeStructures, Maregatti Interiors (all photos)

personal storage

tackable surface

laptop connection

refrigerator

Family area of room.

Commentary

continued on next page

Generally considered to be the origin of the acuity-adaptable room concept, this project, led by Ann Hendrich, MS, RN, F.A.A.N., (opened in 1999), was based on an impressive amount of research. Nurses were video-taped as they hunted for supplies, walked an average of 2 to 6 miles per day in the pursuit of gathering what they needed, and brought their expertise to the bedside. Research showed that patients were moved an average of three times during their stay as their acuity levels changed, resulting in a break in continuity of care – charts being misplaced, discharge dates increased by one-half day for every transport, and 18 individual steps were itemized for every intra-unit transport, (Hendrich & Lee, 2005) costing the organization several million dollars annually for the 56-bed unit. A room was designed that could adjust for acuity so that, in theory, the patient need not be moved. A great deal of thought was given to the placement and design of the toilet room to prevent nurse work-related back strains or twisting injuries and to reduce falls and make it possible for patients to reach it without disconnecting monitors. See page 7.65 for photo and features. [For more detailed discussion about the room and how it currently functions in 2007, refer to the text at the start of the Patient Units chapter.]

Clarian Health CCCCU

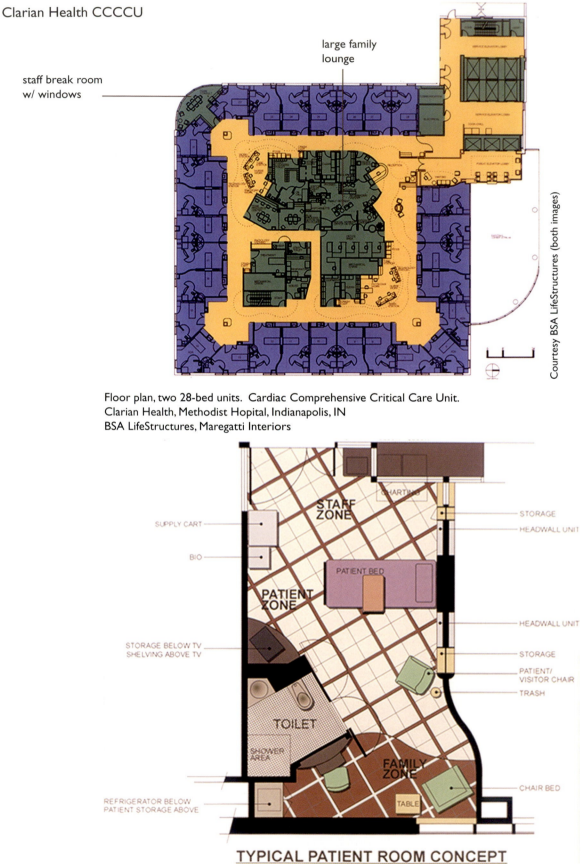

staff break room
w/ windows

large family
lounge

Courtesy BSA LifeStructures (both images)

Floor plan, two 28-bed units. Cardiac Comprehensive Critical Care Unit.
Clarian Health, Methodist Hopital, Indianapolis, IN
BSA LifeStructures, Maregatti Interiors

CHARTING

STAFF
ZONE

SUPPLY CART

BIO

PATIENT BED

STORAGE

HEADWALL UNIT

PATIENT
ZONE

HEADWALL UNIT

STORAGE BELOW TV
SHELVING ABOVE TV

STORAGE

PATIENT/
VISITOR CHAIR

TRASH

TOILET

SHOWER
AREA

REFRIGERATOR BELOW
PATIENT STORAGE ABOVE

FAMILY
ZONE

TABLE

CHAIR BED

TYPICAL PATIENT ROOM CONCEPT

Acuity-adaptable room.

continued on next page

Clarian Health CCCCU

Photo courtesy Don McKahan

E-ICU monitoring center.

Photo courtesy Don McKahan

Closed circuit TV camera.

Photo courtesy Don McKahan

Nurse server pass-through and modular cart
as viewed from corridor.

Photo courtesy Don McKahan

Nurse server pass-through as viewed from patient room.

Commentary

continued on next page

E-ICU: Patients can be monitored by an intensivist from a remote location who, by way of video camera, can observe and talk to the patient. This is linked to the physiological monitor. This has been successful according to the director of nursing. However, she also points out that too much storage has been provided in the rooms, perhaps as an overly-zealous response to formerly having so little. The nurse server has not worked well because when it is restocked, the items push the doors open on the patient room side. Note that the glass above the nurse server cabinet changes from vision to opaque due to activation of an electronic charge.

Clarian Health CCCCU

A

View into nurses "quiet" work area. Note use of curved soffits to "shape" space.

B

View of decentralized nurses' stations. Note use of carpet to reduce noise.

Photographer: Dan Francis, © Mardan Photography (all photos)

C

View into family lounge enclosed with glass.

D

Staff break room with natural light.

Commentary

continued on next page

The unique design of the project was not limited to the patient room. A large core area (A) has both a central "open" nurse station and a glass-enclosed "quiet" work space; nurses also have decentralized nurse stations (B) that provide visibility into two rooms. Families have a large glass-enclosed lounge (C) in which seating is arranged in privacy groupings, some of which face an aquarium and magazine display (E, F, G). The glazed wall makes families comfortable being there because they can still see what is going on. A staff break room (D) has natural light and a prominent location.

Clarian Health CCCCU

E

Photographer: Dan Francis, © Mardan Photography (all photos)

Family lounge, nursing core. Curves in glass wall and in soffits, as well as inset carpet patterns, create a "soft" ambience with few angles.

F

continued on next page

Family lounge, nursing core.

Clarian Health CCCCU

G

Family lounge.

Photographer: Dan Francis, © Mardan Photography (all photos)

CCCC: Performance Outcomes

Performance Measure	1997	2001	% Change
Patient Transports/month:	225	30 *	-90%
Medication Error Index	9.8	2.5 *	-70%
Patient Falls Index	5.8	2.0 *	65%
Overall Patient Satisfaction	96%	97%	+1%
Nursing Turnover (FTE's/Unit)	28%	15%	-47%

*These performance improvements may have declined with increased patient acuity since 2001

Courtesy Don McKahan

The 1997 figures represent the old unit; the new one opened in 1999. In 2001 figures are two years post move-in. Newness and getting used to having family in the room would have stabilized.

St. Joseph's Community Hospital of West Bend

ceiling lift   prairie and nature views

Bathroom located on headwall to minimize falls; handrail on headwall provides continuous support. As patient approaches door a sensor turns bathroom light on.

nursing alcove with glass door to patient room

Courtesy Gresham Smith Partners
Tom Wallen

Standardized patient room, 320 SF with bathroom and nursing alcove. St. Joseph's Community Hospital, West Bend, WI. Gresham Smith Partners

Photographer: Jain Malkin

Patient footwall. Door leads to nurse alcove.

handrail to bathroom

Patient headwall. (photo taken prior to opening; bedside cabinet and lamp were makeshift)

Commentary   *continued on next page*

The first hospital designed around patient safety, this 80-bed facility built on a greenfield site opened in August 2005. Its design features have influenced the design of many new hospitals. CEO John Reiling launched a learning lab to inform the design, looking at the pathophysiology of error and cognitive mechanisms involved in risk awareness. Other industries such as aviation, aerospace, and manufacturing were studied to understand what tactics they employ to enhance safety. The aesthetics of the room are a bit spare as most of the budget went to safety features and the construction cost, per square foot, was modest considering what was achieved.

St. Joseph's Community Hospital of West Bend

patient lift   handrail   nurse work area

Courtesy Gresham Smith
Tom Wallen

Bird's-eye view of patient unit layout. All rooms are same-handed.
Gresham Smith Partners

Commentary

continued on next page

All rooms are absolutely identical, standardized in every way. Numerous strategies were employed to reduce noise to the point that the rooms are almost too quiet. Patients sometimes wonder if anyone else is in the hospital. This is quite an achievement in view of how noisy most hospitals are. Caregivers entering from the door on the footwall, instead of the corridor, reduces noise as does double-stud wall construction around each room. Observing patients from the glazed door of the nurse work area solved the problem of lack of privacy that occurs when the charting area is in a corridor niche.

St. Joseph's Community Hospital of West Bend

Safety by Design

In 2002 planning began on the first hospital dedicated to patient safety. It was inspired by the Institute of Medicine (IOM) report *To Err Is Human: Building a Safer Health System* published in 2000. CEO John Reiling convened a learning lab at the Carlson School of Management, U. of Minnesota. A multi-disciplinary group of individuals met in order to develop a new facilities design and safety model based on strategies from other industries known to have a strong culture of safety. Participants in workgroup sessions interfaced with 28 local and national safety experts in systems engineering, healthcare administration, health services research, human factors research, hospital quality improvement and accreditation, hospital architecture, medical education, pharmacy, nursing, and medicine.

Major causal categories of patient harm in hospitals were identified, followed by a set of facility design recommendations focused on four issues: 1) design principles for creating a safe facility; 2) work process and systems; 3) technology and equipment; and 4) physical environment.

Facility Design Principles[1]

- Use FMEA (Failure Modes and Effects Analysis) on current facility and at every design stage.
- Engage a wide representation of stakeholders in the design process.
- Create an organizational leadership structure to support the design process.
- Design around major organizational processes. Begin mock-ups and equipment planning Day 1.
- Consider human factors and environmental effects on staff as well as patients and families.
- Design around vulnerable populations.
- Design for flexibility, scalability, and accessibility to adapt to changes in technology and work processes.
- Standardize location of equipment, supplies, room layout and care processes.
- Provide accessible information systems at the point of service.
- Address known hazards to patient safety in the physical environment.

Design Around Precarious Events*

During the design process the focus was on strategies to minimize the occurrence of precarious events.

- Operative/post-op complications/infections
- Inpatient suicides
- Medication errors
- Patient falls
- Correct tube–correct connector–correct hole
- Transfusion-related events
- Wrong-site surgery
- MRI hazards
- Oxygen cylinder hazard

[1] Center for the Study of Healthcare Management, Carlson School of Management: Designing a Safe Hospital, Publication 1 series. Minneapolis: University of Mennesota, 2002.

continued on next page

St. Joseph's Community Hospital of West Bend

Latent Conditions*

These are errors in the design, organization, training, or maintenance that lead to operator errors and whose effects typically lie dormant in the system for lengthy periods of time. These often contribute to "active failures," an error that occurs at the level of the frontline operator and whose effects are felt almost immediately (Source: *To Err Is Human*, IOM report).

- Noise
- Standardization (layout, equipment, processes)
- Visibility of patients to staff
- Fatigue
- Automation whenever possible
- Patient handoffs (minimize)
- Patient transport (minimize)
- Scalability, adaptability, flexibility
- Accessibility of information close to the point of service

A Culture of Safety

A culture of safety involves reporting "near misses" and creating a blame-free environment that recognizes human fallibility. It requires shared values and beliefs about safety throughout the organization; a commitment to continuous improvement, to transparency, and the empowerment of patients and families to question and to participate in care.

FMEA (Failure Mode Effects Analysis)

There are two types of FMEA – process and design. The former starts with the assumption that the design is perfect and looks for possible failures that result from the process. The latter assumes the process is perfect and tries to find failures in the design of the facility. The FMEA process is often used in industries like aviation, aerospace, and manufacturing. The St. Joseph team applied FMEA at each stage of design: adjacencies, schematics, and design development.

The design teams determined that the conventional FMEA process was too complex for healthcare facilities and developed a modification in which the traditional numeric scoring was replaced with a FMEA spreadsheet (see sample on next page) in which occurrence and severity of failure were scored as low, medium, or high (Reiling et al 2004).

Technology and Equipment

Vendors were invited to display and demonstrate equipment and technology at an on-site fair to enable staff members to evaluate systems that were currently available or would be available by the time the facility opened. The focus was on automated technology for centralized scheduling, pharmacy, rapid admissions, material management, nurse call and, although the facility did not open with CPOE (Computerized Physician Order Entry) and PACS due to budget constraints it has since added these. Patients' wrist bands as well as medications are bar-coded to reduce the most frequent event – medication error. Each piece of equipment and technology was evaluated according to how they would maximize safety through elimination of latent conditions and active failures.

---

* Information based on presentation given to the author by John Reiling. The list of precarious events was referenced to the Sentinel Event Database of the Joint Commission and the VA National Center for Patient Safety.

continued on next page

St. Joseph's Community Hospital of West Bend

FMEA Application Sample
Design Development Phase
Emergency Department

Failure	Possible Solution	Impact	Cost	Recomm Go/No Go	Describe Solution or Action Taken
Doors are frozen	Heat slab under garage floor and door	Med	Very High	No Go	Barb checked with Sandi - she said non-issue
Garage exit too small for Children's Hospital Transport (and others)	Widen/straighten out swing - contact agencies and demo	Med	Medium	Done	27'-0" turning radius, see new plans
Door in anteroom doesn't lock for forensic patient	Give law enforcement ability to lock	High	Low	Go	Door will be positive latch and will lock
Garage floor slippery/frozen (due to oil, salt, water, from tires)	Heat floor or anti-slip finish & floor drainage	Med	Very High		Discuss with Sandi Course finish on ambulance garage floor Rough, no slip concrete surface, provide drain
Helipad location - arrival and departure cuts off ambulance traffic path clear	Move location to allow ambulance traffic - get Flight for Life involved	Low	Low	Go	Ambulance will transport patients from ED to pad Use golf cart to transport; also provide sidewalk Helipad radius = 75'
Can't wash hands in Exam room	Add sink to toilet room	Med	High	Go	90% of exam toilets will add a sink RELOCATE TUBE SYSTEM IN ASU TO ALLOW SINK IN RM 1-609 TRANS #3
Lack of MD access to ED from parking lot	Add door to garage				Add 3' door into garage; sidewalk to parking, verify site lighting, intercom /C.S. at door

St. Joseph's Community Hospital of West Bend

a member of SynergyHealth

Sample of FMEA process. Courtesy John Reiling.

Patient Room Design

After completing the project, the design team felt strongly that it was key to develop mock-up rooms during schematic design as this is the basic building block of the hospital. To design the building shell in advance of this hampers flexibility in patient room design. In addition, mock-up rooms can be used for training staff in new processes to reduce transition errors.

Planning Features

- All rooms private and same-handed. Standardization in layout, location of supplies, equipment, medical gases. Contrary to conventional wisdom, it actually cost less in this facility to build same-handed rooms versus mirror-image, reflecting the savings derived from being able to produce more standardized units in a factory with very few "existing conditions" variations.

- Nursing alcove enables nurses to observe the patient without entering the room. Since most traffic in and out of the room is through this door, typical corridor noise is greatly reduced. This alcove contains patient supplies which are restocked every evening and allows medication to be stored separately for each patient. Because the nurse does not have to hunt down supplies, fatigue is reduced as well as auditory distraction that can lead to charting and medication errors.

- The bathroom is located on the headwall as this is the shortest distance from the bed and a handrail can support the patient during travel. As well, a sensor turns on the bathroom light as the patient approaches the door.

- The use of infrared technology to notify caregiver if patient sits up and moves toward edge of bed (this was planned but not executed).

- Patients' cardiac rhythms can be monitored across all departments with no dead spots.

continued on next page

St. Joseph's Community Hospital of West Bend

- All existing equipment (IV pumps, for example) was discarded as it was considered imperative to have identical equipment and brands in the new facility to reduce error and enhance standardization.
- Patient access to medication orders.
- Clinical handwash sink located in view of patient; a brochure empowers patients to discuss handwashing with staff members.
- Rooms are wired for cameras.
- The same fluorescent lamp color temperature and color rendering index is used throughout the facility to provide consistent diagnosis from department to department. The team worked with General Electric at Nela Park Research Lab to determine appropriate lamp type. The selection was a high-performance fluorescent at 4100 degrees kelvin and a CRI (color-rendering index) of 82.

HVAC Features*

While patient rooms may have a "sparse" appearance due to budget, considerable money was allocated to the HVAC system which, although it can't be seen, affects patient and staff in the most fundamental and important ways.

- Patient rooms have perimeter heating from a radiant ceiling panel (no finned surfaces to collect bacteria).
- In critical care areas, stainless steel is used for mechanical system components to inhibit corrosion (caused by frequent cleaning) that supports bacterial growth.
- Every room in the facility benefits from HEPA air filtration and ultraviolet-light air sterilization.
- Dual fans are used in critical care air handling systems to ensure cooling and air flow for infection control.
- The building's automation system can self-diagnose and report to address problems before staff notice them.
- Building control systems monitor airborne infections in isolation rooms using differential pressure-sensing devices to allow immediate response to failure of isolation rooms.
- HVAC systems have automated switchover between heating and cooling to provide seamless comfort.
- Closed transfer switches allow emergency generators to be tested without impacting normal hospital operation.
- The ED waiting area has HEPA filtration and ultraviolet self-contained recirculating units to reduce the possibility of airborne pathogens moving to other patient areas.
- Reverse osmosis water is used in the steam boiler (humidification); little to no chemical treatment used.
- Air-handling systems and related components selected to perform at lower than industry-accepted sound levels.

Research Focus

In 2005 baseline "pre" studies were carried out prior to the move. In 2007, post-move studies were carried out, made possible by the Agency for Healthcare Research and Quality through a $1.5 million grant to measure the impact of each safety design principle (e.g., reduction in falls, medication errors, infections, length of stay and costs per discharge). This project represents a milestone for its exploration and analysis of patient safety factors. It has already influenced the design of many new hospitals. The entire process has been documented in a book (Reiling 2007) published by the Joint Commission.

*Information based on Power Point presentation given to the author by John Reiling.

Dublin Methodist Hospital, OhioHealth, Dublin, Ohio

Breaking the Mold

Inspired by Leland Kaiser's dictum "The hospital is a human invention and as such can be reinvented at any time," the design team set out to reinvent the patients' experiences. The reception desk will be replaced by greeters who will walk up and meet patients. Central nurse stations have been replaced by decentralized work areas at which physicians, nurses, patients and family members can interface.

Connection to Nature

Patient rooms are laid out in 20-bed pavilions with components of the building pulled apart to provide more daylight. Building on the research about nature as a therapeutic intervention, there are 13 gardens in the facility, one of which is outside OT/PT, while others may be in the middle of a nursing unit. The connection to nature is also expressed in an extensive collection of original color photographs of nature images, created for the project by photographer Henry Domke. Some of these will be large for circulation spaces, while others will be in patient rooms.

Commitment to Acuity-Adaptable Care

Building on the research about patient safety done by John Reiling (CEO of St. Joseph's Community Hospital of West Bend during the planning and construction of that facility), all rooms will be same-handed and standardized in every aspect; a handrail on the headwall provides support en route to the bathroom; windows are operable; rooms have bedside computers for clinical documentation and patient use. All rooms are acuity-adaptable to ICU with no modifications. The staff will be committed to patients being able to remain in the same room as acuity level changes however it should be noted that ICU-level patients are expected to be treated at tertiary care hospitals within the OhioHealth system. Therefore med/surg and progressive care are what is currently anticipated. If a designated ICU is needed in the future, the shelled area on the fourth floor is available.

Standardization to Reduce Error

Because standardization theoretically makes sense, the 32-bed ED, ORs, PACU and other areas have also been designed to be as standardized as possible with respect to same-handedness and other features.

Commitment to Measuring Outcomes

As a Center for Health Design Pebble project, the research carried out after opening is expected to contribute much to the body of evidence-based design. Following is the research agenda:

1) documentation of the planning process
2) development of the business case
3) patient and family experiences
4) work process and culture
5) risk reduction for innovation
6) safety case

The research will include comparative studies with other OhioHealth hospitals. This facility opened in December 2007.

Dublin Methodist Hospital, OhioHealth

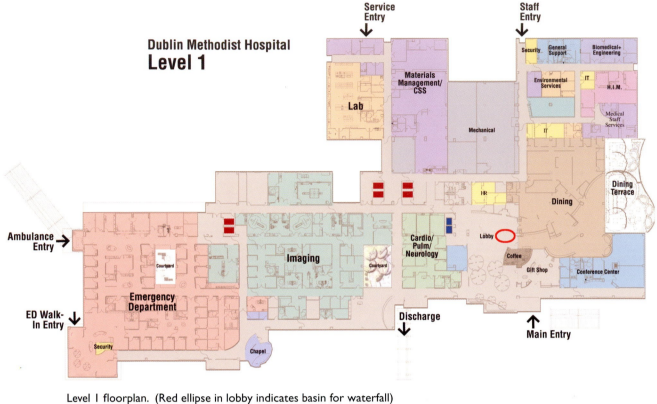

Level 1 floorplan. (Red ellipse in lobby indicates basin for waterfall)
Dublin Methodist Hospital, Dublin, OH
Karlsberger Architects, CAMA Inc. (interior design)

Commentary

continued on next page

This project (325,000 SF facility with 114 beds) is a real-life example of the Center for Health Design's "Fable Hospital," the hypothetical construct that incorporates core values of superior quality, safety, patient-centered care, family involvement, staff support and environmental sustainability with the overall goals of enhancing both clinical outcomes and economic performance. Led by a hospital president with expansive vision, the planning effort was initiated with culture research undertaken by social scientists. As a new facility on a greenfield site, there was no existing culture or mythology. A vision for a new culture had to be created.

Mission Statement

To create a community hospital that revolutionizes healthcare delivery by optimizing the medical, spiritual, and emotional well-being of patients, families, and staff.

Core Values

- Caring for patients medically, spiritually, and emotionally
- Respecting the family of our patients and staff
- Encouraging and promoting education for our staff, patients, and community
- Promoting a close-knit team approach to care

Dublin Methodist Hospital, OhioHealth

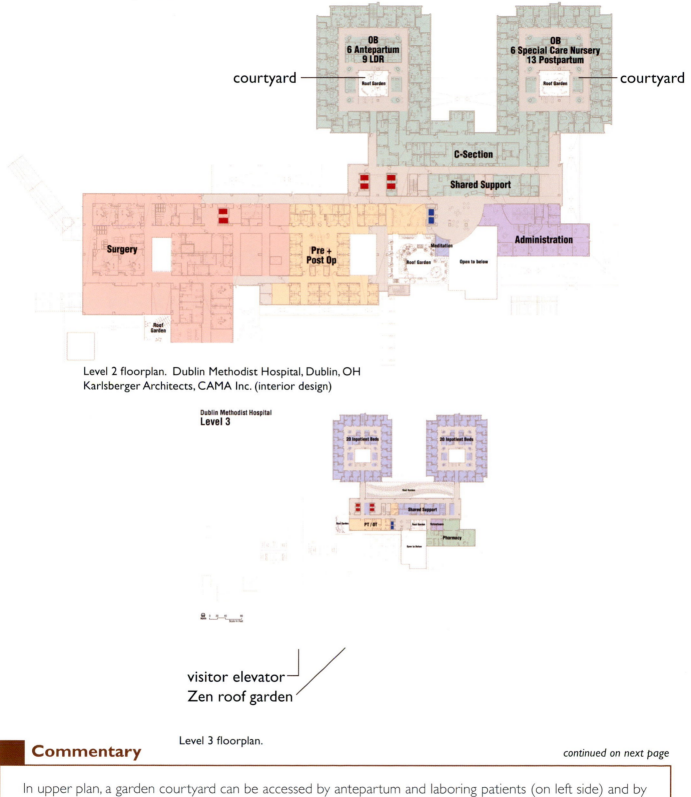

Level 2 floorplan. Dublin Methodist Hospital, Dublin, OH
Karlsberger Architects, CAMA Inc. (interior design)

Level 3 floorplan.

Commentary

continued on next page

In upper plan, a garden courtyard can be accessed by antepartum and laboring patients (on left side) and by post-partum patients and special care nursery family members on right. On level 3 (lower plan) courtyards permit a view into 2nd floor gardens and bring natural light into the core of the nursing unit.

Dublin Methodist Hospital, OhioHealth

Renderings courtesy Karlsberger Architects

Main lobby. Gift shop and coffee bar are on right. Note three-story waterfall at rear.
Dublin Methodist Hospital, Dublin, OH
Karlsberger Architects, CAMA Inc. (interior design)

Zen roof garden, located on third floor, overlooking the lobby below.

Garden located in the center of each patient pavilion.

Commentary   *continued on next page*

The three-story waterfall terminates in an elliptical basin in the lobby adjoining a seating area. Just above the waterfall, on the third level, is the Zen roof garden immediately in front of the visitor elevators. The tree is a piece of commissioned sculpture made of aluminum with polyester discs for leaves. The patient pavilion garden (lower right) brings daylight and a view of nature to staff, patients and visitors.

Dublin Methodist Hospital, OhioHealth

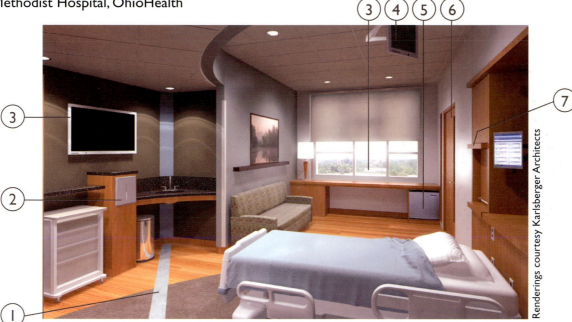

Renderings courtesy Karlsberger Architects

Acuity-adaptable patient room, 340 SF including bathroom, acuity-adaptable.
Dublin Methodist Hospital, Dublin, OH
Karlsberger Architects, CAMA Inc. (interior design)

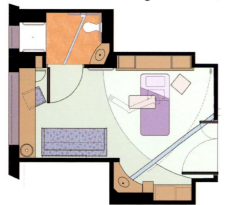

Planview, patient room. Distance from headwall to footwall is 16 feet.

All rooms are same-handed. Corridor niches may house movable equipment or become storage alcoves with cabinets or for movable carts, or become charting alcoves with computers.

Features:

1) Inset diagonal line in floor directs staff to handwashing sink.
2) Paper towel dispenser
3) 37"TV for patient; another monitor for families, on the desk, enables them to watch a different program or watch TV quietly while the patient is sleeping.
4) Pull-down bedside clinical patient station by Cardinal Health used for physician/staff order entry and EMR, as well as patient's access to the Internet, ordering food, and access to educational information.
5) Refrigerator
6) 4-foot-wide bathroom door with frosted glass panel; patient wardrobe to the side
7) Sliding door lifts up to reveal medical gas outlets on both sides of patient. Rooms have full complement of gases for ICU.
8) Beds have deliberately been placed left-facing so that physician must walk around the bed to reach patient's right side in order to enhance the encounter with the family (although this would seem to place the physician's back to the family).

Dublin Methodist Hospital, OhioHealth

Aerial view 20-bed nursing unit with garden or atrium in center and 6 decentralized nurse stations called "perches."
Dublin Methodist Hospital, Dublin, OH
Karlsberger Architects, CAMA Inc. (interior design)

Patient unit corridor.

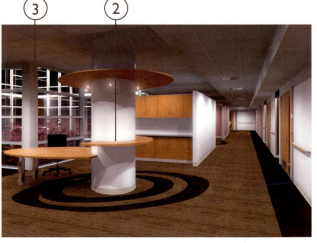

Decentralized work area with garden in rear.

Features:

1) Recessed niches have multiple uses: storage of movable equipment, storage cabinets, or may become charting alcoves with computers.
2) Decentralized work areas facilitate interaction and communication between physicians, caregivers, patients and families and replace the traditional nurses' stations. The intention is that nurses will be in the patients' rooms a significant amount of time.
3) Garden courtyard on 2nd floor and aerial view of garden from 3rd floor of handwashing is done in full view of patient

Florida Hospital, Orlando

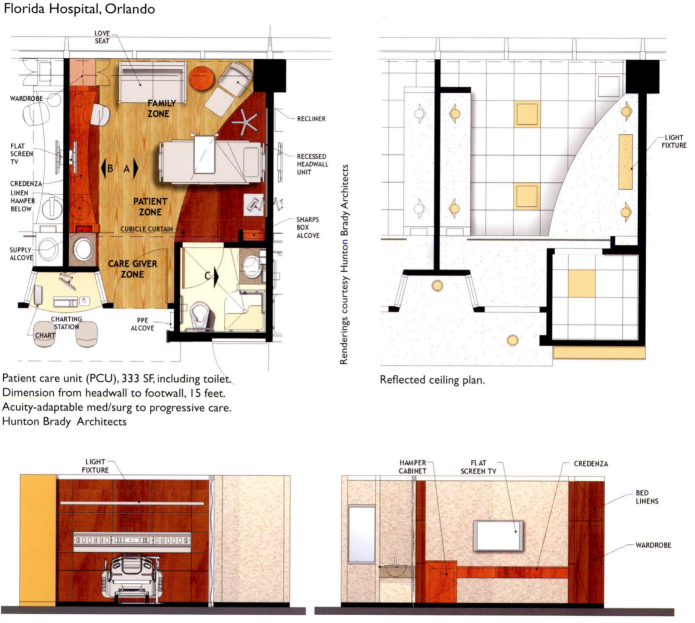

Renderings courtesy Hunton Brady Architects

Patient care unit (PCU), 333 SF, including toilet.
Dimension from headwall to footwall, 15 feet.
Acuity-adaptable med/surg to progressive care.
Hunton Brady Architects

Reflected ceiling plan.

Headwall elevation.

Footwall elevation.

Commentary

continued on next page

Embarking upon three new expansion projects at three sites led Florida Hospital to an intensive visioning and planning process, pooling the talents of several architectural firms and numerous consultants. The Adventist Health leadership teams for all three facilities worked together to make decisions common to all. Full scale mock-up rooms were created with exquisite detail to allow caregivers to continually refine every aspect of the rooms. In addition, panels of "contrarians" from different industries were brought in to review the mock-ups and offer a different perspective. Each site has two types of rooms — critical care and an acuity-adaptable room that combines med/surg and progressive care (mid-level monitored care). The rooms are 15´ × 22´ on center. The acuity-adaptable units are 40-beds divided into (2) 20-bed units which offers a 1:4 or 1:5 nurse-to-patient staffing ratio.

Florida Hospital, Orlando

Patient care unit, acuity-adaptable med/surg to progressive care.
Hunton Brady Architects (architecture and interior design)

Commentary   *continued on next page*

Small nurse documentation stations outside each pair of rooms (see previous page) permit a view of a patient's head but nothing more, to protect the patient's privacy. An inboard toilet allows a 12-foot-wide window view and large family zone. On the lake side of the building, windows run floor to ceiling for maximum view. A fully tiled bathroom has been designed to simulate what one would find in new homes in the community. A 32″ flat panel TV will offer patient education programs, patient scheduling, menu selection, Internet, and entertainment. Rooms have five alternating warm color palettes and a wood-look vinyl floor in two tones of wood.

Florida Hospital, Orlando • Critical Care

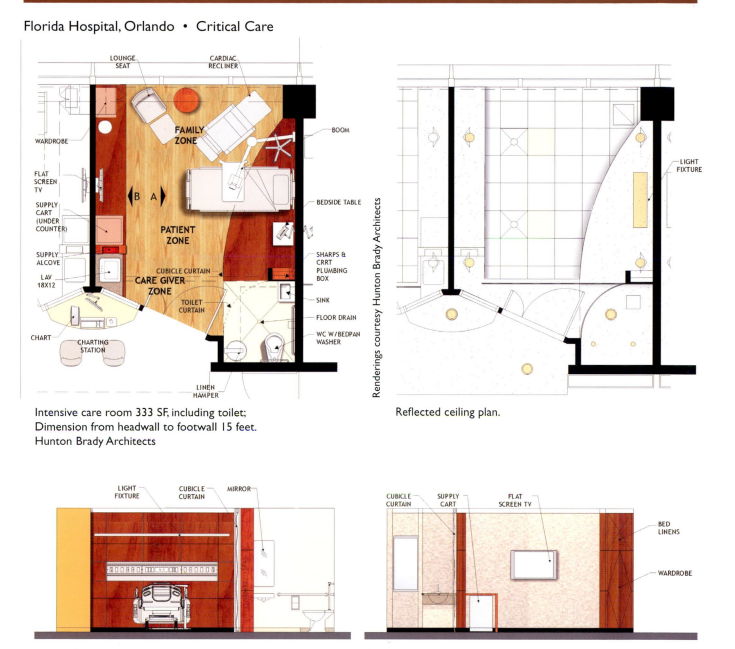

Intensive care room 333 SF, including toilet;
Dimension from headwall to footwall 15 feet.
Hunton Brady Architects

Reflected ceiling plan.

Renderings courtesy Hunton Brady Architects

Headwall elevation.

Footwall elevation.

Commentary

The room size is the same as the PCU (patient care unit) on previous pages. Only the entry/inboard toilet portion of the room differs. In the future, the two types of rooms can be interchanged simply by rebuilding the entry area of the room. The ICU room has large windows to the corridor to enhance caregiver visibility. Unlike the PCU bathroom, the ICU bathroom is "open" with a privacy curtain to give easier access to staff in disposing of waste and to make it easier for patient to access, although many ICU patients will have a bladder catheter. The family zone is the same size as in the PCU room but the presence of family in the room will constitute a cultural change for the nursing staff of this organization, according to the planners.

Photographer: Ed LaCasse

Clarian West Medical Center, Avon, IN
HKS Architects, Maregatti Interiors

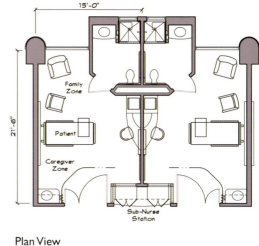

Plan View
255 SF w/o bathroom

14'-6"

20'-8"

Family Zone

Patient

Caregiver Zone

Sub-Nurse Station

Photographer: © Hedrich Blessing

Clarian North Medical Center, Indianapolis, IN
HKS Architects, Maregatti Interiors

Plan View
257 SF w/o bathroom

15'-0"

21'-6"

Family Zone

Patient

Caregiver Zone

Sub-Nurse Station

Commentary

The Clarian Cardiac Comprehensive Critical Care Unit at Methodist Hospital in Indianapolis (see pages 7.17 to 7.22) was the prototype for a research-based acuity-adaptable room designed to provide a high level of patient safety and to avoid transport to another room when acuity level changed. Clarian West and North are more recent adaptations of this concept in new hospitals that opened in 2005 and 2006, respectively. All of these rooms meet the size and med gas requirements for ICU. To accommodate staffing issues (med/surg to ICU), a group of adjacent rooms has been dedicated to the acuity-adaptable concept and staffed accordingly. Any number of rooms can be added as needed.

Photographer: Ed LaCasse (both photos)

Med/surg room with telemetry. Abbott Northwestern Heart Hospital, Minneapolis, MN (both photos)
HKS, Inc. (architecture and interior design) both photos

Nurse station.

Commentary

An outstanding headwall design neatly and attractively organizes medical gases and monitors without taking heroic measures to hide them. The family area is small due to a tight existing column grid but the chair is a sleeper model. Rooms are opposite-handed. The COO set a goal for a design that engaged the mind, body, and spirit of the patient. The five elements (earth, fire, water, wood, metal) were incorporated throughout the project (refer to page 5.8 for lobby photos). The owner requested a neutral palette for the nursing core (lower photo) and public areas, accented with artwork (not in view).

Neil Rashba Architectural Photography

Acuity-adaptable patient room, 300 SF, Baptist Medical Center, Jacksonville, FL
Cannon Design (architecture and interiors)

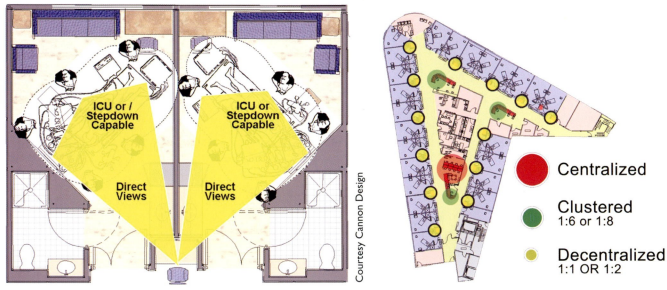

Courtesy Cannon Design

Courtesy Cannon Design

● Centralized

● Clustered
1:6 or 1:8

● Decentralized
1:1 OR 1:2

Commentary

The boomerang shape of the nursing unit derives from a desire to present the river view to as many patients as possible and also to minimize steps for nurses. The 24-bed units can be supervised from the central nurse station or the beds can be split among the three dispersed stations in a 1:6 or 1:8 ratio or, for full ramp-up to ICU, from decentralized stations at 1:1 or 1:2 ratios. All rooms can be stepped up or down between ICU, progressive, or acute care. Clinical handwash sink is just inside entry (obscured by yellow wedge in plan view).

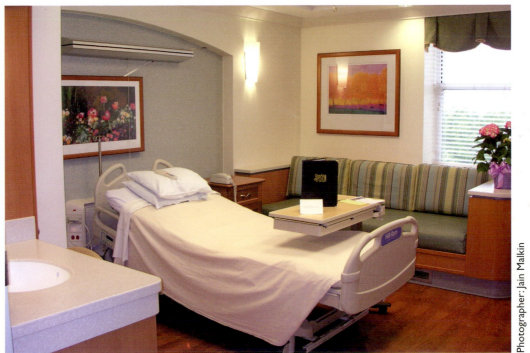

Photographer: Jain Malkin

Med/surg patient room. Gaston Memorial Hospital, Gastonia, NC (both photos)
Designer: unknown

Commentary

This is a pleasant, very comfortable room with clinical handwash sink immediately in view upon entering, variety in lighting, good use of color, good view of the window from the bed. Family sleep sofa opens to full-size twin and there is a desk for office work or for family member dining.

Photographer: Mike Rebholtz Photography (both photos)

Cleveland Clinic, Naples, FL
Marshall Erdman & Associates (architecture and interior design)

Features:

1) Med gases concealed in cabinet; hospitality ambience of room
2) Ample shelving for display of flowers and cards
3) Refrigerator
4) Clinical handwash sink

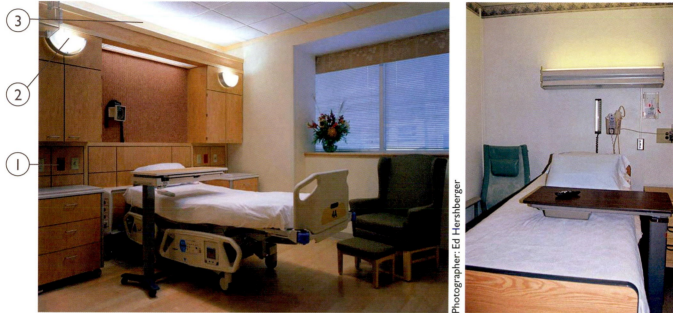

Oregon Health & Science University, Portland, OR
Peterson Kolberg & Associates, Architects
Czopek & Erdenberger (interior design)

Photographer: Ed Hershberger

Before.

Nebraska Orthopedic Hospital, Omaha, NE
Altus Architectural Studios

Photographer: Assassi Productions

Photographer: Assassi Productions

Features:

1) Medical gases nicely placed in composition of wood panels
2) Options for lighting
3) Indirect lighting
4) Medical gases concealed in cabinet; hospitality ambience headwall design
5) Indirect lighting

Photographer: Jain Malkin

Footwall design.
Clarian West Medical Center, Avon, IN
HKS Architects; Maregatti Interiors (both photos)

Photographer: Jain Malkin

Clinical handwash sink in patient room

Photographer: Aker/Zvonkovic

Footwall design.
St. Luke's Community Medical Center, The Woodlands, TX
HGA Architects (both photos)

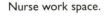

Photographer: Aker/Zvonkovic

Nurse work space.

Features:

1) Patient wardrobe
2) Solid surface countertop with integral sink
3) Plumbing nicely concealed
4) White board for caregiver information
5) Generous area for plants, flowers, and patient belongings
6) Charting outside room
7) Indirect lighting

Commentary

New research indicates that placement of the clinical handwash sink at room entry increases compliance. It should not be behind the door if at all possible. The curve of the countertop in top right photo visually emphasizes the sink.

Photographer: Jain Malkin (all photos)

Niche for waste and linen carts
(can be emptied via doors on corridor side).
Clarian North Medical Center, Indianapolis, IN (all photos)
HKS Architects, Maregatti Interiors

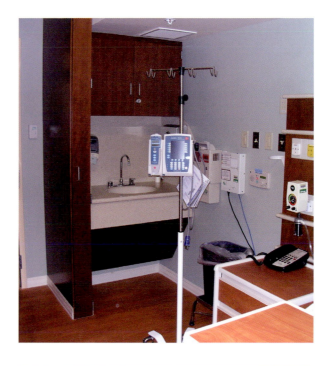

Footwall, pediatric room.

Commentary

Location of handwash sink behind a wall is not optimal. Studies show that immediate visibility upon entering room enhances compliance (Texas A&M, in submission). The checkerboard footwall, although a soothing color, may be too stimulating for a patient who is dizzy or nauseous. When lying in bed it's hard to avoid looking at the footwall; even when watching TV and not nauseous, the checkerboard makes it hard to focus on the TV without distraction.

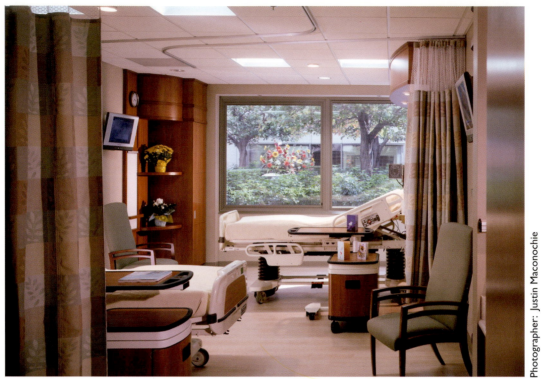

Photographer: Justin Maconochie

William Beaumont Hospital, Royal Oak, MI
Architecture and interior design team: Harley Ellis, HOK, and WHR Architects

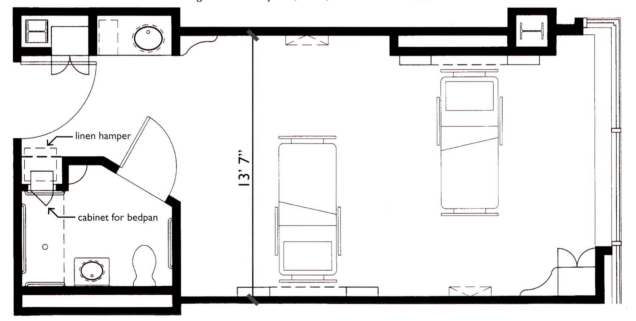

13' 7"

linen hamper

cabinet for bedpan

Commentary

Although single-bed rooms are desirable for a variety of reasons including patient safety, patient satisfaction, reduction of nosomical infection, and privacy, this larger-than-standard semi-private (350 SF plus 42 SF toilet) room offers an option where a minimum number of beds must be achieved and space is limited. Each bed has identical amenities (casework, closets) but they share a bathroom, of course.

Photographer: Jain Malkin

PROVIDE OPTIONS AND
CHOICES TO GIVE PATIENTS
CONTROL

Room service menu enables patients to order food when hungry as opposed to planning food the day before. Studies have shown this costs less operationally as less food is thrown away uneaten. Software programs like this offer entertainment, education, can notify patients in advance of scheduled procedures and provide information about hospital services.

CONNECT PATIENTS
TO NATURE TO
REDUCE ANXIETY AND STRESS

C.A.R.E. Channel ®
(Continuous Ambient Relaxation Environment ®)

Features 60 hours of non-repetitive nature images broadcast on hospital's closed circuit TV, accompanied by soothing instrumental music. A favored image can be selected and "frozen" giving the patient an opportunity to look at a nature scene of special significance. Software manages the programs for 24-hour day/night cycle (www.healinghealth.com).

Courtesy Skyline Art Services

DATE:

NURSE:

MESSAGE:

Courtesy Peter Pepper Products

Commentary

Products like the patient care board used to require custom design; now they are available as manufactured products with numerous custom design options. This board (top photo) also incorporates a photo of nature on the footwall where patients can easily view it. Meeting several needs in one unit, this saves space and is less expensive than buying items separately. Boards such as these help to organize several necessary items and reduce clutter. The unit in the lower photo has a marker board that can be custom silk-screened for patient care data, a tackboard, and a clock that is available with a CDMA (receiver obtains time from cellular phone towers) or a GPS (receives time from global positioning satellites) or a network time protocol (obtains time from local or Internet time servers via the on-board ethernet interface card) master clock.

Kaiser Permanente Care Board

This care board was developed by Kaiser nurses and is used in Kaiser hospitals throughout California.

Used with permission Kaiser Permanente.

Your caregiver will keep the following sections of your Care Board up to date with information you may find useful during your stay:

Who is my doctor? You will find the name of your doctor, nurse, and other care team members, as well as their contact information here in the 'Care Team' section.

What do I need to do today? Review the 'Plan for the Day' section of your Care Board to find out about activities planned for your care. Your care giver will write reminders and notes here.

Where am I? Day, date, room location and contact information can be found in this section of your Care

We encourage you and your family to include your own personal notes and pictures for each other in the 'Family/Patient Communication' section. For example, this is a great place to share smiley faces and 'thinking of you' messages. You may also leave notes for your Care Team here.

Icons to denote eye-glasses, hearing deficit, fall risk, dentures

Tips for Use:

✓ Check regularly

✓ Share with your family

✓ Ask staff questions

✓ Use the clip located along the top edge of the Family/Patient Communication section to display messages and get well cards

When will I go home? Information about your anticipated date/time of discharge and the person coordinating your leave (your 'Discharge Planner') can be found on the bottom left section of your Care Board.

Cove recliner chair.

Reclined position.

All photos courtesy Wieland

Push bar.

Footrest.

Quick change mechanism.

Commentary

Although there are many patient recliner chairs this one has some unique features that were a response to nurses' input. Heavy-duty casters hidden under the chair turn it into a wheelchair (note push bar and foot rest photos). Designed to 500 lb. weight capacity, the casters lock with the kick of a foot pedal on the side of the chair. All upholstery is secured with Velcro and can be easily removed. A "Quick Change Mechanism System" provides easy access to all internal parts of the chair for quick repair. A molded polyurethane strip runs along the base of the chair to protect the edges. Optional elements include IV poles, hook for Foley bag, flip-up table at side of chair and a wide-scale version. Best of all, the chair is incredibly comfortable.

Rendering courtesy the architects

"A hospital in a garden" exterior view.
Palomar Medical Center West, Escondido, CA
Anshen+Allen Architects for Palomar Pomerado Health, an association of CO Architects and Anshen+Allen

Commentary

continued on next page

This is a "hospital within a garden" concept. Courtyards punctuate the diagnostics and testing facility, enhancing wayfinding orientation and offering a view of nature to the users of the ED, diagnostic imaging and surgery departments. Green design is one of the primary project goals in order to minimize the building's impact on the environment. This involves sustainable design principles and analyzing lifecycle impacts of building materials and methods employed. Anything with a five-year payback would likely be approved if it gave the patient more control. The design team is working with the organization Healthcare Without Harm and the project is a pilot for the Green Guide for Healthcare, all in pursuit of Gold LEED status. Reducing water and energy consumption are important aspects of achieving this goal. Note, in photo above, rooftops are "green."

ACUITY
REASSIGNABLE
(24 BEDS)

MED/SURG
(30 BEDS)

Renderings courtesy CO Architects

Typical tower, inpatient unit floorplan.
Palomar Medical Center West, Escondido, CA
Anshen+Allen Architects for Palomar Pomerado Health, an association of CO Architects and Anshen+Allen

Outdoor terrace.

Outdoor terrace.

Commentary

continued on next page

Each tower floor provides access to four outdoor terraces. When departing elevators, there is always exposure to natural light and views. Numerous "cross" or transverse corridors reduce walking distances for staff. Distributed charting areas and supply storage will reduce unnecessary walking, improve patient safety, and increase the time that staff can spend caring for and monitoring patients.

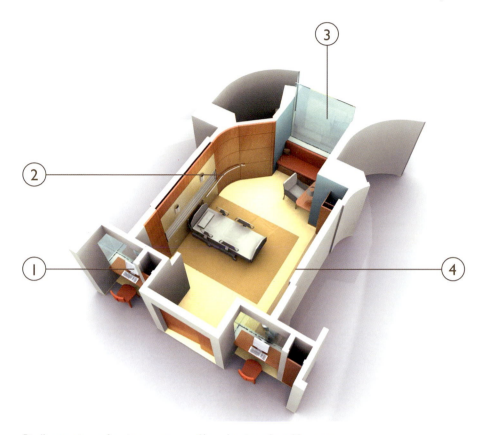

Bird's-eye view of patient room, med/surg/acuity-adaptable room.
325 SF (including bathroom)
Palomar Medical Center West, Escondido, CA
Anshen+Allen Architects for Palomar Pomerado Health, an association of CO Architects and Anshen+Allen

Features:

1) Decentralized nurse charting areas with supply storage in cabinet at night
2) Bathroom is on headwall (shortest distance) and has handrail to reduce falls.
3) Windowsill is low, providing good visibility from bed.
4) Large flat panel monitor for multi-purpose programming: education, entertainment, access to hospital services

Commentary

continued on next page

There is the possibility of two nurses being able to observe each patient, each having good sight lines. The in-house planning effort that underpins the design of this room, as well as other clinical areas, was based on a very participative process for which "Champion Teams" were created and tasked with four areas of influence: Quality, Customer Service, Financial Strength, and Workforce and Workplace Development. The goal was not to simply repeat, in the new hospital, how things were currently done but rather to examine work processes to develop a new model loosely based on the "Fable Hospital" concept explained on a previous page. This is a huge undertaking for a hospital this size and, it should be mentioned, this is a district hospital that reports to an elected board of directors. The biggest champion for the vision was Mike Covert, the CEO. This is being built on a greenfield site that had land acquisition and many other challenges not for the faint of heart.

Patient view, med/surg/acuity-adaptable room.
325 SF (including bathroom)
Palomar Medical Center West, Escondido, CA
Anshen+Allen Architects for Palomar Pomerado Health,
an association of CO Architects and Anshen+Allen

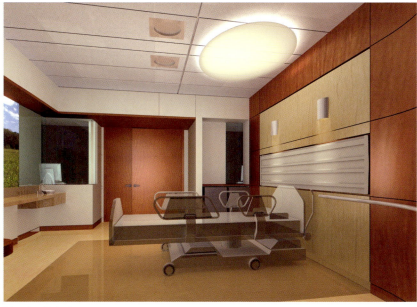

Headwall design.

Commentary

The media panel on the footwall, it is assumed, will be available with emerging technology by the time the hospital opens in 2011. It will be an access portal to medical education resources, entertainment, virtual chaplain, room service menu for food, schedule of procedures, Internet access and photos of restorative nature imagery. The circular light over the bed has the potential to be interactive, an opportunity for the patient to select a preferred color of light. Details of the patient headwall and medical gas layout had not been developed as of this writing.

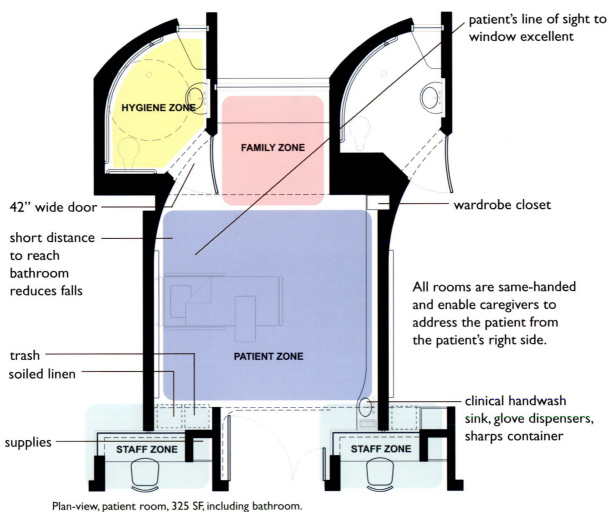

patient's line of sight to window excellent

HYGIENE ZONE

FAMILY ZONE

42" wide door

short distance to reach bathroom reduces falls

wardrobe closet

All rooms are same-handed and enable caregivers to address the patient from the patient's right side.

PATIENT ZONE

trash
soiled linen

clinical handwash sink, glove dispensers, sharps container

supplies

STAFF ZONE   **STAFF ZONE**

Plan-view, patient room, 325 SF, including bathroom.
Palomar Medical Center West, Escondido, CA
Anshen+Allen Architects for Palomar Pomerado Health, an association of CO Architects and Anshen+Allen

Commentary

continued on next page

The Palomar Medical Center West (879,000 SF) is a Center for Health Design (CHD) "super" Pebble, by virtue of its size and scope, and will be an example of CHD's "Fable Hospital," a hypothetical construct that incorporates core values of superior quality, safety, patient-centered care, family involvement, staff support, environmental sustainability and community responsibility. Those values are interwoven with the overall goals of enhancing both clinical outcomes and economic performance. The project is a replacement hospital consisting of 192 acuity-adaptable beds and 168 med/surg acute care beds although this is a moot point, as all rooms are identical, therefore designation can be changed at will. Patient floors are organized into a 24-bed acuity-adaptable wing and a 30-bed med/surg acute care wing. The acuity-adaptable wing, to meet licensing regulations, breaks into (2) 12-bed critical care units. Standardization of room size and design enables maximum operational flexibility:

    a) traditional designation by acuity (ICU, step down or med/surg)
    b) can change unit designations at will (ICU to med/surg or vice versa)
    c) over time operate the unit as a total acuity-adaptable unit (all levels of acuity)

A separate women and children's pavilion will have 96 LDRP rooms in addition to post-partum rooms plus a Level 2 NICU.

Photographer: © Charles Davis Smith

Patient room, new bed tower opened early 2007. The Heart Hospital Baylor Plano, Plano, TX
RTKL Associates, Inc. (architecture and interior design)

Renderings courtesy RTKL

Footwall rendering (electric fireplace was eliminated from project).   Rendering of room.

Commentary

continued on next page

All 68 patient rooms are identical with the goal of not moving patients as their acuity levels change. The building is organized around disease type and procedures, per floor (refer to floorplans). Staff will be trained to care for that patient "type" for all acuity levels. The headwall is 14 feet wide thus meets ICU requirements, has a two-leaf swing door that provides 6-foot clearance and has all physiological monitoring. The room is 287 SF plus 70 SF bathroom. Surgical patients are prepped and recovered in this room. They are brought to their rooms immediately after surgery. The hospital wanted to avoid built-in casework at the foot of the bed, hence the piece of movable furniture. Toilets are inboard. Soffiting of ceiling at footwall is a nice design detail (with light cove) but in some jurisdictions this would be considered a "dust shelf."

Nursing unit corridor with decentralized nurse station.
The Heart Hospital Baylor Plano, Plano, TX (both renderings)
RTKL Association, Inc. (architecture and interior design)

Central nurse station.

Commentary

continued on next page

Decentralized nurse observation station has visibility into two rooms. As there is also a central nurse station this provides maximum flexibility for desired nursing protocol. Swing door opens to 6-feet-wide to serve ICU patients. Note clerestory glass over door to bring more light into the nursing core.

First floor plan. The Heart Hospital Baylor Plano, Plano, TX
RTKL Associates, Inc.

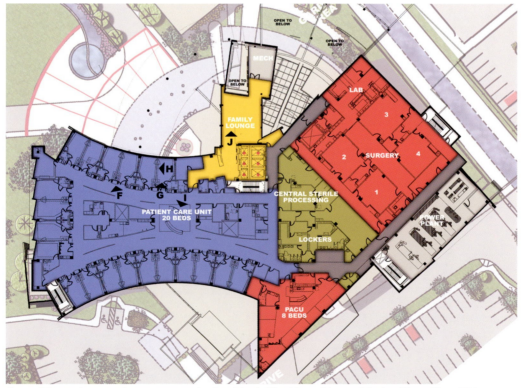

Second floor plan – cardiac surgery and related beds. The Heart Hospital Baylor Plano, Plano, TX
RTKL Associates, Inc.

continued on next page

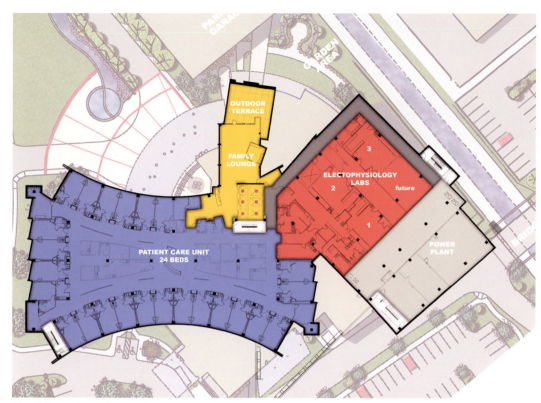

Third floor plan – electrophysiology and related beds. The Heart Hospital Baylor Plano, Plano, TX
RTKL Associates, Inc.

Fourth floor plan – interventional labs and related beds. The Heart Hospital Baylor Plano, Plano, TX
RTKL Associates, Inc.

WARDROBE

ORGANIZER
FOR GLOVES,
MASKS & GEL

PLASMA TV
LINEN
HAMPER

6'-9"

15'-6½"

WIPES
& WASTE

DIAG. SYS.

6'-8¾"

8'-3¼"

2'-10¾"   4'-0¾"

14'-4¾"

14'-6"   2'-1"

Acuity-adaptable patient room, 283 SF without bathroom; 315 SF w/ bathroom.
Heart and Vascular Institute and Critical Care Building, Hoag Memorial Hospital, Newport Beach, CA
KMD Architects (both renderings)

View of footwall from bed.

Commentary

continued on next page

Rooms designated as ICU will have glass slider/breakaway doors. Med/surg rooms may have same or a hinged door with a fixed leaf to fill the opening to make it easy to re-license beds from one type to another. (See next page for planview of nursing unit.)

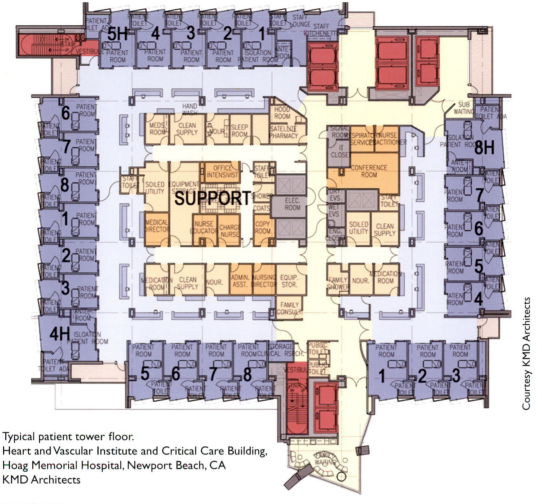

Typical patient tower floor.
Heart and Vascular Institute and Critical Care Building,
Hoag Memorial Hospital, Newport Beach, CA
KMD Architects

Courtesy KMD Architects

Commentary

The new 8-story Critical Care Building (to open 2011) on the Hoag campus has a 96-bed tower over a 3-story podium. The roof garden will be accessible to all hospital occupants. The building serves the Heart and Vascular Institute "Center of Excellence" as well as replaces and expands inpatient surgery (14 ORs plus 30 prep/recovery beds) in addition to providing a surgical interventional platform (refer to page 9.19 for a plan) of 14 interchangeable "boxes" all 750 SF in size. The heart program also includes a 24-bed ICU and (2) 24-bed telemetry units (included in the 96 beds). Rather than devote an entire floor to ICU, they will likely do a floor with a 16-bed ICU and the remainder med/surg beds. All patient rooms are identical and are sized to serve both acute and critical care without remodel of the toilet room. Rooms are same-handed and the window is centered to give all patients the same relationship to the view on four sides of the building. The room meets both acuity-adaptable and universal design standards giving the hospital the flexibility to staff modules of 8 beds as either acute or critical care which meets licensing requirements of California.

Nursing support rooms are grouped "off-stage" in the core, which prevents visitors from looking into them. All elevator lobbies have access to natural light. It would have been desirable to have more natural light flowing into the core but at least most corridors terminate at a window. There is a satellite pharmacy on each floor. Nurses work out of central stations as California does not accept decentralized stations in lieu of a central station, according to the architect.

Photographer: Ed Hershberger

Oregon Health & Science University, Portland, OR
Peterson Kolberg & Associates, Architects
Czopek & Erdenberger (interior design)

Before.

Photographer: Assassi Productions

Nebraska Orthopedic Hospital, Omaha, NE
Altus Architectural Studios

Commentary

High-profile patient bathroom design costs minimally more as a percentage of overall construction cost but is a sure way to uplift a patient's spirit. These bathrooms have large tile with fewer grout joints, adequate towel bars, shower with no curb, hotel-like accessories and easy-to-clean sinks and countertops. Most of us look at the bathroom when we first check into a hotel room. It's a benchmark of overall quality.

Photographer: Hershberger Photography

Salem Hospital, Salem, OR
KMD Architects

Photographer: Jain Malkin

UCLA Replacement Hospital

The two bathrooms above are almost indentical in size and layout but very different in ambience, yet it is unlikely the one on the left cost more. Below, built-in shelves provide a place for toiletries.

Photographer: Gary Kessel, TRO Jung/Brannen (both photos)

Trinity Medical Center, Birmingham, AL
TRO/The Ritchie Organization (architecture and interior design)

Clarian West Medical Center, Avon, IN
HKS Architects, Maregatti Interiors

Photographer: Jain Malkin

Memorial Hermann Texas Medical Center Signature Suites, Houston, TX
WHR Architects, Inc. (interior design also)

Photographer: Fran Brennan

Features:

1) Decorative tile adds punch of color
2) Corian top with integral sink
3) Make-up mirror
4) Recessed Corian shelf for toiletries
5) Illuminated mirror makes patients look healthy.
6) Access panel for flush value system

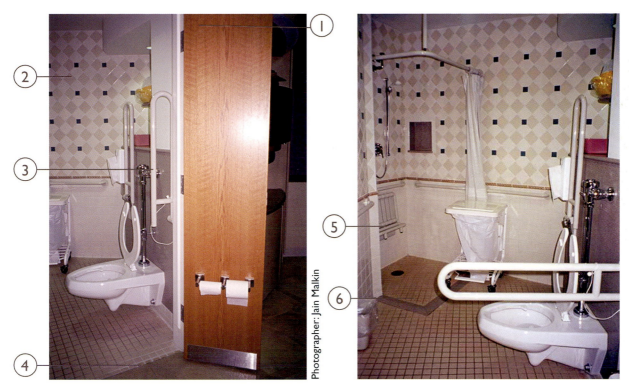

Photographer: Jain Malkin

Clarian Health, Methodist Hospital, Indianapolis, IN, Cardiac Comprehensive Critical Care Unit
BSA LifeStructures, Maregatti Interiors

TOILET

SHOWER AREA

FAMILY ZONE

TABLE

Courtesy: BSA LifeStructures

PLAN VIEW OF BATHROOM ABOVE

Features:

1) Double-leaf doors fold back to enable oversized wheelchair or patient in a bed (one designed to "fold up" to enable transport of patient to bathroom without disconnecting monitors and IVs) to be moved into bathroom. Provides more dignity for patient over using a commode chair. Note that larger door, when folded back, provides a privacy screen for family zone.
2) Patterned ceramic tile creates attractive ambience
3) Fold-down grab bars provide leverage for rising from a seated position but fold up to make possible a double caregiver assist.
4) Level transition at threshold
5) Fold-down shower seat
6) No curb to create fall hazard

Photographer: Jain Malkin (all photos)

Clarian North Medical Center, Indianapolis, IN (all photos)
HKS Architects, Maregatti Interiors

Commentary

Inset flooring patterns enhance corridors and create a warm ambience. Note colored lights (photo left) emphasizing curved soffit.

Photographer: Ed LaCasse Photography

Nursing unit corridor has generously sized workstations for nurses outside patient rooms. This reduces distraction and increases patient visibility. Sound attenuation is achieved through the use of carpet and high-NRC (noise reduction coefficient) acoustical tile in ceilings.
South Jersey Healthcare Regional Medical Center, Vineland, NJ
HKS Architects (architecture and interior design)

Commentary

A warm, non-institutional ambience has been created with color, curved soffits, lighting, and the graceful shape of the countertop and niches of the decentralized nurse workstations.

Photographer: Assassi Productions

Nebraska Orthopedic Hospital, Omaha, NE (both photos)
Altus Architectural Studios

Features:

1) Interesting nurse station design
2) Indirect lighting
3) Privacy screen
4) Carpet (absorbs foot traffic noise)
5) High, durable baseboard

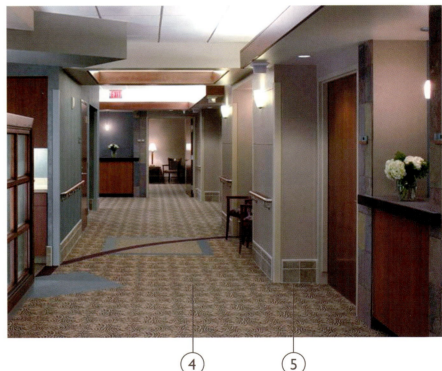

Photographer: Assassi Productions

Commentary

Design features and ambience from lobby are carried into patient care areas. Good use of color and pattern. Also see pages 7.43 and 7.62.

Photographer: Ed LaCasse

Nurse station. Parker Adventist Hospital, Parker, CO
HKS, Inc. (architecture and interior design)

Photographer: Jain Malkin (both photos)

Nurse station. Clarian North Medical Center, Indianapolis, IN
HKS Architects, Maregatti Interiors

Nurse station. Clarian North Medical Center

Commentary

The two photos are polar opposites for central nurse station design. In the upper photo, features include a clinical handwash sink, plenty of storage to avoid clutter, and a variety of work settings from "quiet" to more exposed. Detailing in ceiling, lighting and casework, as well as flooring pattern carry design concepts from public areas to the clinical setting. In the lower photos, a small work space with little storage and a shallow desk top has a make-shift appearance. In addition, chairs are not ergonomic. This was most likely an attempt to downsize the central nurse station.

Photographer: Ed Hershberger

Oregon Health & Science University, Portland, OR
Peterson Kolberg & Associates Architects, Czopek & Erdenberger (Interior Design)

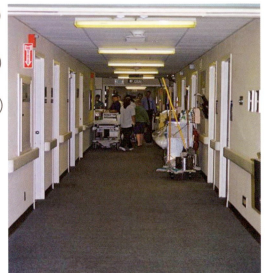

Courtesy Peterson Kolberg & Associates

Before.

Photographer: Ed Hershberger

Oregon Health & Science University, Portland, OR
Peterson Kolberg & Associates Architects, Czopek & Erdenberger (Interior Design)

Before.

Features:

1) Indirect lighting
2) Nurse server
3) Carpet absorbs noise of foot traffic

Commentary

A dramatic change in ambience was achieved in a 1950s-era nursing unit all within the medical center's "standard" budget for this type of renovation. The architect refers to this as "perceived opulence" as opposed to "real" opulence which is costly. Also see pages 7.43 and 7.62.

LDR room, 340 SF plus 43 SF bathroom. Emory Crawford Long Hospital, Atlanta, GA (all photos)
HKS Inc. (all photos)

Photographer: Ed LaCasse (all photos)

NICU.

Post-partum room.

Features:

1) Infant warmer folds up into cabinet.
2) Fetal monitor is housed in cabinet; case cart is stored in closet within the room.
3) Interesting ceiling with indirect lighting (reduces glare) NICU design has similar detailing as birthing rooms.
4) Wood-look vinyl floor.

Photographer: Rick Gardner (both photos)

LDRP room, 365 SF including bathroom. Brazosport Memorial Hospital Dow Women's Center, Lake Jackson, TX (both photos)
WHR Architects (interior design also)

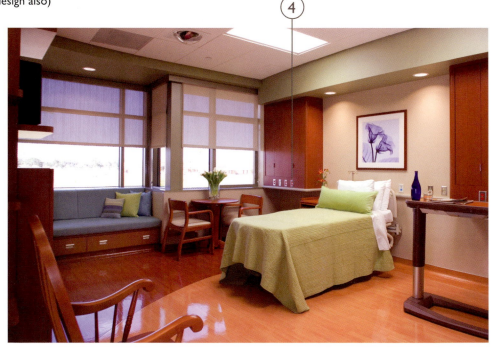

Features:

1) Ample room for display of flowers, cards
2) Armoire for clothing and storage
3) Large windows, view of school playground and running track
4) Electrical outlets on face of cabinet; med gases are inside cabinet accessed by bi-fold doors; suction, with cannister attached, inside cabinet
5) Case cart stored in equipment room and brought into room when needed.

Photographer: ©Vance Fox

LDRP room, 280 SF, including bathroom which is inboard, to preserve maximum window area.
Carson Tahoe Regional Medical Center, Carson City, NV
Moon Mayoras Architects, Inc; Brandt Design Group (interiors)

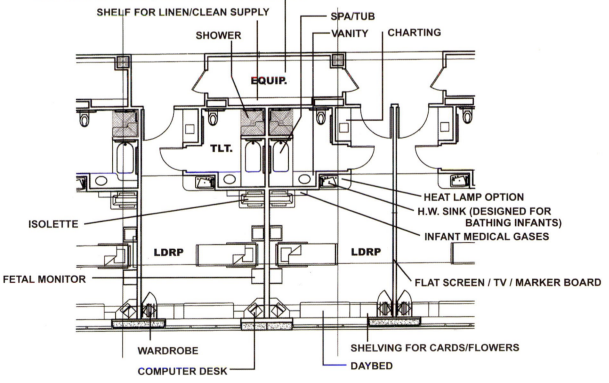

Planview courtesy Moon Mayoras Architects

Photographer: © Eckert and Eckert

LDR room. Legacy Salmon Creek Hospital, Vancouver, WA
Zimmer Gunsul Frasca Partnership

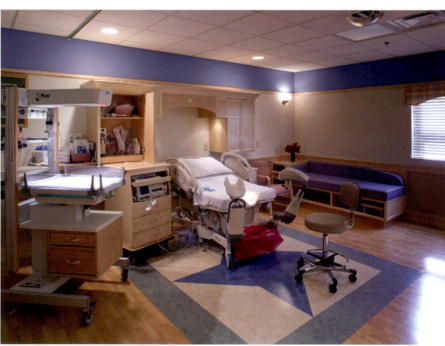

Photographer: Brad Feinknopf

LDR room. Memorial Hospital of Union County, Marysville, OH
Karlsberger Architects (architecture and interior design)

Commentary

Two LDR rooms with very different aesthetic styles. The top photo has clean, contemporary detailing and the lower image is country casual with an inset flooring pattern reminiscent of a patchwork quilt. No doubt each is a response to the community served.

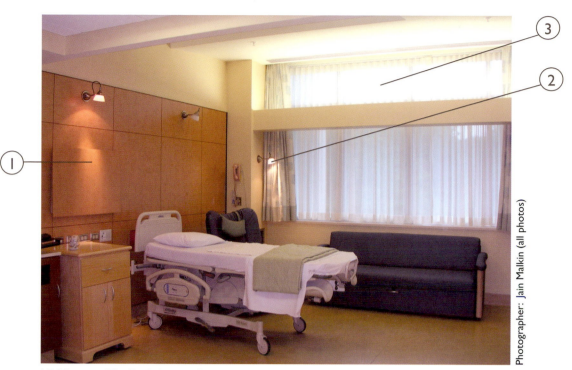

LDRP room. The Birthplace at Gaston Memorial Hospital, Gastonia, NC
KMD Architects (all photos)

Photographer: Jain Malkin (all photos)

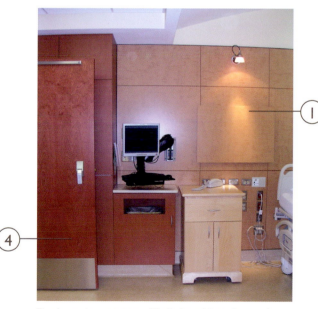

Fetal monitor on top of built-in cabinet for trash.

Recessed medical gas cabinet (door slides up).

Features:

1) Panel slides up to expose medical gas cabinet.
2) Reading light for family member in recliner chair
3) Clerestory window offers an option for ambient light independent of the large window.
4) Door to bathroom

continued on next page

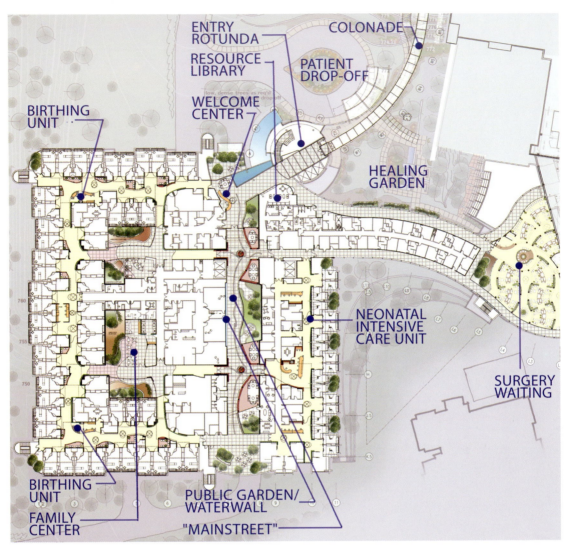

ENTRY ROTUNDA
COLONADE
RESOURCE LIBRARY
PATIENT DROP-OFF
WELCOME CENTER
BIRTHING UNIT
HEALING GARDEN
NEONATAL INTENSIVE CARE UNIT
SURGERY WAITING
BIRTHING UNIT
FAMILY CENTER
PUBLIC GARDEN/ WATERWALL
"MAINSTREET"

The Birthplace at Gaston Memorial Hospital, Gastonia, NC
KMD Architects

Commentary

This is a remarkable maternity center with 56 LDRPs, and 16 private NICUs. All services are located on one floor. Not only is the interior architecture and planning uniquely interesting, the concept of family-centered care is taken to new heights. Every aspect of the patient's and family's experience was choreographed. For example, as the mother is being wheeled back to her room after a C-section, the father walks alongside holding the baby. Every protocol has been developed to create early bonding with the baby and to support the family. The responsibilities for neonate care "assigned" to the parents (based on teaching and training) build their confidence in caring for the infant. Nurses communicate by Vocera wireless system. Only a personal tour of this facility can do it justice. Healing environment amenities include gardens specifically for staff and for families, quick break areas for nurses near the nurse station; the main circulation spine has a 100-foot-long water wall, and commissioned artwork has been integrated into the interior design in such a way that it's evident it was carefully planned. The art is colorful, uplifting and interesting in its variety. The architects took great advantage of the high ceiling and natural light available due to its top-floor location. Large oval light wells punctuate the nursing core and patient room entries are set back creating a corridor with a meandering flow.

Infant bathing sink. UC Davis Medical Center, Davis, CA
Anshen+Allen Architects

Photographer: Matthew Millman

Rendering courtesy RTKL Associates, Inc.

One of 60 LDRP maternity suites.
Size: 388 SF + 70 SF equipment storage + 57 SF bathroom = 515 total SF.
Community Hospital North, Indianapolis, IN
RTKL Associates, Inc.

Photographer: Ed LaCasse

LDR room. Parker Adventist Hospital, Parker, CO
HKS, Inc. (architecture and interior design)

Commentary

Both of these projects have a level of sophistication and clean contemporary design not often found in birthing rooms. In top photo, case cart with fetal monitor tucks into headwall niche; white vertical panel on footwall is marker board; rooms are not same-handed. In the lower photo, the handwash sink is on the footwall; case cart is on headwall; the "bow" design behind infant warmer was created by an inlay of cherry laminate into the maple field. The window is to the side of the rocker/recliner chair. (Refer to next page for Community Hospital North patient unit floorplans.)

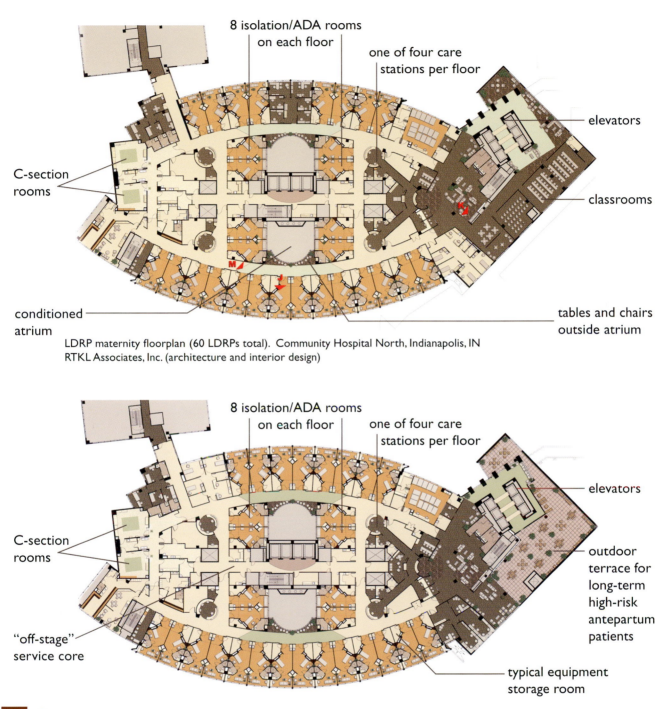

8 isolation/ADA rooms on each floor

one of four care stations per floor

elevators

C-section rooms

classrooms

conditioned atrium

tables and chairs outside atrium

LDRP maternity floorplan (60 LDRPs total). Community Hospital North, Indianapolis, IN
RTKL Associates, Inc. (architecture and interior design)

8 isolation/ADA rooms on each floor

one of four care stations per floor

elevators

C-section rooms

outdoor terrace for long-term high-risk antepartum patients

"off-stage" service core

typical equipment storage room

Commentary

Refer to page 7.78 for rendering of LDRP room. Interior atrium brings natural light into nursing units (five-story atrium is accessible only at second floor); exterior roof plazas and gardens are beneficial for long-term high-risk antepartum patients. The building's oval shape creates a hybrid racetrack with an east-to-west service corridor that reduces noise. The four care stations provide visibility of ambulating patients in labor and the chairs and tables at the atrium provide rest stops. The curvilinear corridor form ensures better visibility of patient room entries from any of the care stations and visually reduces the appearance of a large floor plate.

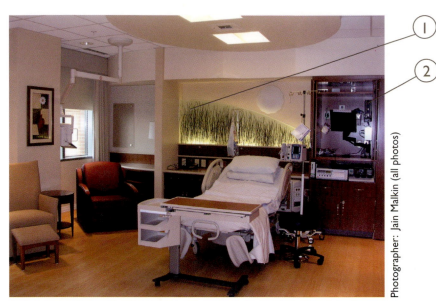

LDR room. Clarian North Medical Center, Indianapolis, IN (all photos)
HKS Architects, Maregatti Interiors

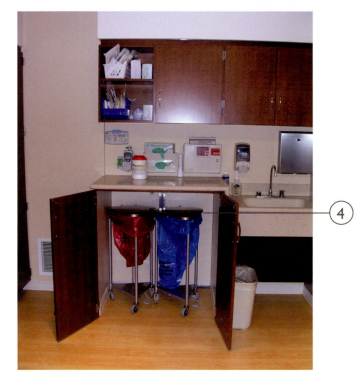

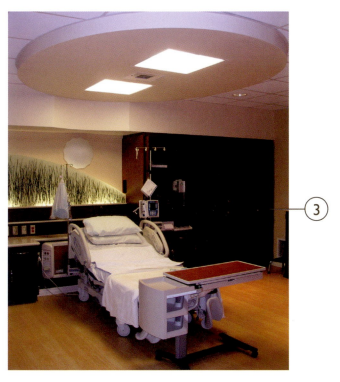

Features:

1) Back-lit resin panel with embedded grasses on headwall introduces nature and also serves as a night light.
2) Monitors and other equipment are neatly tucked inside cabinet with retractable doors.
3) Case cart stored inside cabinet.
4) Trash carts wheel into cabinet and can be exchanged from corridor without entering the room.

continued on next page

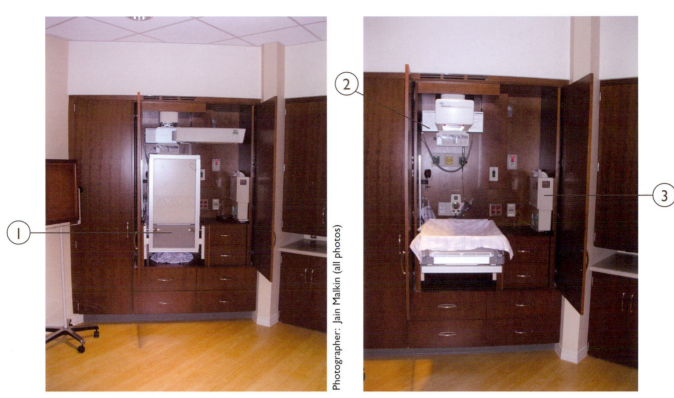

Photographer: Jain Malkin (all photos)

LDR room. Clarian North Medical Center,
Indianapolis, IN (all photos)
HKS Architects, Maregatti Interiors

Features:

1, 2) Infant warmer folds up and stores in cabinet.
3) Sharps container is conveniently located inside cabinet.
4) Carts for waste roll inside cabinet (see previous page).
5) Cubicle drape stores inside cabinet which keeps it from getting splashed by sink; also keeps it cleaner than if it were exposed to multiple hands tugging at it all day but the trade-off is that the cabinet is a visual barrier to immediately seeing the handwash sink upon entering. The "hand" of the door also adds to that problem.

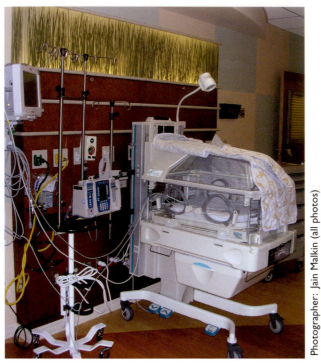

Photographer: Jain Malkin (all photos)

Level 3 NICU (private rooms). Clarian North Medical Center, Indianapolis, IN
HKS Architects, Maregatti Interiors

Decentralized nurse station.

NICU corridor.

Commentary

NICU headwall "matches" design of LDR headwall (see previous page); rooms are private with sleepover sofa for parents. There is no central nurse station for this unit, which may be why a nurse is sitting at a tablet-arm chair in the corridor. There is a remarkable lack of clutter (housekeeping carts, linen carts) in corridor. Bravo. The soffit in corridor would constitute a dust shelf in some jurisdictions and this forces the call lights to be ceiling-mounted, which makes them less visible, it would seem, than if they were above the door.

Photographer: Strode Eckert

Kern Critical Care Unit at Legacy Good Samaritan Hospital, Portland, OR
Tom Sagerser, Architect

Photographer: Nursing Director

Garden outside ICU rooms.

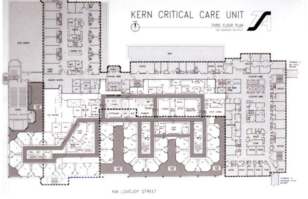

Courtesy: Tom Sagerser

Outdoor garden/courtyard wraps into
and around ICU rooms.

Commentary

This project set a new benchmark for the design of critical care units. It was the first to use a rotating boom for delivery of medical services and made possible rotation of the bed to face the nurse station or the garden. The architect made use of the research indicating that a view of nature is restorative and therapeutic. This challenged the widely-held notion that critical care patients are comatose and therefore won't benefit from a window view, hence many ICU rooms place a narrow window behind the patient's head. The Director of Nursing has noted that patients seem to recover sensory awareness more quickly in this setting. Another advantage of the garden is that family can enjoy fresh air and sunlight and still be nearby to notice if the physician comes into the room or if there is unusual activity that might cause alarm.

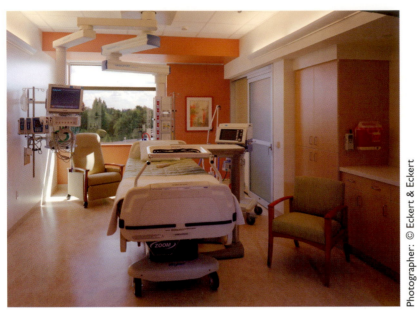

Photographer: © Eckert & Eckert

Photographer: © Eckert & Eckert

ICU patient room. Legacy Salmon Creek Hospital, Portland, OR (both photos)
Zimmer Gunsul Frasca Partnership

ICU waiting area.

Photographer: © Eckert & Eckert

Critical care room, 302 SF. Kadlec Medical Center, Richland, WA
Zimmer Gunsul Frasca Partnership

Commentary

In both rooms, ceiling-mounted boom with power and medical gas connections enables bed to be rotated to face the view as patient becomes more stable. Indirect lighting offers an option. Nice to see color in an ICU room. ICU waiting area has ample natural light. Bathrooms (top photo) are on exterior wall (with sliding frosted glass door) and shared between rooms. Bathrooms in lower photo in same location; note 10-foot ceiling height to maximize light into the room.

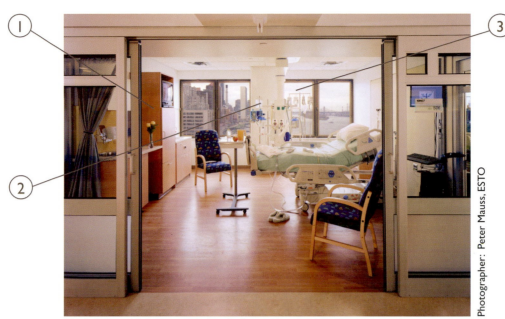

Critical Care Unit Consolidation. Bellevue Hospital, NY (both photos)
Guenther 5 Architects

Photographer: Peter Mauss, ESTO

Photographer: Peter Mauss, ESTO

Features:

1) Footwall storage/entertainment cabinet unusual, but welcome, in an ICU room.
2) Medical gases on 360° rotating ceiling-mounted power column makes possible rotation of bed.
3) Natural light/views visible to patients
4) Universal ICU room works for all types of critical care patients. Total 56 rooms, 240 SF in size.
5) Nurse desk for every two rooms; behind each desk, in core area, are meds rooms, conference rooms, utility rooms, and administrative offices.
6) A feng-shui consultant was used to develop color palettes which are based on exposure:
   East – green: morning; brings in the energy of the rising sun
   North – blue: night; brings in the energy of the full moon
   South – brick orange; brings in the energy of accomplishment and creation
   West – white silver; brings in the energy of the setting sun

Photographer: © 2006 Dimitre Photography

Nurse station. Provena Mercy Medical Center, Aurora, IL (both photos)
Proteus Group

Photographer: © 2006 Dimitre Photography

Features:

1) Indirect lighting reduces glare and eye strain.
2) Hybrid decentralized nursing areas serve two nurses, which reduces isolation problems at typical decentralized nursing station
3) Sconces balance overhead lighting and allow nurses to dim lighting at night
4) Colored walls and inset flooring patterns create a pleasing ambience not often seen in a critical care unit.
5) General: The unit is adjacent to surgery; support spaces include a large equipment room and multiple cart alcoves located off patient corridors to prevent carts being stored in corridor. There are two family sleep rooms with bathroom/shower for family members who stay overnight. A general waiting room is complemented by a private family waiting room.

continued on next page

Photographer: © 2006 Dimitre Photography

Provena Mercy Medical Center, Aurora, IL
Proteus Group

Provena Mercy Medical Center
ICU Relocation

16 bed ICU
Proteus Group

Commentary

Decentralized nurse stations are across the corridor from patient rooms (see previous page); medical gases and power are fixed on headwall which prevents bed from being rotated to enable patient to see outdoors. No TV is available for patients. Patient room is 250 SF. A lay-in combination exam light/reading light over bed is complemented by downlights to provide varied lighting options.

Photographer: Scott Williams Photography

Decentralized nurse station is larger than "standard," offering good visibility, a large work surface and storage. St. Joseph Regional Health Center, Bryan, TX
WHR Architects, Inc. (interior design also)

Photographer: Jain Malkin

ICU nurse station with drawers for supplies opening from the front (faces patient rooms). St. Joseph's Community Hospital of West Bend, WI
Gresham Smith Partners

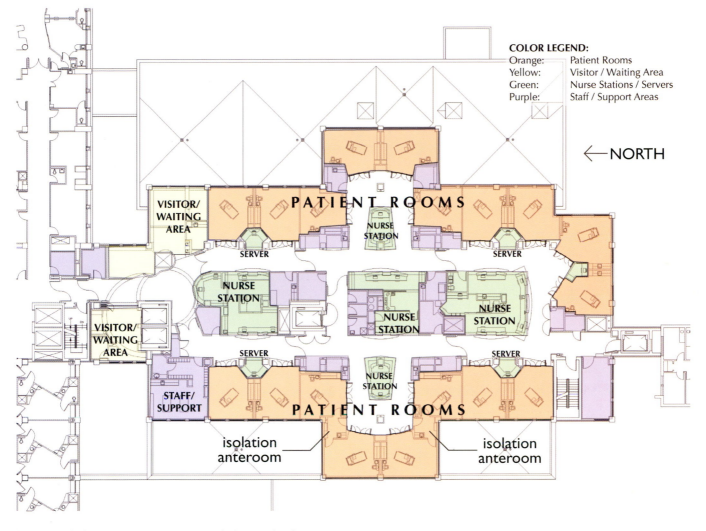

COLOR LEGEND:
Orange: Patient Rooms
Yellow: Visitor / Waiting Area
Green: Nurse Stations / Servers
Purple: Staff / Support Areas

← NORTH

Remodeled 18-bed intensive care unit with decentralized nursing.
Exempla Lutheran Medical Center, Wheat Ridge, CO
H+L Architecture (architecture and interior design)

Commentary

The layout of the unit was dictated by column size and floors below, which resulted in the crucifix form. This did not allow for full decentralized care for all rooms. Whether a room has a rotating boom for gases and services or a fixed power column depended on a visual analysis of each room by nurses to ensure optimal observation from nurse stations. Eight rooms have booms; rooms with nurse servers have fixed columns. Isolation anterooms each serve two rooms. Rooms are 265 to 315 SF in size. Patient mix is surgical and medical ICU. Separate cardiac and neuro units are located elsewhere. Note that corridors are carpeted to reduce noise. Refer to a discussion of the care process and patient outcome statistics at the end of Chapter 5.

Planview, ICU Room of the Future. Plan at left shows open toilet room; plan at right shows enclosed toilet for ambulatory patients.
Hennepin County Medical Center, Minneapolis, MN
Perkins+Will Architects

Renderings courtesy Perkins+Will Architects

Bird's-eye view of patient room and charting alcove.
(Note: black rectangles are light fixtures overhead)
Patient room 435 SF; toilet 61 SF; nurse alcove 80 SF.

Commentary   *continued on next page*

The ICU Room of the Future was a design study to determine if a common floorplan could be used for the varying acuity ICUs located within the medical center (Hennepin is a Level 1 trauma center and also has a burn unit). Issues of patient safety and family-centered care were paramount. The deeply recessed charting area enables a nurse to view two patients and provides storage for universal precaution protective equipment, computers and patient room supplies. Informal consults with staff and family can occur here and, to reduce noise for the patient, access to the room can be through the sliding doors of the alcove, instead of corridor doors.

Headwall, ICU Room of the Future.
Hennepin County Medical Center, Minneapolis, MN
Perkins+Will Architects

Footwall.

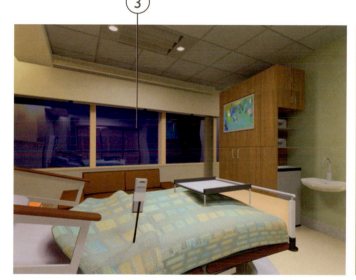

The entry to the bathroom is to the left of foot-wall/TV casework (along the window wall).

Nurse workstation.

Features:

1) Multiple types of lighting, including indirect
2) Family area
3) Patient has access to views and natural light.
4) Glove boxes and sharps containers are out of patient's view.
5) Location of handwash sink at room entry

Examination Room | The Scripps Center for Integrative Medicine
La Jolla, CA. Jain Malkin Inc. in collaboration with Schmidt, Scanlon, Gordon Architects. Photography: Michael Campos

Diagnostics: Discovering the Invisible 8

Diagnosis is fundamental to the practice of medicine. This is the province of physicians who, depending upon the condition, may be able to rely upon experience and training to diagnose an illness or may require a battery of tests such as laboratory analysis, pulmonary function tests, electrocardiography, or diagnostic imaging modalities, to name a few. It is not uncommon for patients to become anxious while awaiting test results that may be revealed the same day as the test or perhaps a week later. While a standard chest radiograph (X-ray) prior to surgery may not engender much psychological stress, a patient has a lot riding on the results of a CT scan that may reveal the return or growth of a tumor. Expectant parents wait anxiously as the fetus becomes visible through an ultrasound examination, ever vigilant about discovering something unexpected.

In settings other than healthcare, moderate amounts of stress are tolerable and may even improve performance. In healthcare, however, stress reactions are a clinical problem as they often result in negative or worsened medical outcomes (e.g., elevated blood pressure, increased muscle tension, and anxiety) through effects on stress hormones and immune function (Ulrich, Simons, and Miles 2003). This can even impact behavior, such as keeping office appointments and compliance with treatment regimens (Gatchel, as cited in Ulrich, Simons, and Miles 2003).

RESTORATIVE BENEFITS OF NATURAL ENVIRONMENTS

Sometimes, just the sight of the equipment is enough to cause anxiety. Many individuals can't bear the sight of a needle, making phlebotomy (blood draw) very stressful. Research indicates that anxiety is highest during the anticipatory phase and declines substantially by the end of the blood-drawing experience (Ulrich, Simons, and Miles 2003). In the same study, the presence or absence of television provided convincing evidence, as measured by physiological responses, that stress was significantly higher during television viewing. The investigators caution that the widespread practice of playing daytime television programming continuously and uncontrollably as a distraction in waiting rooms should be reexamined.

Another hypothesis tested was whether nature settings alleviate stress more effectively than views of built/urban environments. This is based on evolutionary theory that humans are hard-wired to experience nature environments as restorative (Ulrich 1991; Ulrich et al. 1991; Wilson 1984; Kellert and Wilson 1993). Moreover, people respond to the natural environment with consistency regardless of geography or cultural diversity (Kaplan and Kaplan 1989). This makes it an ideal strategy for reducing stress in emergency rooms (Image page 9.5, top photo), cancer treatment facilities (Image pages 10.8, 10.10, 10.11, 10.12, and 10.14), and in diagnostic testing areas.

A simulated view of nature is as effective as the real thing, according to Ulrich (1991). Photographic images of nature (landscapes) can be placed on the wall in blood-draw cubicles in view of the patient or they can be back-lit transparencies placed overhead in treatment or procedure rooms (Image page 10.12). Another strategy is the implementation of nature programming on a closed-circuit television station. Systems such as the Continuous Ambient Relaxation Environment (CARE) channel offer 72 hours of nonrepetitive nature images accompanied by soothing instrumental music (Image page 7.47). This would be preferable to television programming in waiting areas throughout inpatient or outpatient settings. In creating an optimal experience for patients, when a patient is escorted to a room, the television monitor could have images of nature as the default channel. This can be a task assigned to housekeeping personnel in preparing the room for a new patient.

In the aforementioned study by Ulrich, Simons, and Miles (2003) subjects watched either a videotape of nature or one of urban environments lacking nature. Stress was considerably lower when viewing nature. The evidence suggests that stressful healthcare environments should have low environmental stimulation levels rather than high and intrusive ones.

POSITIVE DISTRACTION

It makes no sense to spend upward of $1 million on a piece of diagnostic imaging equipment without setting aside $10,000 to $20,000 for environmental amenities to distract patients and reduce their stress. The mere visual presence of such a large piece of equipment and the noises emitted during the procedure as the scanner gathers images can be frightening.

Magnetic resonance imaging (MRI) can be particularly intimidating, especially after having to pass through a metal detector (a safety precaution in some hospitals) and having to answer numerous questions about implanted medical devices, orthopedic pins to hold bones in place, and so forth prior to the procedure. Having one's head inside a snug cylinder and having to lie perfectly still for a minimum of 45 minutes is pure torture for anyone who is claustrophobic. Those minutes pass very slowly. Certainly, MRI rooms should have soothing lighting and color palette, perhaps a wood-look floor and even images of nature to relax the patient at least in the anticipatory phase of the procedure upon entering the room. A good example can be seen on Image page 5.17, upper left photo. Headsets enable patients to listen to their choice of music, which can help to block the noise of the machine.

Several Notable Examples of Positive Distraction

A hospital in Orlando, Florida, created a "beach" experience for patients with murals on the wall depicting sand castles and colorful striped umbrellas. Patients are given beach sandals and patterned bathrobes and the scent of suntan lotion is sprayed periodically. Far more common are MRI rooms devoid of any amenities with the most basic of finishes and lighting. It is the responsibility of design professionals to include stress-reducing amenities as a standard part of planning and design of imaging facilities. It's a rare radiology department manager or vice president of ancillary services who thinks about these issues and questions the architect about how it is being handled.

Patients with cardiovascular disease may undergo studies on a PET/CT scanner, which is also often used for staging cancer treatment. The remarkable aspect of this machine is that it enables diagnosticians to observe metabolic function in body organs accompanied by images of tissue and anatomical data, creating three-dimensional images. In The Scripps Center for Integrative Medicine in La Jolla, California, (Image page 8.1) patients undergoing examination by a PET/CT scanner have the benefit of looking at a ceiling designed to simulate a section cut through a chambered nautilus shell. Constructed of gypsum board and deeply sculpted, segments of the shell are highlighted with fiber-optic lighting that cycles through a spectrum of color. After the patient is positioned on the table, the ambient lighting of the room is dimmed and the focus is on the ceiling as colors sequence from magenta to green to lavender and blue—providing a compelling positive distraction. The nautilus shell design is repeated in the flooring.

Cardiology is the service line that anchors The Scripps Center for Integrative Medicine, but the emphasis is on lifestyle change. Sacred geometry, based on the golden mean (a mathematical proportion found in nature and even human DNA and the basis for many outstanding works of architecture over many centuries), informs the design of the entire facility, using the chambered nautilus shell, considered to be one of the most harmonious forms in nature, as a pattern. Patients requiring the administration of radioactive isotopes or contrast media prior to the scan are prepped in a room with dimmable lighting so that the subdued shoji-screen wall sconces and back-lit sky image overhead create a relaxing ambience (Image page 9.12).

A hospital in Nashville, Tennessee, has created a memorable experience for patients in its CT scanner suite to celebrate country music (Image page 8.2). The room has considerable attention to detail, including musical notes on the ceiling. This is a great example of understanding regional culture.

Using healing environments research in a breast care center

The specter of breast cancer is so powerful that many women dread having an annual screening mammogram. It creates huge anxiety for many women. The design of the Scripps Polster Breast Care Center in La Jolla, California, uses healing-environments research to reduce patients' stress and anxiety (Image pages 8.3 to 8.6).

This research falls into five categories:

1. connection to nature
2. control (options and choices)
3. positive distraction
4. access to social support
5. elimination of environmental stressors (noise, glare)

The text on the photo pages explains how the research was translated into design features that create a positive experience for patients. Access to social support is a fundamental concept in the care process: if a patient is symptomatic, she is immediately counseled as to options and next steps so that she doesn't leave the facility in a frantic state of mind. A referral to an oncologist can be made. The patient will meet the same caring staff when returning for diagnostic mammograms or for stereotatic biopsy. Direct access to an ambulatory surgical center is provided so that the patient doesn't have to travel outside the setting with a needle placed in her breast to get to a surgery center. Convenience and privacy are paramount. Another aspect of social support is the concierge/greeter who checks patients in for their appointments. This is friendlier than checking in at a reception window. While patients wait for their procedures, they are offered a 10-minute neck and shoulder massage by a massage therapist, one of several high-touch amenities.

EXAMINATION ROOMS

As physicians become more comfortable with paperless offices and can afford to purchase electronic medical record (EMR) systems, all aspects of patient care will be electronically managed. The scale will download the patient's weight to the EMR. Other types of diagnostic instruments (otoscope and ophthalmoscope, for example) can record a photo of the ear or eye and store it on the EMR. Handheld electronic devices or PDAs (personal digital assistants) enable physicians to have quick access to huge clinical practice databases to aid in diagnosis or best practices for treating various diseases or conditions.

The integration of technology into exam rooms is being studied by a number of organizations that have a vested interest in changing the layouts that have characterized examination rooms for much of the past century. Companies that develop and market information technology (IT) systems are trying to rethink the process. Since many patients do not have to disrobe and only need to speak to a physician across a desk or at chairs placed at right angles, is the traditional exam room even necessary or appropriate? Perhaps these patients could be seen in a room without an exam table, one furnished with lounge seating and a large monitor on the wall on which lab tests and radiographs could be displayed.

We are seeing the Gretsky effect: the great hockey player once said his success is due to skating not where the puck is, but where it will be. Others who are trying to figure out where it will be are large furniture manufacturers like Steelcase, whose research and development team is collaborating with the Mayo Clinic in the SPARC (see, plan, act, refine, communicate) Innovation Program (http://mayoresearch.mayo.edu/mayo/research/sparc/). In a physical space designed as a working laboratory, exam room concepts can be tested without having to actually build them in the clinical setting.

Moreover, patient care process and flow concepts can be tested. This type of change is disruptive in a healthcare setting, but staff can be brought into the SPARC space to test new room layouts, furniture, and equipment, as well as evaluate the integration of technology into the patient care experience. The patient-caregiver interaction is, of course, essential to the equation.

One of the innovations being tested is a touch pad that physicians activate when entering the room. This, in turn, activates the computer and opens the patient's file, thus cutting wasted time and allowing physicians to turn their focus immediately to the sick patient in front of them. Collaborating on this project are Mayo; Hammel, Green and Abrahamson Architects; IDEO; and Steelcase.

The Scripps Center for Integrative Medicine has exam rooms "divided" into a clinical side and a consultation area. The change in flooring from sheet vinyl to carpet reinforces the duality of the room (Image page 8.7, top photo). To reduce patient anxiety, diagnostic instruments, sharps containers, and glove boxes are behind tambour doors that slide up to reveal these items as needed. A two-panel door rolls out to create a private dressing area. The computer is placed on the desk.

The exam rooms in LifeScape Medical, a large family practice group in Scottsdale, Arizona, make use of a built-in bench for family. This makes the room less cluttered than individual chairs and accommodates several persons in an 8 x 12-foot room. All rooms are same-handed (not mirror image) so that the physician always addresses the patient from the patient's right side. While seated at the corner desk, the physician can chart while facing those seated on the bench. The room is well-organized and tidy with no electrical cords snaking down the wall. This office is totally paperless, and it is a pilot site for a major IT vendor's integrated software.

Mayo Clinic has, for years, used an exam room design that is often referred to in the industry as a "Mayo room." It has an examination side and a consultation area with a built-in sofa alongside a desk for the provider (Image page 8.8).

References

Kaplan, S., and R. Kaplan. 1989. *The experience of nature: A psychological perspective.* Cambridge, MA: Cambridge University Press.

Kellert, S. R., and E. O. Wilson, eds. 1993. *The biophilia hypothesis.* Washington, DC: Island Press/Shearwater.

Ulrich, R. S. 1991. The effects of interior design on wellness: Theory and recent scientific research. *Journal of Healthcare Design* 3:97–109.

Ulrich, R. S., R. F. Simons, B. D. Losito, E. Fiorito, M. A. Miles, and M. Zelson. 1991. Stress recovery during exposure to natural and urban environments. *Journal of Environmental Psychology* 11:201–230.

Ulrich, R. S., R. F. Simons, and M. A. Miles. 2003. Effects of environmental simulations and television on blood donor stress. *Journal of Architectural and Planning Research* 20(1):38–47.

Wilson, E. O. 1984. *Biophilia: The human bond with other species.* Cambridge, MA: Harvard University Press.

Photographer: Michael Campos

PET/CT in Scripps Center for Integrative Medicine, La Jolla, CA (both photos)
Jain Malkin Inc. in collaboration with Schmidt, Scanlon, Gordon Architects

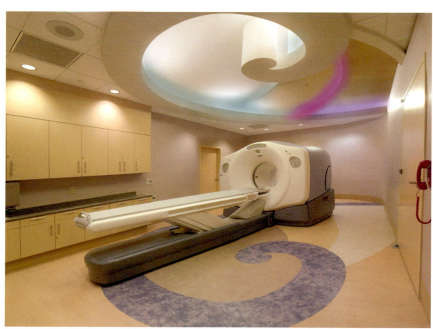

Photographer: Michael Campos

Commentary

The ceiling is a representation of a chambered nautilus shell, an expression of sacred geometry or the Golden Mean, due to the harmony of its proportions. Fiber optic lighting outlines the segments with a rainbow of colors as it sequences from magenta to teal, green, and lavender. When the lights in the room are dimmed, it is a compelling positive distraction.

Sink cabinet enclosure with Nashville memorabilia in the background.

"CT Country" employs Nashville musical memorabilia as a positive diversion.

Photos courtesy Adventist Health

"Stage" entrance to CT suite.

The view through the bore of the machine.

"Guest artist" dressing room.

Commentary

While some may view this as over the top, it delights the local community in a city where music is as important as air to breathe. To design an experience that distracts patients during a potentially frightening or overwhelming procedure, it's important to know what resonates for them. In Nashville, it's country music!

Photographer: Glenn Cormier, InSite

Reception area with concierge desk.
Scripps Polster Breast Care Center, La Jolla, CA
Jain Malkin Inc. (planning and interior architecture)

Commentary

continued on next page

The most advanced breast care is provided in a setting focused on the link between mind, body, and spirit. Many women experience tremendous anxiety in anticipation of a mammogram. To reduce anxiety, patients have opportunities to select, from a wide number of options, what would be most comforting to experience while waiting for the procedure. Many positive diversions are offered in a setting, which is in itself an architectural experience. Patients may research a health topic on the Internet, or enjoy the Zen fountain carved out of a huge boulder. One may mosey about exploring a unique collection of fine arts and crafts. The Confident Reflections shop offers a selection of gift items and prostheses to help women look as confident and vibrant as they feel. Gowned waiting areas named East of the Sun and West of the Moon after a Norwegian folk tale, offer a tea service and comfy chairs as the sounds of nature are enjoyed through small speakers concealed within the upholstered walls of the room at shoulder level. The East of the Sun gowned waiting lounge is dedicated to the Summer Solstice when female energies are at their peak. An exhibit in that space simulates the solstice concept. The West of the Moon gowned waiting lounge celebrates the Triple Goddess of the Moon legend, representing three stages of a woman's life. This is metaphorically expressed in a sculpture as the three phases of the moon, waxing (youth), full (middle-age) and waning (elder) create a niche in the room. In addition, an artist was commissioned to create a series of three large paintings (seen through an opening in the lounge) celebrating the stages of a woman's life, employing metaphors (for example butterfly: metamorphosis; onion: fecundity; lotus: wisdom) integrated into powerful images.

SCRIPPS BREAST CARE CENTER

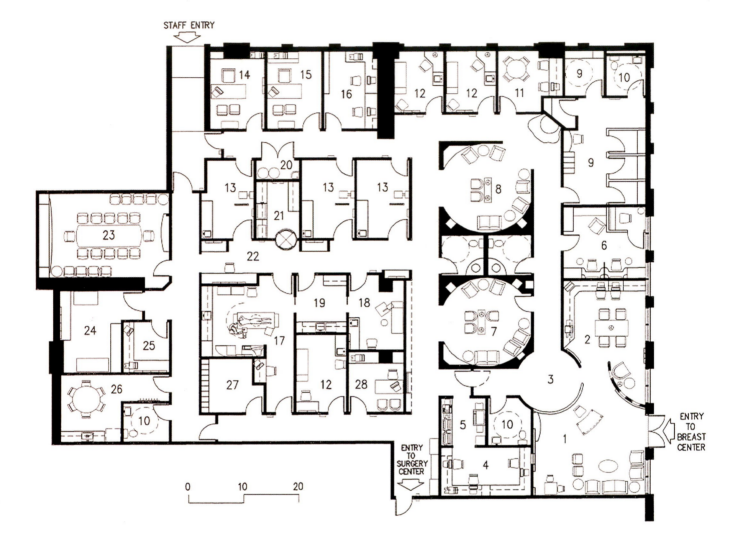

1	RECEPTION	15	ADMINISTRATOR
2	RESOURCE LIBRARY	16	NURSES' OFFICE
3	ROTUNDA	17	STEREOTACTIC
4	BUSINESS OFFICE	18	ULTRASOUND
5	WORKROOM	19	WORKROOM
6	POSITIVE APPEARANCE CENTER	20	DARKROOM CHEMICALS
7	EAST OF THE SUN LOUNGE	21	DARKROOM
8	WEST OF THE MOON LOUNGE	22	TECH WORK CORRIDOR
9	DRESSING ROOMS	23	CONFERENCE ROOM
10	RESTROOM	24	FILM READING
11	VOLUNTEER'S OFFICE	25	RADIOLOGISTS' OFFICE
12	PATIENT EDUCATION / EXAM	26	STAFF LOUNGE
13	MAMMOGRAPHY ROOM	27	STAFF LOCKER ROOM
14	MEDICAL DIRECTOR	28	PRE-OP CONSULTATION

HEALTH CARE
DESIGN
CONSULTANTS

INTERIOR
ARCHITECTURE

JAIN MALKIN INC.
5070 SANTA FE STREET, STE C
SAN DIEGO CA 92109

continued on next page

Ethel Rosenthal Resource Library.
Scripps Polster Breast Care Center, La Jolla, CA
Jain Malkin Inc. (planning and interior architecture)

Photographer: Glenn Cormier, InSite (all photos)

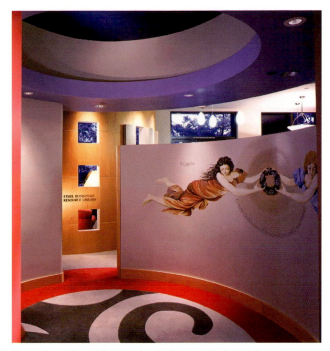

Rotunda with goddesses Hygeia (prevention) and Panacea (treatment), daughters of Aesclepius, Greek God of Healing.

Walls of the two 18-foot diameter screening and diagnostic gowned waiting lounges are lined with a thick construction of sound-absorbing material so that there is absolute quiet in these rooms, only the sounds of nature — a bubbling brook, birds chirping — can be heard from speakers concealed in the wall at shoulder level.

West of the Moon screening gowned waiting.

Commentary

continued on next page

Passing through the entry rotunda, women are greeted by a mural of Hygeia and Panacea, goddesses from fourth century Greece, underscoring the dual functions of the Center (prevention and treatment). Patients proceed to a private dressing salon. For devotees of feng shui, the granite fountain is placed so that water flows from the north and the principal accent color — geranium red — provides an extra measure of good fortune during the visit.

Trompe l'oeil mural facing East of the Sun diagnostic gowned waiting lounge.
Scripps Polster Breast Care Center, La Jolla, CA
Jain Malkin Inc. (planning and interior architecture)

Photographer: Glenn Cormier, InSite

Scripps Center for Integrative Medicine, La Jolla, CA
Jain Malkin Inc. in collaboration with Schmidt, Scanlon, Gordon Architects

Photographer: Michael Campos

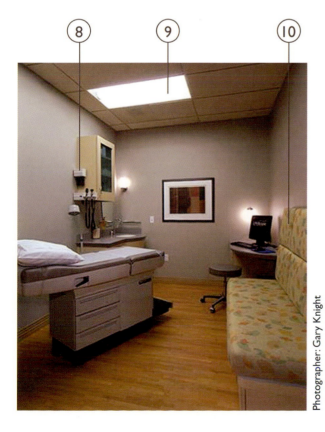

Photographer: Gary Knight

Features

1) Indirect lighting
2) Wood soffit below arched gysum board ceiling
3) Sharps container/gloves behind tambour door
4) Dressing cabinet
5) Diagnostic instruments behind tambour door
6) Vessel sink
7) Consultation area
8) Diagnostic instruments mounted to side of cabinet avoids electrical cord snaking down wall
9) Indirect "perforated basket" light fixture
10) Bench accomodates 3-4 family members; physician can easily face family when speaking

Photographer: Joel Koyama

Exam room. Mayo Clinic, Gonda Bldg., Rochester, MN
Ellerbe Becket (architecture and interior design)

Features:

1) Indirect lighting
2) X-ray film illuminator
3) Consultation desk enables physician to face patient and family
4) Note that exam rooms are mirror image layout, which has been Mayo's tradition for 100 years. This puts the physician on the patient's left side in half of the rooms (physicians are trained to examine from the patient's right side in medical school), but this lack of standardization has, according to the architects, not posed a problem for them.

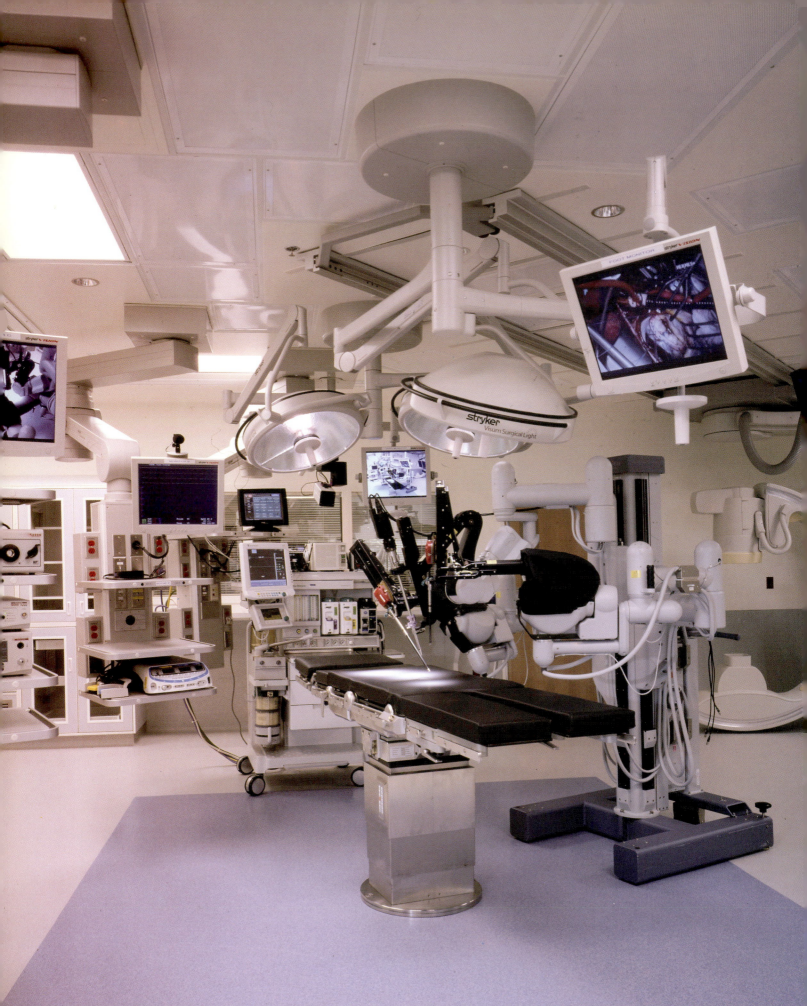

Digital Operating Suite | Providence St. Vincent Medical Center
Portland, OR. Zimmer Gunsul Frasca Partnership. Photography: Eckert & Eckert

Procedures: Fear of the Unknown 9

There are many types of procedures: endoscopy; cardiac catheterization; cardiac stenting; coronary artery bypass graft (CABG); surgical; emergency department (ED) trauma care; ED stabilization procedures for insulin shock or for pulmonary or cardiac insufficiency; tissue biopsies acquired with ultrasound or other imaging modalities, including stereotactic breast biopsies; and procedures using radiation to precisely target brain or other tumors. The list is endless, but what is common to all is the anxiety of the patient and family in anticipation of the procedure, some degree of relief when it is over, followed by anxiety about the outcome. Fear of the unknown can be as stressful for someone undergoing a colonoscopy as it can be for a cardiac cath procedure or CABG. Much has been written on the biological and physiological effects of stress (see Chapter 1). If persistent, it can lead to immune dysfunction.

A well-designed environment cannot reduce the fear associated with waiting for a biopsy or mammogram report, but it can help to reduce anxiety and create a more positive patient experience prior to and during a procedure. Since patients cannot evaluate the clinical competency of the care team, they assess the built environment and interactions with staff as a surrogate to form an impression of competency or lack thereof. A cluttered, poorly maintained reception and waiting area, for example, makes one wonder about the cleanliness of the surgical suite. The built environment sets expectations from the time one walks through the door and, even before, when one considers parking issues and wayfinding problems that often exist.

CAN A LESS STRESSFUL HOSPITAL EXPERIENCE LEAD TO BETTER POSTSURGICAL OUTCOMES?

As it turns out, there are many benefits resulting from a less-stressful hospital experience pre- and postsurgically (Kiecolt-Glaser et al. 1998). Physical and psychological comfort prior to surgery may result in less pain and use of fewer narcotic pain medications, and patients may experience less anxiety and depression and have fewer postsurgical complications such as bleeding.

An interesting journal article that discusses many studies relating to influences on surgical recovery reveals the following (Kiecolt-Glaser et al. 1998):

- Greater distress or anxiety prior to surgery is associated with a slower and more complicated postoperative recovery.
- The healing process is a cascade, and success in the later stages of wound repair is highly dependent on initial events. Immune function plays a key role in this cascade.
- Stress can alter multiple aspects of immune function.
- Even transient, relatively mild stressors can delay wound healing 24% to 40%.
- Stress-related deficits in wound repair have broad implications for surgical recovery.
- Pain, like other stressors, adversely affects immune function. Anesthetics that block transmission of neuroendocrine pain impulses are also associated with better immune function and reductions in postoperative infections.
- Fragmented sleep results in reduced GH [growth hormone] secretion, a hormone that facilitates wound healing; even one night's partial sleep loss results in elevated cortisol (a stress hormone) levels the next evening. Postsurgical sleep deprivation may itself be a significant stressor.
- Greater self-reported anxiety and stress are typically related to more severe postoperative pain.
- High preoperative fear or stress is predictive of a variety of poorer outcomes, including greater pain, longer hospital stays, more postoperative complications, and poorer treatment compliance.
- Interventions that enhance coping skills and reduce preoperative fear or stress may also modulate immune and endocrine function, in turn improving surgical recovery. Such interventions include teaching relaxation techniques to reduce pain. In a large number of studies, such strategies were shown to reduce length of stay and use of narcotic and analgesic pain medications, reduce postoperative complications, result in better treatment compliance, and decreased anxiety and stress.
- Several studies suggested that presurgical psychological status can influence physiological responses during the surgery itself…as well as the speed of physical recovery (time to open eyes) following the discontinuation of anesthesia.

High-Impact, Low-Cost Interventions

It is likely that the aforementioned research is not well known or it would result in more proactive measures and, indeed, become the standard of care for surgery patients. Surgical teams no doubt focus on their individual skills and protocols employed to keep patients safe and may underestimate the benefits of low-cost, simple presurgical preparation interventions. Cardiac surgeon Mehmet Oz, who practices at New York's Columbia Presbyterian Medical Center, has, since the mid-1990s, employed complementary therapies such as hypnotherapy, relaxation techniques, massage, reflexology (manipulation of pressure points on the feet to restore imbalances in the body), and guided imagery to relax patients prior to heart transplant and other cardiac surgeries and to keep them relaxed postsurgically (Oz 1998).

Another well-respected physician, Harvard's Herbert Benson, the creator of the Relaxation Response, believes that the placebo effect, which he calls *remembered wellness*, is 70% to 90% effective (Benson 1996). He comments: "In my 30 years of practicing medicine, I've found no healing force more impressive or more universally accessible than the power of the individual to care for and cure him- or herself." He calls self-care the third leg of a three-legged stool, the other two legs being pharmaceuticals and surgery/procedures: all three are necessary for health and well-being. Benson cautions, however, that for remembered wellness to be effective, physicians and other caregivers dispensing medication and performing procedures must believe in their efficacy and communicate this confidence to patients. In a very interesting book, Benson (1996) documents the power of belief in altering brain physiology and chemistry. More recently, a number of researchers who have been studying the placebo effect have concluded that expecting benefit can trigger the same neurological pathways of healing as real medication does (*Wall Street Journal* 2005).

The relationships between the major types of presurgical stress-reduction interventions (procedural intervention, sensory information, behavioral instruction, cognitive intervention, relaxation, hypnosis, or emotion-focused intervention) and eight outcome variables (negative affect, pain, pain medication, length of stay, behavioral and clinical indices of recovery, physiological indices, and satisfaction) were addressed in a meta-analysis by Johnston and Vögele (1993). They concluded that each of the eight outcomes showed significant benefit. Procedural information and behavioral instruction produced the most widespread improvements across all outcomes, whereas relaxation studies showed benefits for all indices except behavioral recovery (Kiecolt-Glaser et al. 1998).

Contrada, Leventhal, and Anderson (1994), in summarizing results from several meta-analyses of presurgical intervention studies (as reported in Kiecolt-Glaser 1998), found that two-thirds to three-quarters of intervention patients had better outcomes than controls with 20% to 28% improvement. Using two or more interventions (information, coping-skills training, and psychosocial support) led to even better results.

What is so remarkable is that these interventions are brief, often executed only once, and accomplish such profound benefits for patients. If this were a pharmaceutical, everyone would prescribe it and want to buy stock in this company.

In the aforementioned studies, the interventions had a median length of 30 minutes; some were individually executed while others were group sessions. Even low-cost alternatives such as booklets, audiotapes, and videotapes achieve successful results; 79% to 84% of the studies showed positive effects, and 79% were associated with a shorter length of stay, averaging 1.5 days less than control groups (Kiecolt-Glaser 1998).

THE BUILT ENVIRONMENT AS A THERAPEUTIC INTERVENTION

A less-stressful hospital experience is as much about people and processes as it is about the built environment. However, this has been discussed in previous chapters of this book. As well, throughout this book, research has been introduced documenting effects of the physical setting on reduction of stress. Clearly, patients are affected psychologically and physiologically by all aspects of the built environment, and this is why high-quality design must be carried into all patient care areas. It is not appropriate or equitable to have lobbies with two-story waterfalls and gardens, commissioned works of art, and beautiful lighting supported by patient care areas that resemble a 1980s hospital. Bereft of any design detail or healing environment amenities that would bring a measure of joy or delight to a weary or frightened patient, too many treatment areas, procedure rooms, and nursing units have suffered this fate in our newest hospitals. It was a challenge, in fact, to collect photos for this book in which design details from the lobby were extended into the "back of the house." That term is used with tongue in cheek, of course, as nothing is more important than the spaces in which patients receive treatment and care.

A good example of carrying design features from the reception/lobby into diagnostic and treatment areas is the Maria Nathanson Center of Excellence for Gastrointestinal, Pulmonary, and Renal Medicine and Research in Nashville, Tennessee (Image pages 9.1 to 9.4). All the more credit is due for accomplishing this as a remodel within existing hospital space.

The preparation and recovery area of Nebraska Orthopedic Hospital in Omaha, Nebraska, (Image page 9.13) and the postanesthesia care units (PACU) of Parker Adventist Hospital in Parker, Colorado, and Kettering Medical Center-Sycamore in Miamisburg, Ohio, (Image page 9.14) are other good examples in which color, lighting, the use of wood, and interesting ceiling design are the antithesis of stark clinical spaces. This has been accomplished without lapsing into warm and fuzzy homelike styling that seems too much of a disconnect with a high-tech clinical setting.

Previously in this chapter, research was introduced about the importance of postoperatively stabilizing a patient's stress levels as quickly as possible; we learned that stress increases during preparation for the procedure, and ramps up for several days prior to the procedure. One can connect this research to using the built environment as a therapeutic intervention to reduce stress:

- Introduce images of nature or the real thing (top photo Image page 9.12, top right Image page 9.23).
- Provide access to social support by families and by caring healthcare workers who can offer a variety of brief stress-reducing interventions that are known to be highly effective.
- Offer options for the patient to be in control, to walk into the operating room if practical (this is routinely done in ambulatory surgical centers to enhance the patient's sense of wellness), select preferred music to listen to via headset or ear buds during the procedure, or listen to a guided-imagery audiotape.
- Prepare and recover patients in private rooms (Image pages 9.20 and 9.24, top photo). This enables a family member to be present and provides maximum confidentiality for the patient. In addition, the patient does not have to listen to other patients as they are being prepped for procedures or as they awaken from anesthesia. It is stressful to overhear unwanted conversation of such an intimate nature. Private rooms greatly reduce PACU noise levels.
- Treat patients in settings with natural light when possible (Image pages 9.12, top photo; 9.13, top photo; 9.14, bottom photos; 9.20, top photo; and 9.24).
- Offer positive distractions, such as back-lit images of nature on the ceiling, whenever possible (Image pages 9.12, 9.23, 10.11, 10.12, 10.13, and 10.14).
- Eliminate environmental stressors such as glare from fluorescent fixtures placed directly over gurneys (Image pages 9.12 and 9.13) and noise (reduced by private preparation/recovery rooms and by managing telephones, monitor alarms, and other communication devices to reduce their auditory cacophony). Consider glare from direct light fixtures in corridors and elevator lobbies that serve patients on gurneys. Solutions such as those on Image pages 5.19, 7.57, 7.67, 7.68, 7.70, and 7.86 are preferable.

EMERGENCY DEPARTMENTS (EDs)

The nation's emergency care system is at the breaking point (Institute of Medicine 2007). The number of patients visiting EDs increased by 23% from 1992 to 2002, while the number of hospital EDs declined by 15% during that period (McCaig and Burt 2004). Overcrowding results in long waits and patients being stacked up in a line like airplanes in a holding pattern when inpatient beds are filled. The practice of holding them in the ED, in beds in hallways, is known as boarding, and it is not unusual for this to occur for up to 48 hours until a bed becomes available (Institute of Medicine 2007).

During this period, patients have no privacy, no place for a family member to sit, and they do not have the benefit of the expertise and specialized equipment they would get within the inpatient setting (Institute of Medicine 2007). According to a study published online in the *Annals of Emergency Medicine*, patients in this situation prefer to be boarded in inpatient hallways as opposed to the ED (*Scope* 2007). In light of the discussion earlier in this chapter about the negative effects of stress, this would seem to be high on a list of stressors and would make bunking with a roommate who moans or snores seem like nirvana next to being in a corridor with a Florence Nightingale-type movable privacy screen nestled next to the gurney or bed (one would hope the latter, not the former).

A Few Statistics (McCaig and Burt 2004)

- On average, patients spent 3.2 hours in the ED.
- Abdominal pain, chest pain, and fever are the most commonly recorded reasons for visits.
- Most commonly diagnosed condition: acute upper-respiratory infection.
- 25% of patients are seen in less than 15 minutes (Centers for Disease Control 2007).
- Just over 1% of visits result in admission to an intensive care unit or coronary care unit (Centers for Disease Control 2007).
- 12% of ED visits result in hospital admission.
- Diagnostic imaging was provided for 40.7% of visits.
- Diagnostic/screening services were provided for 86.8% of visits and procedures for 43.2% of visits.

A Call to Action

The Institute of Medicine report brief (2007) identifies five principal problems creating the crisis in the nation's EDs:

Overcrowding: Lack of universal coverage means many people use the ED for primary care or when a medical condition has gone untreated for too long and has reached urgent status.

Fragmentation: In many cities, poor coordination among emergency medical services agencies and EDs means that care is fragmented and variable.

Shortage of on-call specialists: Hospitals have difficulty in getting paid for ED services by uninsured patients, while physicians assume high risks and liability working on ED patients with whom they rarely have an existing relationship. Servicing the ED is also disruptive to private practice and family life.

Lack of disaster preparedness: Many EDs, already operating beyond capacity, are ill-equipped to handle a major disaster. Funding of this effort by the federal government has been minimal.

Shortcomings in pediatric emergency care: Children make up 27% of all visits to the ED, yet only 6% of EDs have the necessary supplies for handling pediatric emergencies and only half of EDs have even 85% of the essential supplies.

Proposed solutions to these problems are outside the scope of this book; however, the American College of Emergency Physicians and the Emergency Nurses Association are good resources for further study.

Common Risk Factors in the ED*

The emergency department is unique and unlike any other hospital department in its workflow design, staffing, organizational factors, and the high-stress physical environment. The following commonly occurring factors increase the risk of committing an error in the ED setting (Hospitals and Health Networks 2006).

1. Overcrowding
2. Multiple individuals involved in the care of a single patient
3. Patients with a high-acuity illness or injury
4. Rapid healthcare decisions under severe time constraints
5. High volume of patients and unpredictable patient flow
6. Barriers to communication with patients, families, and other health professionals
7. Interaction with multiple types of diagnostic and/or treatment technology
8. Shortage of healthcare workers
9. Increased service expectations of patients and families
10. Lack of established, long-term relationship between ED providers and ED patients
11. Role of ED as the provider of care to those who have no established source of regular healthcare
12. Rapidly expanding need for a greater knowledge base due to evolving field of healthcare
13. Uncontrollable nature of workflow (for example, surges in patient visits, frequent distractions and interruptions)
14. Declining health status of the patient population (for example, increased chronic conditions)

Emergency Rooms—the Hospital's Front Door

The ED is the hospital's front door for an increasing number of patients. Although statistics show that 12% to14% of ED patients are admitted, 40% to 80% of the hospital's patients come through the ED. This may sound confusing, but it can be explained by an example. If a hospital has 400 beds and it receives, on average, 13% of the ED's volume each day and that volume is 125 cases, 13% is 16 admits per day or 112 per week. It's easy to see how it adds up. While unable to find documented statistics on this, the author's informal survey of a dozen hospitals revealed 40% to 80% of patients were admitted by way of the ED. Those with 80% of admissions served a community with a high number of uninsured or Medicaid patients.

*Sources: Emergency Nurses Association, 2006; American College of Emergency Physicians, 2001; H&HN research, 2006.W

Creating optimal patient experiences

Despite the grim statistics about the burdens afflicting many of the nation's EDs, there is a new focus on creating optimal experiences for patients. In recognition of this being the hospital's front door and access point for a large number of patients, many of whom are insured, hospitals see a competitive advantage to be realized. Among the hospitals with luxury hotel ambience are St. Vincent's in New York City, Kettering Medical Center in Dayton, Ohio, (Image page 9.7) and Emory Crawford Long Hospital in Atlanta, to name a few (Landers 2006).

It used to be common to see EDs furnished with seating that looked like it could be hosed down if someone vomited or bled on it. Metal frames, vinyl upholstery, or the type of mesh one finds in patio furniture sends a nonverbal message that the patient's comfort is a secondary concern after maintenance. In one ED (in fact, it had just been refurbished) an 8-inch high horizontal band of acrylic wall protection was placed at an odd height where only someone's head could hit it. Upon inquiry, it was explained that this would protect the wall from hair grease. In this same ED, the visual focus of the waiting room was patients being off-loaded from ambulances. The leaders of this hospital are good people who really care about providing the best experience for their patients, they were just unaware of the impact of these decisions.

Fortunately, the newer EDs have stepped away from the hose-it-down mentality. One now sees a combination of carpet and hard-surface flooring, interesting lighting and ceiling design, coffee bars instead of vending machines, and upholstered furniture that is comfortable. Healthcare fabrics are easy to maintain and durable, although for an ED, vinyl on the seat is a good option with solution-dyed nylon or Crypton woven fabric on the back and side panels, if any. Arm caps should be wood or metal, not fabric, for ease of cleaning.

Applying healing environments research

Healing environments research can be applied to the ED waiting experience:

- Views of nature (water elements, trees, gardens) help to relieve stress (Image pages 9.5, top photo; and 9.7).
- Furniture arranged in privacy groupings enables family to sit together (Image pages 9.5, 9.6, 9.7, and 9.8). It is much less institutional than sitting in ganged-seating arranged around the perimeter.
- Positive distractions such as a fireplace (Image pages 9.7 and 9.8), a waterfall (Image page 9.5), a coffee bar, and an aquarium (Image pages 9.7 and 9.8) provide stress relief. Children enjoy watching the fish. (The ED staff often frowns on play toys for kids in this setting because they are hard to disinfect.)
- Social support from a concierge who can report on the patient's progress to family in the waiting room. Most EDs allow at least one family member to accompany a patient into the treatment core.
- Many options and choices for patients and family to restore a sense of control. These may include a meditation room, coffee bar, television area, and different styles of seating to accommodate individual preferences. An area of the waiting room with a lower lighting level may appeal to those who prefer a quiet experience, while another area with brighter lighting may have more appeal to those who wish to socialize.

- Use noise-reduction coefficient (NRC) acoustic ceiling tile to reduce noise (Image page 9.6). Locate a reception area where patients' comments cannot be overheard when they check in. Attractive room dividers (Image page 9.6) can be used to distribute seating to provide more privacy.

Healing environments research can also be applied to the treatment room. Most new EDs have all-private treatment rooms (Image pages 9.10 and 9.11) and many have televisions, DVD players, individual temperature and lighting controls, and seating for family members. Occasionally there is a rocking chair.

Typically patients entering the ED check in at a reception desk and, from there, are called to a private nurse triage room. In some EDs, nursing assessment occurs at the bedside. The goal is to get the patient into the treatment room as quickly as possible. The most serious cases will arrive by ambulance; however, ambulatory patients complaining of chest pain will get an immediate electrocardiogram (EKG) and blood tests to determine status. Innovative planning concepts for EDs are outside the scope of this book, because this is a complex subject that cannot be briefly discussed in a few pages. There are a number of well-known architects who specialize in ED design and are consultants to more generalist healthcare architects.

Because workflow is such a critical issue in ED planning, careful time and motion studies are executed to see where bottlenecks occur. Typically, waiting for laboratory results or an imaging report keeps a treatment room tied up. One solution is a subwaiting area within the treatment core where patients can sit awaiting discharge instructions. This frees up the treatment room for another patient. Putting a stat (quick results) lab in the ED also speeds up the process. A general X-ray room and even a CT scanner may be contained within the ED, which also increases throughput.

A hospital in Orlando, Florida, planning a 72-bed ED, decided to cluster the rooms with a subwaiting room for family close to each cluster. These subwaits are on an exterior wall with a lake view. Natural light flows into the ED core from this corridor, and glimpses of the lake can be seen. All rooms will be universal—same size and setup—and each will have a bathroom. Staff respite locations are integrated into the plan, which, unfortunately, was not available in time for publication of this book.

Doing an experience audit

The nature of the ED—high stress, a lot of activity—makes it a difficult environment in which to roll out a guest relations/customer service program. Physicians and nurses who select ED as a specialty thrive on the fast-paced, high-stakes, adrenalin-rush environment that is emergency medicine. In this setting, saving someone's life seems a lot more important than being nice. The goal is to make staff aware that both are important.

Doing an experience audit is discussed by Berry, Carbone, and Haeckel (2002); this is a first step to understanding where and how improvements can be made. A specific example of an audit for a university hospital ED is discussed in Chapter 5. It should also be noted that there are a number of Planetree-affiliated EDs that can serve as resources and models for patient-centered care.

A reality check

Inner-city EDs face unique problems of gang violence and many repeat customers termed "frequent flyers," that is, mentally ill homeless people, alcoholics, and drug abusers. When a gang member is shot and taken to the ED, it is not uncommon for the rival gang to show up to finish the job. For this reason, some EDs have multiple waiting rooms with cameras to separate gangs, and they have a treatment core with no windows, for fear someone will climb up and shoot through the glass. In these hospitals, armed guards are visible (even at the main entrance to the hospital) and, within a few feet of entering, one must show photo identification at the visitors' desk, whereupon a badge will be issued. This is a very different scene than at a suburban or community hospital where one can walk right by the lobby visitor/information desk and take the elevator to patient units.

Despite the extreme conditions inner-city EDs face, with a bit of searching one can find furniture and upholstery fabrics that cannot be cut with a knife; cannot be punctured, unraveled, or stained; and are impervious to inscriptions (graffiti) by pen or knife. Although it's not the friendly look hospitals would choose to have, reception staff must be protected by bullet-proof glass or decorative Lexan panels that are bullet-proof. These are an attractive option, although panels with grass and other natural materials embedded in them will reduce the necessary visibility.

SURGERY

Much has been discussed previously in this chapter about stress associated with surgery. This is surely a high-stakes stressor, with possible outcomes that include death, disfigurement, pain, functional impairment, uncertainty about length of recovery, economic losses while away from work, and perhaps changes in social roles.

Is it because of the high-stakes nature of surgery, the focus on equipment, and the interface of so many systems that surgery suites usually lack any color or design features? Or is it considered an unnecessary frill? Patients are conscious while they are being wheeled into the preparation area; why not have interesting ceilings enhanced here and there by back-lit images of nature? Why not have indirect lighting to eliminate glare in patients' eyes?

Apparently Memorial Sloan-Kettering Cancer Center in New York City thought these issues were important when developing a new surgical platform with 21 high-tech operating suites (Image pages 9.15 to 9.17). Even the scrub area has inset designs in the flooring and the adjacent corridor in the flooring; and the adjacent corridor has light sconces, color, and artwork as well as indirect lighting. The color palette and design features in the clinical areas are consistent with the reception area and physician consultation room (Image page 9.17).

Note that the operating rooms (ORs) have two shades of blue insets in the flooring. This is an aesthetically attractive feature, but it also has a functional role. It is a law of perception that, after focusing on a color, when one looks away the eye produces the after-image, which is the complementary color (a complementary color is one that is directly opposite on the color wheel). After staring at blood (red), the after-image is blue-green. If surgical scrubs weren't green (which absorbs the after-image), surgeons would see green spots whenever they looked away from the surgical site. As robotic surgery becomes more common and the surgeon is even in a different room (Image page 9.18), perhaps this will be less of an issue. Note that the digital operating suite in this photo also has a blue inset in the floor.

In new surgery platforms, there is a tendency to design the ORs as large interchangeable rooms (Image page 9.19) to achieve maximum flexibility. As more hospitals adopt interventional technologies, this flexibility will be key to not having to remodel existing surgical suites. Note that all preparation and recovery beds are private rooms in this plan (Image page 9.19).

Focus on Improving the Patient's Experience

The trend toward private preparation/recovery rooms in surgery, cardiac cath labs, and endoscopy suites (Image pages 9.13, lower photo; 9.20, and 9.24), addresses issues of privacy and makes it more comfortable for a family member to be present. The prior discussion (in this chapter) about the many benefits of psychological and physiological stress-reducing interventions prior to procedures and surgeries points to a need for private rooms, provided 20 minutes to 30 minutes can be integrated into the preparation schedule for this purpose. Preparation varies somewhat depending upon the procedure, but it is possible for the patient to be listening to an audio relaxation tape with headphones while staff members do their work. There is a listening device made for clinical use that cuts out the audio when staff members address the patient and require a response.

The Cyberknife suite on Image pages 9.22 and 9.23 demonstrates attention to the patient's experience from the initial annotated rendering prepared by the design team to the final product. The project is being completed in phases; therefore, other areas of the cancer center that one might like to see had not yet been built or photographed.

CONCLUDING REMARKS

What can be more frightening than undergoing a surgical procedure? Whether minor or major, they all carry risk associated with anesthesia, infection, errors of all types, in addition to anatomical anomalies only to be discovered once under the knife. The built environment can be a therapeutic intervention in reducing stress so that patients require less narcotic pain medication and can be discharged sooner.

Emergency departments are increasingly becoming the hospital's front door, and this is why there is a greater focus on ambiance and on the total patient experience. Hospitals across the nation are dissecting their processes to discover inefficiencies and waste in an effort to reduce wait times and achieve higher levels of patient satisfaction.

References

Benson, H. 1996. *Timeless healing: The power and biology of belief.* New York: Scribner.

Berry, L. L., L. P. Carbone, and S. H. Haeckel. 2002. Managing the total customer experience. *MIT Sloan Management Review* 43(3):85–89.

Centers for Disease Control. 2007. Emergency department visits. National Center for Health Statistics. http://www.cdc.gov/nchs/fastats/ervisits.htm.

Contrada, R. J., E. A. Leventhal, and J. R. Anderson. 1994. Psychological preparation for surgery: Marshaling individual and social resources to optimize self-regulation. In *International review of health psychology*, Vol. 3, eds. S. Maes, H. Leventhal, and J. Johnston, 219–266. New York: John Wiley & Sons.

Hospitals and Health Networks. (2006). Patient safety in the ED: A guide to identifying and reducing errors in the emergency department. http://www.hhnmag.com/hhnmag_app/jsp/articledisplay.jsp?dcrpath=HHNMAG/PubsNewsArticle/data/2006May/0605HHN_FEA_Gatefold&domain=HHNMAG.

Institute of Medicine. 2007. The future of emergency care: Dissemination workshop summaries. Washington, DC: Institute of Medicine.

Johnson, M., and C. Vögele. 1993. Benefits of psychological preparation for surgery: A meta-analysis. *Annals of Behavioral Medicine* (15):245–256.

Kiecolt-Glaser, J. K., G. G. Page, P. T. Marucha, R. C. MacCallum, and R. Glaser. 1998. Psychological influences on surgical recovery: Perspectives from psychoneuroimmunology. *American Psychologist* 53(11):1209–1218.

Landers, P. 2006. Hospital chic: The ER gets a makeover. *Wall Street Journal,* July 11.

McCaig, L., and C. W. Burt. 2004. National hospital ambulatory medical care survey: 2002 emergency department summary. *Advance data from vital and health statistics*, 340. Centers for Disease Control.

Oz, M. 1998. *Healing from the heart: A leading heart surgeon explores the power of complementary medicine.* New York: Dutton.

Scope. 2007. ED patients prefer to board in inpatient hall while waiting for room. June.

Wall Street Journal. 2005. Research links placebo effect to changes in the human brain. Nov. 29.

The Maria Nathanson Center of Excellence for Gastrointestinal, Pulmonary and Renal Medicine and Research. Nashville, TN

Photographer: Alan McGee (all photos)

Entry to Center.
Southeast Venture, LLC (architecture and interior design)

Waiting room.

Commentary

continued on next three pages

This project is an excellent example of the theme of this book: carry the design details from the lobby into the diagnostic and treatment areas to create a better, less stressful, experience for patients. According to the architect, the client articulated this intention. Located within a hospital, good wayfinding landmarks at the entry were essential. Curved metal ceilings, indirect lighting, and undulating flooring patterns expressing an Asian influence, are featured throughout. The Center is divided into three functional areas: *Education* (resource coordinator offices, library/conference room, patient education); *Procedures* (includes capsule endoscopy and minimally invasive vascular procedures – rooms have hand-painted clouds and star-shaped lights on ceiling); and *Recovery* (6 inpatient beds/8 private rooms with toilets for outpatients). For providers who feel they cannot afford to do this level of design, the cost will be a pleasant surprise.

Statistics: 8,750 SF (new), 2,450 SF (renovation); $160 SF (new), $41 SF (renovation).

Maria Nathanson Center

Courtesy: Southeast Venture, LLC

Floorplan.

Resource/Consultation Center corridor.

Photographer: Alan McGee (both photos)

Conference and resource center.

continued on next page

Maria Nathanson Center

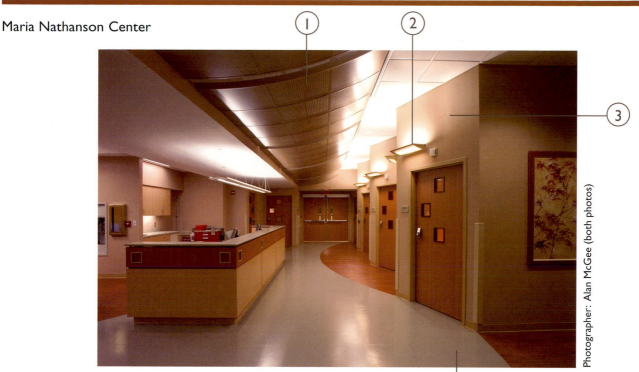

Nurse station and private recovery rooms.
Southeast Venture LLC (architecture and interior design both photos)

Photographer: Alan McGee (both photos)

Procedure corridor.

Features:

1) Perforated metal ceiling panels add design interest to a clinical area.
2) Indirect lighting (less glare)
3) Recovery rooms are "stair-stepped" to add interest, and doors have colored glass windows
4) Inset flooring design

continued on next page

Maria Nathanson Center

Photographer: Alan McGee (both photos)

Endoscopy procedure room.
Southeast Venture LLC (architecture and interior design both photos)

Inpatient recovery area. (Light fixtures are actually indirect/direct and have less glare
than depicted in photo.)

Commentary

It would have been ideal if this area had windows. Color palette and flooring inset design have been carried
into this space from other areas to provide consistency.

Photographer: Eckert & Eckert

Providence St. Vincent Medical Center, Portland, OR
Zimmer Gunsul Frasca Partnership

Photographer: Jain Malkin

Entry view. Good Samaritan Hospital, Dayton, OH
Earl Swensson Architects

◼ Commentary

This project (top photo) represented a radical change in the ED experience when it opened about 15 years ago. The retaining wall provides privacy for those waiting and the exposure to a nature setting with boulders, plants and waterfall is a response to the research indicating that nature is restorative. A more recent ED (lower photos), breaks seating into groupings, uses several types of lighting, makes good use of wood detailing and employs an appealing color palette. Design features from the main lobby carry into the ED and other destinations. Both projects on this page use carpet in the seating area. (See telephone carrels on page 9.8 that are part of this project.)

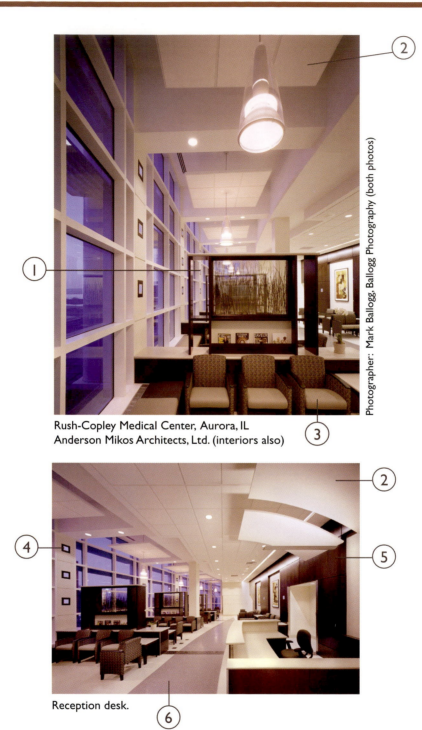

Rush-Copley Medical Center, Aurora, IL
Anderson Mikos Architects, Ltd. (interiors also)

Photographer: Mark Ballogg, Ballogg Photography (both photos)

Reception desk.

Features:

1) Seating is divided into privacy groupings by semi-open partitions that incorporate magazine display. Partitions feature resin panels embedded with tall grass.
2) Curved acoustic panels are suspended over the desk and each seating grouping.
3) Seating is faux leather, elegant but washable.
4) Small blue "squares" on exterior wall are LED lights set into wall for accent.
5) Wall behind reception desk is walnut veneer set off by art display and square blue LED lighting accents.
6) Terrazzo floor is easy to clean and highly durable.

Photographer: Andy Snow

Photographer: Andy Snow

Kettering Medical Center, Dayton, OH (both photos)
Jain Malkin Inc. with Lorenz + Williams Architects

Features:

1) Art glass accessories and books
2) Garden with audio rock (sounds of birds, frogs) and fountain
3) Salt-water aquarium; cast resin panel with wave pattern overhead
4) Carpet tile
5) Vending concealed behind curved wall
6) Variety in ceiling and lighting
7) First impressions: fireplace, cantilevered hearth (double-sided)
8) Numerous options in seating, arranged in privacy groupings
   Design incorporates research relative to access to nature; options and choices of positive distraction reduce stress as well as numerous options of types of seating, including bariatric; reduction of environmental stressors (noise, glare).

Photographer: Paul Warchol

HealthEast Woodwinds Health Campus, Woodbury, MN
NBBJ, Jain Malkin Inc. (interior design)

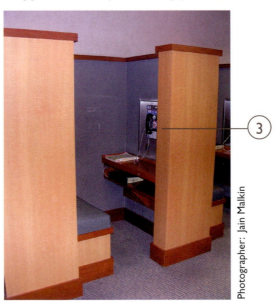

Photographer: Jain Malkin

Good Samaritan Hospital, Dayton, OH
Earl Swensson Architects

Features

1) Fireplace with cluster of lounge chairs. Different types of seating are offered to respond to individual comfort preferences. Chairs can be moved or rearranged by occupants.
2) Salt-water aquarium, a positive diversion while waiting
3) Private telephone carrels accommodate two persons and offer auditory privacy (acoustic treatment on walls).

Level 2 trauma room. Riverside Methodist Hospital, Columbus, OH
Karlsberger (architecture and interior design)

Photographer: Brad Feinknopf

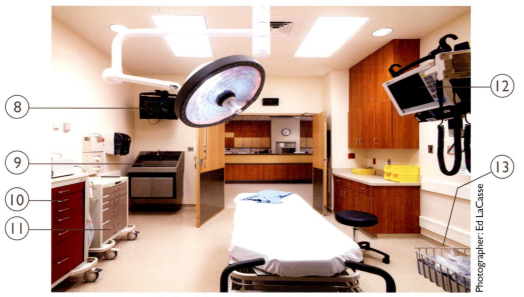

Level 3 trauma room. Parker Adventist Hospital, Parker, CO
HKS (architecture and interior design)

Photographer: Ed LaCasse

Features:

1) Ceiling-mounted radiography (note tracks) computed radiography (CR) chosen over digital because table was sturdier.
2) Control area serves two trauma rooms
3) PACS reading station
4) Passage to other trauma room for staff
5) 8-foot wide opening.
6) Color inset in floor adds nice punch of color.

7) Low air returns as in ORs (upper photo—not in view)
8) TV monitor
9) Scrub sink
10) Crash cart with portable suction
11) Supply cart
12) Physiological monitor with defibrillator
13) Basket on headwall for immediate supplies

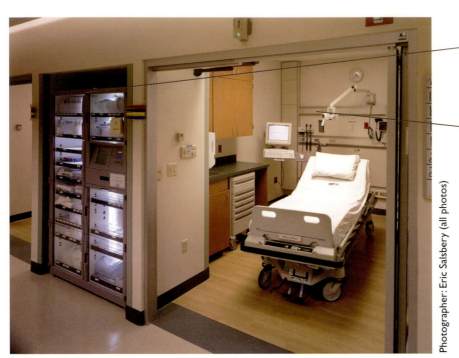

Photographer: Eric Salsbery (all photos)

Features:

1) Pyxis dispensing for supplies
2) Rail on headwall has power and medical gases
3) Decentralized workstations

Sinai Hospital ER-7, Baltimore, MD (all photos)
Anshen + Allen Architects

Commentary

This project, when opened in 1998, represented a new approach to ED design. The main waiting area had 12 individual waiting rooms so that families could have privacy, and it was a strategy for dealing with gang violence. It was also a strategy for containing the spread of infectious diseases like TB as it is easier to manage HVAC (negative pressure) in a small room. In the core area, another feature of the design was private treatment rooms and decentralized workstations. Comments offered by the medical director of the ED for this book are that the unit was designed for 55,000 visits and they currently have 80,000 visits causing them to deal with understaffing and over-volume. The multiple waiting rooms have been closed off due to security problems, even with video cameras. The decentralized workstations have been expensive to staff and do not allow for enough "cross-over" and visual overlap.

Photographer: Ed LaCasse

Staff work stations are decentralized and have good visibility into Level 3 treatment rooms.
Emory Crawford Long Hospital, Atlanta, GA
HKS, Inc. Architects (interior design also)

Photographer: Jeff Goldsberg, ESTO

Staff work stations facing private treatment rooms.
Little Company of Mary Hospital, Torrance, CA
KMD Architects

Commentary

Both facilities have private treatment rooms and good visibility from workstations. Use of wood in both projects creates a nice ambience in lieu of what is often a frightening high-tech environment for families. Both projects are mid-level community emergency centers. The project in the lower photo was designed to handle about 55,000 cases per year.

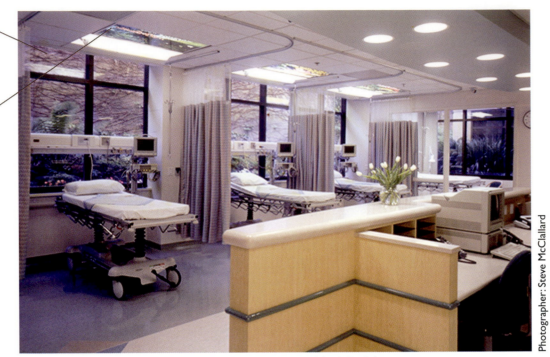

Cardiac catheterization prep area. Scripps Memorial Hospital, La Jolla, CA
Rodriguez & Park Architects and Jain Malkin Inc. (interior design)

Photographer: Steve McClallard

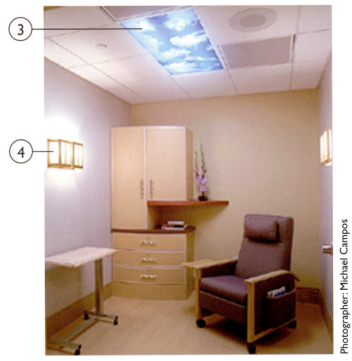

PET/CT prep room.
Scripps Center for Integrative Medicine, La Jolla, CA
Jain Malkin Inc. in collaboration with Schmidt, Scanlon,
Gordon Architects

Photographer: Michael Campos

Features:

1) Garden with retaining wall provides privacy and places garden at height of gurney
2) Views of tulip gardens in Holland are placed over each bed
3) Backlit image of sky provides some relief in a room without windows
4) Shoji-screen lantern wall sconces provide soft light

Photographer: Assassi Productions

Prep/recovery. Nebraska Orthopedic Hospital, Omaha, NE
Altus Architectural Studios

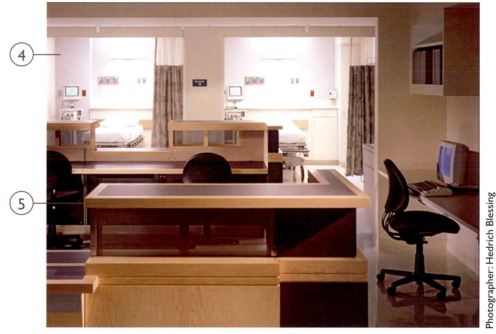

Photographer: Hedrich Blessing

Endoscopy recovery. St. Francis Hospital, Boston, MA
TRO/The Ritchie Organization

Features:

1) Interesting ceiling, soffits, lighting
2) Natural light
3) Flooring pattern, color palette and nurse station design are consistent with lobby and nursing unit
4) Private rooms, good acoustic integrity, good visibility from nurse station
5) Punch of color and wood trim add interest

Post-anesthesia care unit. Parker Adventist Hospital, Parker, CO
HKS Inc. (architecture and interior design)

Photographer: Ed LaCasse

Kettering Medical Center-Sycamore,
Miamisburg, OH
Lorenz + Williams Architects
in collaboration with Jain Malkin Inc.

Photographer: Jain Malkin

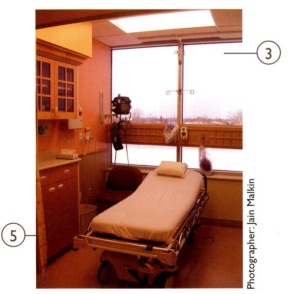

Kettering Medical Center-Sycamore, Miamisburg, OH
Lorenz + Williams Architects in
collaboration with Jain Malkin Inc.

Photographer: Jain Malkin

Photographer: Jain Malkin

Features:

1) Wood tones, soffits, and lighting aesthetically enhance the space; design detailing from lobby and nursing areas has been carried into procedure and treatment spaces.
2) Nurses document at the bedside in tablet arm chairs
3) Access to natural light
4) Interesting ceiling design over nurse station; cheerful color palette
5) High-impact edges of oak casework protected with Corian

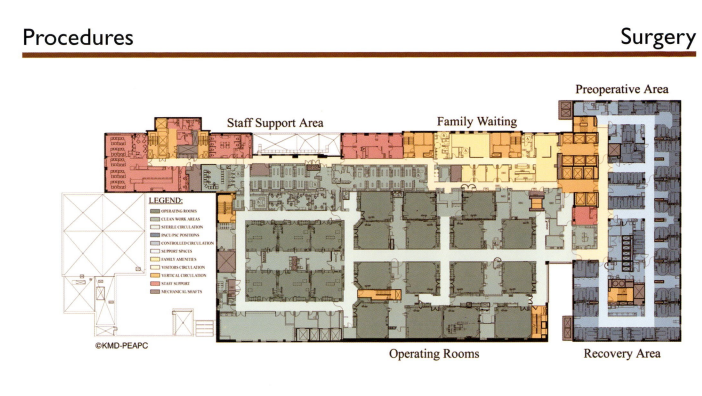

Total Floor Area: 72,000 sf
New Construction: 21,000 sf

MEMORIAL SLOAN-KETTERING
SURGICAL PLATFORM

Surgical platform with 21 high-tech operating suites. Memorial Sloan-Kettering Cancer Center, New York, NY
KMD in association with Perkins Eastman Architects
Granary Associates, Executive Architect and Project Manager

Commentary

continued on next page

Each cluster of 3 - 4 operating rooms has its own supply and core area. The construction occurred over an occupied space, including existing surgical suites. It involved building a massive truss and super-column structure without compromising the hospital's existing operations. (This was designed by Granary Associates in a previous project.)

Corian scrub sinks. Memorial Sloan-Kettering Cancer Center, New York, NY
KMD in association with Perkins Eastman Architects (all photos)
Granary Associates, Executive Architect and Project Manager

Photographer: Chuck Choi

Main corridor to surgery.

Photographer: Chuck Choi

OR for robotic minimally invasive surgery using Intuitive Surgical's da Vinci robot.

Photographer: Paul Warchol

OR with "green" light makes it easier to see monitors during robotic surgery. This is the final design based on prototype model.

Photographer: Chuck Choi

Commentary

continued on next page

Indirect lighting keeps glare out of patients' eyes as they are wheeled to surgery (top photos). Protective wall features are nicely integrated. Although the patient can't see the inset patterns in the flooring, they are likely to be appreciated by the surgeons and nurses who traverse this corridor. Even more unusual, is the presence of artwork and wall sconces in a surgical corridor.

Photographer: Chuck Choi (both photos)

Reception. Memorial Sloan-Kettering Cancer Center, New York, NY (both photos)
KMD in association with Perkins Eastman Architects; Granary Associates,
Executive Architect and Project Manager

Physician consultation room.

Commentary

continued on next page

It's rare to see design details that are introduced in the reception/visitor waiting area carried into the surgical corridor (see next page). Ample use of wood warms up the space. Varied lighting and ceilings add interest.

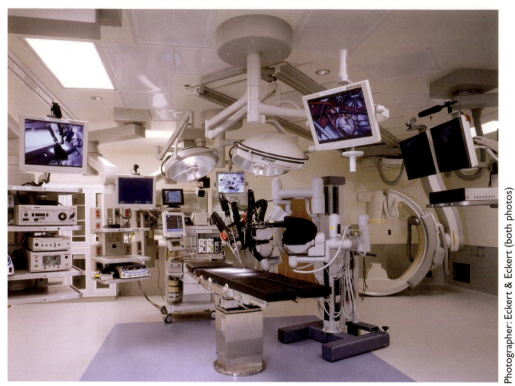

Photographer: Eckert & Eckert (both photos)

Digital operating suite. Providence St. Vincent Medical Center, Portland, OR (both photos)
Zimmer Gunsul Frasca Partnership

Surgeon operates the robot from control room.

Features:

1) The first robotic-assisted cardiac surgery west of the Mississippi River was performed here. Includes 31 x 31 foot OR with adjoining control and viewing rooms.
2) Utilizes Intuitive Surgical's da Vinci surgical system. Includes surgeon's console, patient side cart, high-performance vision system, and additional instrumentation.
3) Digital OR features ceiling-mounted C-arm fluoroscopy.
4) Adjacent five-person viewing room features two flat screen monitors.

Courtesy KMD Architects

Interventional platform. Heart and Vascular Institute and Critical Care Building
Hoag Memorial Hospital, Newport Beach, CA
KMD Architects

Commentary

The first floor of the new tower is dedicated to the interventional platform with 14 interchangeable "boxes" all 750 SF in size. Offering maximum flexibility, these ORs can be built-out as interventional, hybrid, or high-tech operating rooms. Adjacent is a 30-station prep/recovery suite. The second floor contains 14 inpatient ORs and a 30-bed prep/recovery suite. Refer to page 7.61 for inpatient nursing unit layout.

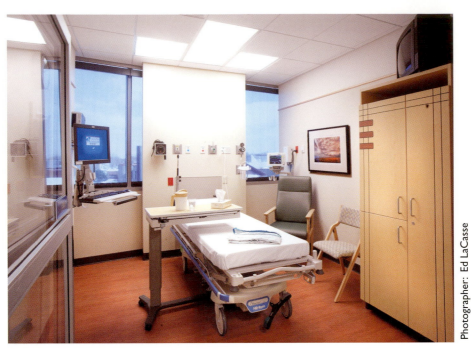

Private prep and recovery room. Abbott Northwestern Heart Hospital, Minneapolis, MN
HKS, Inc. (interior design also)

Photographer: Ed LaCasse

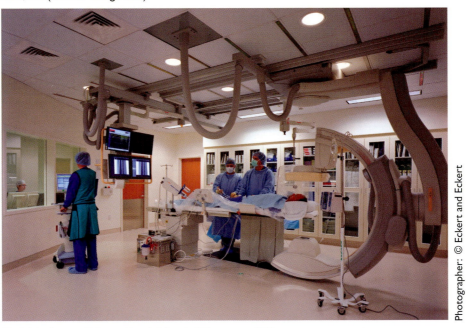

Cath lab. Legacy Salmon Creek Hospital, Vancouver, WA
Zimmer Gunsul Frasca Partnership

Photographer: © Eckert and Eckert

Features:

1) In top photo, natural light, artwork, and seating for family make these private rooms patient-centered.
    The cabinet has the same detailing as that in patient rooms, nurse stations and procedure areas.
2) Also in top photo, left side of cabinet contains gowns and linens; door with lock on right side
    is for patient's belongings.

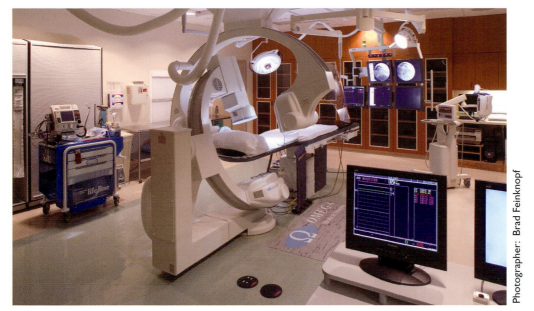

Photographer: Brad Feinknopf

Electrophysiology lab. The McConnell Heart Hospital at Riverside Methodist Hospital, Columbus, OH
Karlsberger (architecture and interior design)

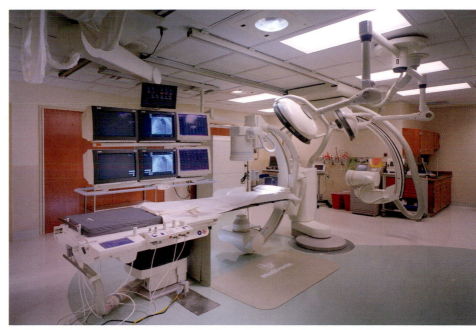

Photographer: Brad Feinknopf

Cardiac catheterization lab. Heart Center Mount Carmel East, Columbus, OH
Karlsberger (architecture and interior design)

Commentary

Top photo: The room is set-up to be as flexible as possible with most of the floor space open. The room is entered from two directions—one for patients along a private corridor and the other for staff from the sub-sterile area which connects to other labs for staff support. This room is designed to cath lab standards for flexible expansion. Supplies are located in the custom wood cabinets along footwall. Both rooms have monitors on a boom and inset flooring incorporating an accent color (centered around the table) and C-arm radiography unit.

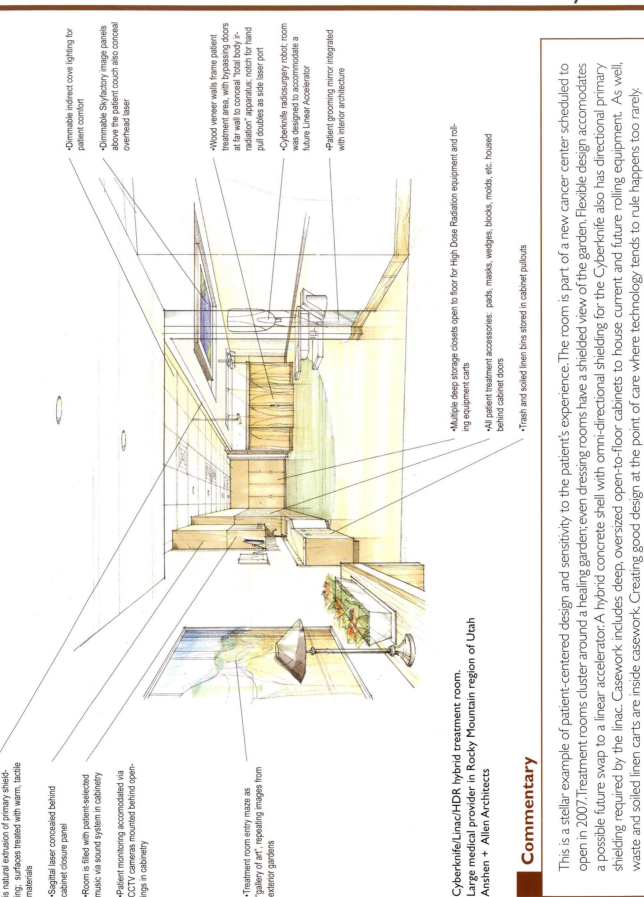

- Patient treatment area within room is natural extrusion of primary shielding; surfaces treated with warm, tactile materials
- Sagittal laser concealed behind cabinet closure panel
- Room is filled with patient-selected music via sound system in cabinetry
- Patient monitoring accomodated via CCTV cameras mounted behind openings in cabinetry

- Treatment room entry maze as "gallery of art", repeating images from exterior gardens

- Dimmable indirect cove lighting for patient comfort
- Dimmable Skyfactory image panels above the patient couch also conceal overhead laser

- Wood veneer walls frame patient treatment area, with bypassing doors at far wall to conceal "total body irradiation" apparatus; notch for hand pull doubles as side laser port
- Cyberknife radiosurgery robot; room was designed to accommodate a future Linear Accelerator
- Patient grooming mirror integrated with interior architecture

- Multiple deep storage closets open to floor for High Dose Radiation equipment and rolling equipment carts
- All patient treatment accessories: pads, masks, wedges, blocks, molds, etc. housed behind cabinet doors
- Trash and soiled linen bins stored in cabinet pullouts

Cyberknife/Linac/HDR hybrid treatment room.
Large medical provider in Rocky Mountain region of Utah
Anshen + Allen Architects

Commentary

This is a stellar example of patient-centered design and sensitivity to the patient's experience. The room is part of a new cancer center scheduled to open in 2007. Treatment rooms cluster around a healing garden; even dressing rooms have a shielded view of the garden. Flexible design accomodates a possible future swap to a linear accelerator. A hybrid concrete shell with omni-directional shielding for the Cyberknife also has directional primary shielding required by the linac. Casework includes deep, oversized open-to-floor cabinets to house current and future rolling equipment. As well, waste and soiled linen carts are inside casework. Creating good design at the point of care where technology tends to rule happens too rarely.

Simulator room.
Intermountain Health, Huntsman Cancer Center, Salt Lake City, UT
Anshen + Allen Architects (all photos)

Radiation therapy.

Photographer: David Wakely (all photos)

Gowned waiting area overlooks garden.

Dressing area: dressing rooms are just beyond entry casework.

Commentary

These photos depict the first areas to be completed in this large cancer center. On a previous page, a rendering for the Cyberknife suite describes the attention to patient comfort that is the basis for all patient care areas. The radiation therapy room above (identical in room design and amenities to the Cyberknife suite yet to be completed) has the latest Varian accelerator with on-board fluoroscopy (the "arms" on sides of table). Cabinet doors/drawers are opened to show that everything is stored neatly out of patient view.

Photographer: Gary Kessel

Endoscopy prep/recovery room. Massachusetts General Hospital, Boston, MA
TRO/The Ritchie Organization

Photographer: Gary Kessel

Exam room. Massachusetts General Hospital, Boston, MA
TRO/The Ritchie Organization

Commentary

Both rooms are cheerful and have natural light. Private endoscopy prep and recovery rooms offer the maximum in HIPPA compliance and preserve a patient's dignity. The exam room desktop enables the provider to face the patient while taking a history or discussing a diagnosis.

Radiation Therapy Suite | Windsor Regional Cancer Center
Windsor, ON. Vermeulen/Hind Architects. Photography: Ben Rahn/A-Frame

Cancer Treatment: Touching the Spirit | 10

No word strikes terror in our hearts quite as much as the word *cancer.* Initially the news is perceived as a death sentence and, for some, it ultimately is. Occasionally the disease may be permanently arrested, yet for others it recurs, requiring periodic courses of radiation therapy or chemotherapy. Surgery is often the first step in what is, for some, a long journey. Early diagnosis and treatment by a multidisciplinary team of specialists is essential for success, but also important is the patient's psychological attitude, which can be influenced positively or negatively by the environment in which treatment is provided.

PSYCHOLOGICAL AND BEHAVIORAL ISSUES ASSOCIATED WITH CANCER

If patients are hospitalized for medical or surgical treatment of cancer, the issues raised in Chapter 7 of this book will be relevant. The diagnosis of cancer does not create a need for specialized patient rooms except for bone marrow transplantation and hemopoietic stem cell transplants (HSCT), which require positive air pressure and exquisite attention to infection-control measures, because these patients are immunocompromised (have suppressed immune systems). It is outside the scope of this book to discuss the planning of such spaces except to say that psychological and behavioral issues factor prominently into the design of the facility. [For an in-depth discussion of cancer treatments, psychological, and other issues, see Malkin 1992.]

Research in psychoneuroimmunology demonstrates that the mind can have a powerful effect on the course of treatment. At least 100 books have been written for patients to guide them in dealing with cancer. Most notably, books by Bernie Siegel have made us aware of an individual's potential for self-healing (not as a substitute for medical care, but as an adjunct to it). Siegel's nonprofit organization, Exceptional Cancer Patients, founded in 1978, promotes a specific form of individual and group therapy using patients' dreams, drawings, and images to facilitate personal change and healing. His books and lectures have helped many cancer patients to live full lives one day at a time.

Elisabeth Kubler-Ross: The Five Stages of Response

Although each cancer patient is unique, and individual personality traits to some degree determine how each person will deal with the disease, certain common physical and psychological symptoms are imposed by the life-threatening nature of the disease and treatment protocols. Elisabeth Kubler-Ross (1969, 1972) defined the five stages of response as denial, anger (why me?), depression, acceptance, and bargaining.

Other psychological factors associated with a diagnosis of cancer include:

Anticipatory grief: Preparation for future loss of one's life, body part, or function; anticipation of pain.

Depression: A response to onset of the disease; a coping mechanism for dealing with anxiety.

Uncertainty: The patient may not know for a period of years whether the disease has been effectively arrested; uncertainty about the future can be difficult for the victim and his or her family.

Isolation: The "why me?" phenomenon causes feelings of separation and isolation at the start of the illness. Friends are reluctant to talk about the disease for fear they will say the wrong thing. For terminally ill patients, social isolation increases as friends, family, and sometimes even physicians or caregivers withdraw to protect themselves from anguish and a feeling of failure.

Touching the Spirit

While one is being treated for cancer or when one becomes a cancer survivor, there is a lot of camaraderie in the form of support groups, national events such as walks for breast cancer, and identification with the disease and others who may be undergoing treatment. During treatment, it is so important to keep mind, body, and spirit aligned. The reflection space at the Assarian Cancer Center in Novi, Michigan, (Image page 10.1) is an excellent example of how a space can be designed to touch the spirit.

Connecting patients to nature is another strategy for touching the spirit. Previous chapters of this book have presented research about the importance of nature for human well-being and restoration after a stressful event.

A garden visible from cancer-treatment spaces, especially chemotherapy infusion, is a welcome distraction (Image pages 5.14, 10.4, 10.7, 10.8, and 10.10). In radiation therapy rooms, simulated views of nature can be introduced in the ceiling (Image pages 10.11, 10.12, 10.13, and 10.14). Water is soothing, both the sound and the touch of it (Image pages 5.16 and 5.17).

Even when a garden view is unavailable, interesting ceilings give patients something to look at (Image page 10.3, top left photo; 10.8, top photo; and 10.9). Partitions separating rooms or treatment areas may have cast glass with flowers and other naturalistic images along with quotations celebrating hope and courage. This can be an expression of the healthcare organization's culture of healing and encourage the patient to find the placebo within (Image page 5.10).

DESIGN CONSIDERATIONS

Because radiation therapy and chemotherapy involve a series of treatments that may extend from two weeks to three months, there are unique design considerations around issues of socialization, privacy, territoriality, waiting, and sense of control.

Socialization versus Privacy

Patients should have the option of socializing or enjoying privacy in the chemotherapy setting. The same individual may prefer either option, depending on how he or she feels on a particular day. Many chemotherapy facilities have patients arrayed in chairs, placed closely together, in a large room. Often there is one common television, which means there is a loss of control without options. In settings like this, nurses will often say that patients much prefer being able to chat as opposed to having an option for a private space.

However, research indicates (see Chapter 1) that having choices reduces stress. Individual treatment stations (Image page 10.2) enable patients to have their own television, DVD player, and a place for personal belongings. This caters to the human need to stake out and create boundaries around one's personal space. Patients who are feeling ill or tired may be treated in totally private infusion rooms as in Image page 10.3, lower photo. A large private treatment room can be seen in the top photo, Image page 10.5, while considerably larger-than-standard open bay spaces can be seen in the lower photo Image page 10.5. The Hansen Center at Margaret Mary Community Hospital in Batesville, Indiana, offers garden views and the choice of privacy or socialization by virtue of a sliding glazed door.

Gowning

Gowning is a significant part of the treatment protocol in radiation therapy because it symbolizes the transfer from autonomy to committing oneself for treatment. Separate men's and women's dressing/gowned waiting areas should be provided to address issues of privacy and modesty. Wearing a gown may produce anxiety for patients whose cultural backgrounds have strong taboos about nudity or for those who are disfigured by surgery. The patient's personal standard of modesty dictates the level of comfort or discomfort experienced. The dressing room should have a door that can be locked, a secure place for personal belongings, a bin for the soiled gown and robe, a bench, and a mirror. (Note: The Joint Commission on Accreditation of Healthcare Organizations [the Joint Commission] does not allow a stack of clean gowns to be placed in a dressing room on an open shelf; they must be in an enclosed cabinet for reasons of hygiene. A clean gown can be handed to the patient or the patient can take one from inside a cabinet.) A carpeted floor is desirable in a dressing room, provided there is a commitment to clean it properly and often enough. Patients are normally weighed after gowning to achieve consistency from one treatment to the next. The combination of gown and bathrobe helps gowned patients feel more comfortable and not quite as vulnerable.

Personal Comfort

There are many types of recliner chairs designed for healthcare use. To be practical for chemotherapy, it must be able to go into trendelenburg (head lower than the heart) position. These chairs may have an attached pole for hanging bags of infusion drugs, although a mobile stand is generally preferable as it allows the patient to get up and move around or use the restroom. The chair depicted on Image page 10.6 has a lift mechanism, an option for heating the chair, a personal DVD player, and a tray table for work or snacks. Patients may spend many hours in these chairs, so comfort and ease of operation are very important.

DESIGNING THE PATIENT-CENTERED FACILITY

The benefits of a reduced-stress environment have been well-documented in Chapter 1. A hospital that implemented a number of cosmetic renovations to create more of a healing environment saw a remarkable decline in patients' self-administered use of narcotics. Patients with sickle-cell anemia used 53% less pain medication in the renovated unit, and radical prostatectomy patients used 23% less narcotics (Oncology Roundtable 2004).

Amenities

The newest cancer centers are offering a number of amenities to create a better experience for patients and their families. This includes stylish coffee bars and gift shops that offer wigs, scarves, and prostheses. This requires a private dressing room with a big mirror and flattering shadow-free lighting where these items can be fitted. Often these shops have interesting jewelry, hats, and trinkets that are whimsical and a boost to the spirit. In larger cancer centers, a retail pharmacy may be located there for patient convenience. Resource centers used to be common in cancer and breast centers but, because so many people have Internet access at home, they are sometimes not well-utilized. If patient volume warrants, a resource librarian may work out of an office to assist patients in finding appropriate books, videos, DVDs, and websites or to gather journal articles on specific types of cancer or treatment protocols for individual patients.

Exam rooms are getting larger because it is common for family members to accompany patients. Providing an audio recording device to capture what the physician is saying is helpful because patients are sometimes so stressed that they don't remember what was actually said when they arrive home. This enables them to hear it again and lets family hear it verbatim.

Small things can make a difference in feeling nurtured. Since fragrance preferences are very personal, aromatherapy diffused through the HVAC system may be less successful than offering a variety of aromatherapy scents that can be sprayed on a pillow case or other object in the immediate vicinity of the patient. While aromatherapy uses expensive highly distilled essential oils and the sprays are inexpensive—often synthetic—agents, they can still be successful in reducing stress if the scent is individually pleasing and offers choice to the patient. Some cancer centers have employed aromatherapy diffusers with the scent of vanilla to reduce nausea.

Complementary therapies

Mainstream acceptance of complementary therapies has steadily increased. The most utilized therapies are presented in Table 10.1.

Most Utilized Complementary Therapies	Table 10.1
Massage therapy	47%
Stress management	40%
Yoga	37%
Relaxation techniques	32%
Pastoral counseling	29%
Acupuncture	21%
Biofeedback	20%
Source: Oncology Roundtable (2004)	

Sixty percent of complementary and alternative medicine (CAM) programs are profitable, and startup costs are not significant (49% of hospital programs spent $150,000 or less) according to the American Hospital Association (Oncology Roundtable 2004).

Toolkit for cancer patients

A nurse-architect at HGA Architects, which is based in Minneapolis, Minnesota, developed a mock-up of a toolkit for cancer patients. The small binder was covered in a beautiful fabric. The goal of the kit was to define the steps in a patient's journey. It included photos of the patient's care team, a CD with the medical record, a compilation of diaries written by oncology patients, notes on how to access the treatment plan online, maps of the hospital campus, and an identification card for the patient's dashboard providing free parking.

Patient navigator

A patient navigator helps patients coordinate their care, booking consultations and appointments on different campuses, if required, and linking the patient to social workers and psychological counseling. Doing this for oneself can be overwhelming to patients already depleted by aggressive treatment modalities, worries about family, missing work, and finances. The navigator, often an oncology nurse, can be a lifeline of support for patients.

Patient safety

Patient safety has been discussed in detail in Chapter 3 and throughout this book. Boston's Dana-Farber Cancer Institute (2007b) implemented patient safety rounds to manage risk. A toolkit is available to share with other organizations. The patient safety team for each unit is led by the institute's risk manager and includes the unit's nurse manager or charge nurse, a pharmacist, and a clinical champion, and a member of the staff who serves as a liaison between the team and staff on the unit. Patients are also involved in patient rounds to deal with patients' concerns about safety.

FAMILY-CENTERED CARE

The Institute for Family-Centered Care helped the Dana-Farber Cancer Institute to develop an ideal experience for patients and families in the adult oncology program (Dana-Farber 2007a). Patients and families had key roles in program development, which resulted in these initiatives:

- The formation of a pain and symptom management team
- The development of the Zakim Center for Integrative Medicine
- Input into hospice care and how to structure psychosocial programming
- The development of programs to deal with end-of-life situations
- The development of hospital policies and procedures such as visiting policies, the admissions process, and the handling of emergency care for cancer patients
- Participation in the planning of new facilities: outpatient infusion and radiation therapy, family resource center
- Creation of the Arts and Environment Committee to review furniture, fixtures, fabric, art, and signage
- Involvement in staff recruitment and training
- Development of a curriculum for oncology fellows that focuses on communication and information sharing and educational sessions for surgical residents and fellows

The Patient and Family Advisory Council

The Patient and Family Advisory Council was formed to provide input on the hospital's quality improvement measures. Members of this council participated in a Joint Commission survey; they review falls and accidents, medication errors, and patient survey results. The council was instrumental in changing the billing system and the ways information is shared with families and patients. Other successful endeavors included improving parking for ambulatory patients and reducing clinic waiting times; the data they collected and studied and their recommendations for change had a significant impact on clinic policies and expectations of physicians and other staff (Dana-Farber 2007a). Finally, a quarterly newsletter called *Side by Side* is written and edited by members of the advisory council.

So often healthcare organizations say they embrace family-centered principles, but much of the time it's a token effort in which patients are surveyed for opinions but the input changes policies not at all or very superficially. Kudos to Dana-Farber for truly partnering with patients and families. The Institute for Family-Centered Care (http://www.familycenteredcare.org) is a valuable resource for healthcare organizations that really want to reach out to families.

A MODEL OF CARE WORTH NOTING

Comprehensive Cancer Care in Windsor, Ontario, Canada, is a provincial system operating eight regional cancer centers. Ninety percent of these facilities have wet-bench research. The care is organized around the goal of preventing hospitalization with ambulatory centers ranging from 65,000 to 300,000 square feet. The largest center has 20 linear accelerators and 70 exam rooms (Faven and Vermeulen 2001).

Linac rooms (approximately 900 square feet) are designed with maximum shielding to accommodate new technology, and room utilities have been designed to be flexible for any vendor. All exam rooms double as small procedure rooms. An interesting feature of the therapy rooms is that they are doorless. An active infrared beam facing two entry points reacts to movement that shuts down the machine. There is a 10-second delay between activating the machine before it starts up. The doorless design is 17% larger, but the cost was a wash in the end as the extra concrete was offset by not having the expense of the door. The walls are lined with special material to absorb neutrons.

Other features of these clinics are electronic medical records, exceptionally nice design features, and pharmacists who consult directly with patients. Art glass is used in corridors and core areas have high ceilings. Many rooms have views of gardens and water elements. There are no direct fluorescent fixtures; wherever possible, cove lights and downlights are used. An example of this design can be seen on Image page 10.13, top photo.

CONCLUDING REMARKS

Cancer treatment can be brutal to the body and the spirit. A lifetime fear of the dangers of radiation must give way in an instant to regarding it as therapeutic. In the treatment room, the patient is at the mercy of the machine and the technologist; autonomy is impossible. The tedium of rounds of chemotherapy, sitting in a chair tethered to pumps that diffuse toxic chemicals, sometimes for the better part of a day, can be debilitating. The patient- and family-centered initiatives embraced by cancer centers, along with beautifully designed facilities, help to restore dignity and a sense of control, as well as help patients achieve unity of mind, body, and spirit.

References

Dana-Farber. 2007a. Family-centered care in an adult oncology program. http://www.familycenteredcare.org/profiles/prof-danafarber.html (accessed July 14, 2007).

Dana-Farber. 2007b. Implementing Dana-Farber Cancer Institute patient safety rounds in your organization—A toolkit. http://www.dana-farber.org/pat/patient-safety/patient-safety-resources/patient-rounding-toolkit.html (accessed April 9, 2007).

Faven, L., and F. Vermeulen. 2001. Cancer care, a Canadian model: Comprehensive cancer treatment through patient-focused multidisciplinary care. Presentation at National Symposium on Healthcare Design, Nashville, TN.

Kubler-Ross, E. 1969. *On death and dying*. New York: Macmillan.

Kubler-Ross, E., E. Wesslav, and L. Avioli. 1972. On death and dying. *Journal of the American Medical Association*: 221:174–79.

Malkin, J. 1992. *Hospital interior architecture*. New York: John Wiley & Sons.

Oncology Roundtable: Future Cancer Care Strategy. 2004. Marina del Rey, CA.

Photographer: Hedrich Blessing (all photos)

Reflection space. Assarian Cancer Center at Providence Cancer Institute, Novi, MI (all photos)
Albert Kahn Associates, Inc.

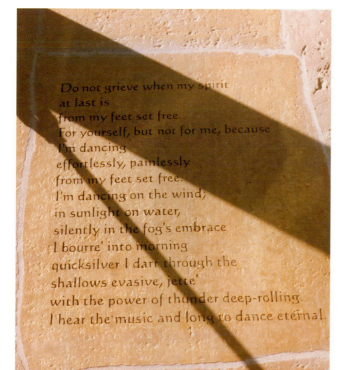

Do not grieve when my spirit
at last is
from my feet set free.
For yourself, but not for me, because
I'm dancing
effortlessly, painlessly
from my feet set free.
I'm dancing on the wind;
in sunlight on water,
silently in the fog's embrace
I bourre' into morning
quicksilver I dart through the
shallows evasive, jette'
with the power of thunder deep-rolling.
I hear the music and long to dance eternal.

Inscription detail, stone floor.

Commentary

A glass-enclosed area, 40-feet in diameter, the Center's Reflection space offers patients and their families a place for spiritual and emotional healing. Mankato stone structures of varying sizes, along with inscriptions carved into the Mankato stone floor, "lead" a person through the stages of one's life journey. In the center of the space, a small "healing pool" represents the Biblical Pool of Bethesda whose waters, when stirred, were believed to have cured the sick. The pool is periodically stirred by drops of water coming from a steel rod that connects the pieces of the stained glass mobile.

Photographer: Tom Crane

Photographer: Tom Crane

Memorial Sloan-Kettering Cancer Center, Commack, NY
Ewing Cole Architects

Features:

1) Art glass privacy dividers introduce color and pattern
2) Indirect lighting
3) Good use of wood to add warmth
4) Non-clinical lighting (pendant fixture)
5) Natural light; landscape views
6) Work surface for patients
7) Individual TVs and VCRs
8) Storage for supplies
9) Storage for patient's belongings
10) Wood ceiling creates interest for reclined patients
11) Design features start in lobby and are applied consistently throughout patient treatment areas.

Research

A missed opportunity here is not making the window operable in the partition between chairs. This would have given the patient access to additional social interaction if desired. A choice of privacy versus socialization gives the patient control which reduces stress. Access to views of nature are available. Personal TV/VCR optimizes choice. Glare from overhead lighting (a stressor) has been avoided.

Photographer: Steve McClallard

Lucy Curci Cancer Center at Eisenhower
Medical Center, Rancho Mirage, CA
Jain Malkin Inc. interior design in collaboration with
Moon Mayoras Architects

Photographer: Steve McClallard

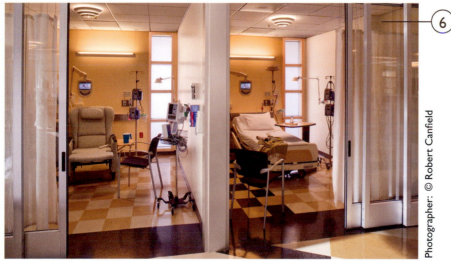

Photographer: © Robert Canfield

Private infusion rooms.
Rebecca and John Moores Cancer Center. UC San Diego Medical Center, La Jolla, CA
Zimmer Gunsul Frasca Partnership (architecture and interior design)

Features:

1) Interesting ceiling gives patients something to look at.
2) High noise reduction acoustic tile
3) View of garden
4) Wood-look vinyl floor adds to non-institutional ambience.
5) Patient's handwash sink (used prior to treatment) and beverage station
6) Privacy is a nice option, but patients can't look out windows.

NURSE STATION

Photographer: Jeff Miles © Hedrich Blessing

Patients have option of privacy or socialization.
The Hansen Center, Margaret Mary Community Hospital, Batesville, IN
BSA LifeStructures; Maregatti Interiors

Photographer: © Hedrich Blessing

View of garden from treatment room.

Commentary

Patients have views of nature through large expanses of glass; they have the option of privacy or socialization by closing or opening the sliding door between chairs.

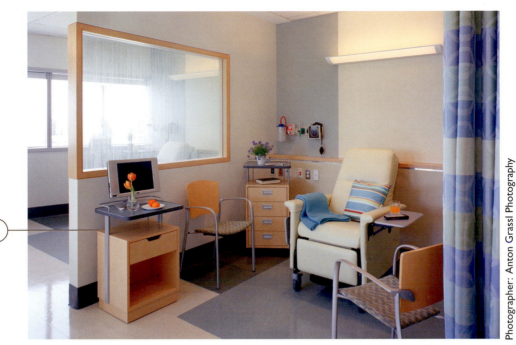

Photographer: Anton Grassl Photography

Yawkey Center for Outpatient Care at Massachusetts General Hospital, Boston, MA
Perkins+Will (architecture and interior design)

Photographer: Chris Little Photography

Infusion. Edwards Comprehensive Cancer Center, Cabell Huntington Hospital, Huntington, West Virginia
Perkins+Will (architecture and interior design)

Features:

1) Generously sized private treatment rooms have ample space for family or friends
2) Nurse station (out of view)
3) Chair for family member
4) High windows behind patient chair bring in natural light but not view
5) Supply cart
6) Open shelves for patient's belongings behind chair (out of view)

Personal DVD player.

Lift assist feature.

Warm seat and lumbar support (oval in center of back).

Reclines to flat position and beyond to trendelenburg.

Commentary

The Oncology Care Chair by IoA Healthcare Furniture is an example of a chair that offers a few new features as vendors try to improve the patient's experience. The personal DVD player is removable for security storage at night; the tray table folds flush to the side of the chair when not in use; it also features a heated seat and lumbar support (ideal for dialysis patients as well). The chair is motorized and adjusts to a flat position, trendelenburg, and has a lift feature.

Photographer: © Robert Canfield

Bamboo garden. Rebecca and John Moores Cancer Center at
UC San Diego Medical Center, La Jolla, CA
Zimmer Gunsul Frasca Partnership (all photos); Katherine Spitz (landscape architect)

Photographer: Nick Merrick © Hedrich Blessing

First floor clinic corridor with view into bamboo garden. Note the ceiling and
innovative lighting.

Commentary

continued on next page

A consistent vocabulary of design details introduced in the lobby follow into many treatment areas.
Especially notable is the bamboo garden (the bamboo had yet to reach substantial height when photos were
taken). It is truly an oasis for staff and patients. Upper floors are research labs that enable translational research
to be brought into the clinical setting.

Oncology waiting room.
Rebecca and John Moores Cancer Center at UC San Diego Medical Center, La Jolla, CA
Zimmer Gunsul Frasca Partnership (architect and interior design)

Photographer: © Robert Canfield

Stress-relieving oasis in clinic corridor. Looks onto bamboo garden.
Rebecca and John Moores Cancer Center at UC San Diego Medical Center, La Jolla, CA
Ziimmer Gunsul Frasca Partnership (architect and interior design)

Photographer: © Robert Canfield

Commentary

The gardens, on two levels, (see previous page) offer: areas for socialization and contemplation; shade as well as sun; bamboo plus a number of low shrubs and water elements. The oncology waiting room (above) has interesting ceilings, access to the garden, and a nice mix of texture and color. The focus on a garden throughout this building is based on the copious amounts of research (by Ulrich, Kaplan, and others) demonstrating the stress-reducing benefits of a view of, and contact with, nature.

Photographer: Chris Little

AFLAC Cancer Center at Children's Health Care of Atlanta
(outpatient center for blood disorders).
Perkins+Will (architecture and interior design)

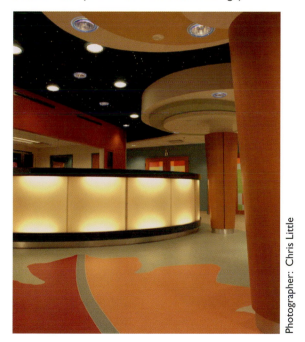

Photographer: Chris Little

Commentary

This facility exudes happiness and joie de vivre. Why shouldn't facilities designed for adults look more like this? This is a 22,000 SF outpatient clinic dedicated to treatment of blood disorders. It has a 16-chair infusion area with seven private rooms. The design theme celebrates the four seasons which bridges the gap between toddlers and teenagers. As patients exit the elevator they are greeted by "spring" and an interactive video wall depicting the four seasons. The adjacent play area, celebrating summer, features floor-activated touch pads that enable the change of seasonal imagery on the video wall. As patients move toward the infusion area, they encounter the colors of fall.

Floor-to ceiling windows provide an intimate view of the water garden.

Courtesy LCH Foundation

Courtesy Kurisu International, Inc.

Courtesy LCH Foundation

Waterfall.

View from the infusion therapy unit.
The Healing Garden at Samaritan Lebanon Community Hospital,
Lebanon, OR
Kurisu International (landscape designer, all photos)

Commentary

The 11,000 SF garden is centrally located between the Emenhiser Center (the infusion therapy wing), the birthing wing, the education wing, and the cafeteria. A path draws diners out of the cafeteria into the nature setting with its Japanese-style raked sand garden and luxurious plantings. The healing garden was a priority for the CEO of the hospital who was familiar with the research documenting the ability of nature to be restorative. In the future, research will be conducted to measure its impact on clinical outcomes.

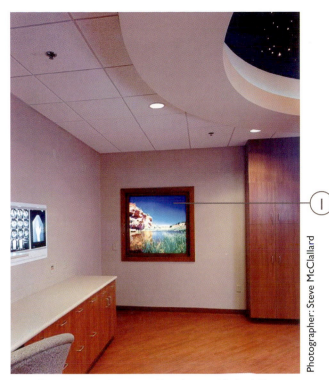

Photographer: Steve McClallard

Lucy Curci Cancer Center at Eisenhower Medical Center,
Rancho Mirage, CA
Moon Mayoras Architects in collaboration
with Jain Malkin Inc.

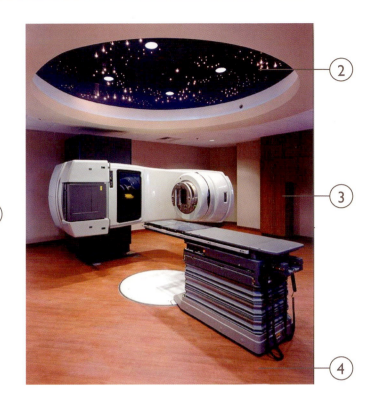

Photographer: Andrew Wagner

The Weinberg Center for Women's Health & Medicine at Mercy, Baltimore, MD
RTKL Associates, TESS (Therapeutic Environmental Solutions) USA, Inc.

Features:

1) Backlit film transparency view of nature. Frame hinges for access to lamping
2) "Midnight Sky" has fiber optic lights in constellation formation (astronomy). Perimeter has fiber optic color "rainbow" that cycles through five colors.
3) Cabinetry provides concealed storage for all accessories.
4) Wood-look floors add warmth.
5) 10-foot-diameter backlit film transparencies introduce stress-relieving image of nature (positive distraction).

Photographer: © 2002 Chris Burkhalter

Radiation Oncology Center, Troy, William Beaumont Hospital, Royal Oak, MI
SSOE Inc. Architects

Photographer: Steve Richardson

Deaconess Hospital, Radiation Therapy, Evansville, IN
BSA LifeStructures, Maregatti Interiors

Features:

1) Stimulated view of nature reduces stress. Image has sufficient detail to engage one's attention for a period of time.
2) Entry to the maze features artwork.
3) Indirect lighting and luminous sky create a feeling of outdoors, a psychological "escape."
4) Adequate storage for accessories out of patient's view
5) Carpet makes room less clinical in ambience.

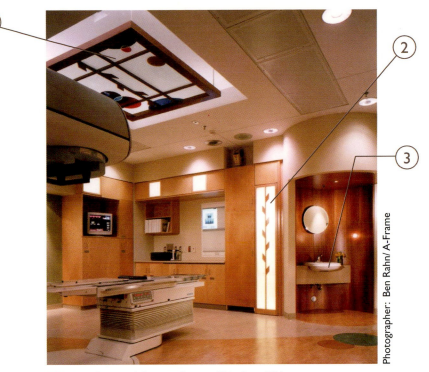

Photographer: Ben Rahn/ A-Frame

Windsor Regional Cancer Center, Windsor, ON
Vermeulen/Hind Architects

Photographer: Michael Dorsin

Baltimore Washington Medical Center, Glen Burnie, MD
Cannon Design

Features:

1) Art glass in ceiling (positive distraction)
2) Backlit art panel
3) Clinical handwash sink in high-profile design, located on curved wood wall — one component of an uncommonly beautiful room
4) Luminescent panels with 10 pre-programmed color and light patterns allow the technologists to alter the effects according to a patient's preference.

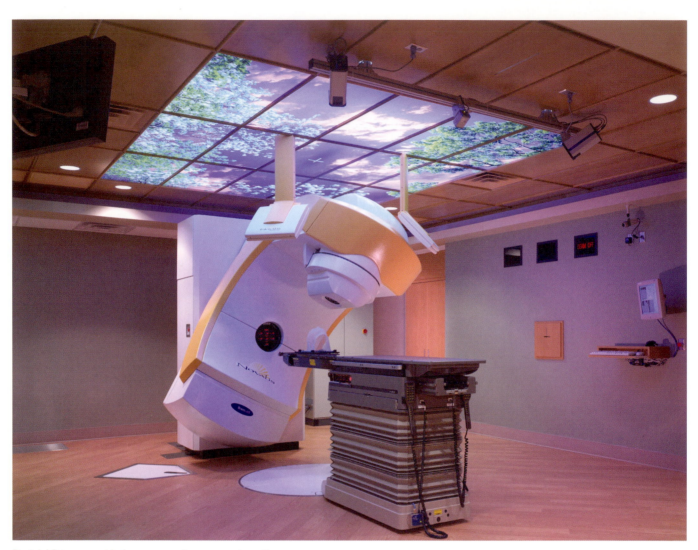

BrainLAB image-guided surgery and stereotactic radiosurgery room.
Saint Alphonsus Regional Medical Center, Boise, ID
HDR Inc. (architecture and interior design)

Commentary

The BrainLAB Novalis device is a linear accelerator used for treating all types of tumors of the body, including cancer. It is the software that distinguishes it from other linear accelerator devices. According to Novalis, neurological sites can be precisely targeted while patient pain and anxiety are minimized due to shorter treatment times (10-15 minutes), frameless positioning (a face mold is used instead), and completely non-invasive procedures. Devices like this are designed to deliver extremely focused radiation, confined to the tumor, and in one dose. This is called radiosurgery. Alternately, larger volumes of tissue are treated in small doses of radiation over a number of days. This is called radiotherapy. The ceiling, by Sky Factory, offers patients a view of nature. The floor is wood-look sheet vinyl.

Index

Geboy, Lyn, 15
Gen-X, 84
glove(s), CDC infection control guide, 45–46
glove boxes, placement of, 47, 126, 7.7, 7.12, 7.13
Golden Mean, 133, 8.1
gowns, CDC infection control guide, 45–46
grab bars, infection control choices, 59
green design, 121, 5.6, 7.51
Granary Associates, 9.15
Gresham Smith Partners, 7.24, 7.88
grief, Kubler-Ross stages, 150
Guenther 5 Architects, 5.6, 5.7, 6.1, 7.85

H

H+L Architecture, 7.89
Hammel, Green and Abrahamson Architects, 135
hands, infection transmission, 39, 43–44
handwashing
   CDC guidelines, 45–46
   compliance problem, 39
   gel cleanser. *See* alcohol-gel cleanser
   sink, placement of, 48, 117, 7.7, 7.13, 7.14, 7.41, 7.44, 7.45
HDR Inc., 10.14
headwalls, 125–126, 7.5, 7.7, 7.23, 7.39, 7.54
healing environments
   defined, 4–5
   emergency department (ED), 144–145
   false claims, 18
   research support for, 2
   stress reduction strategies, 8–10
   See also evidence-based design
Health Information Portability and Accountability Act (1996), 69
HEPA filtration, 53–54
HICPAC, 43, 55
HIPAA, 69
HGA Architects, 153, 7.44
HKS Architects, 5.2, 5.3, 5.4, 5.10, 5.20, 7.38–7.39, 7.45, 7.64, 7.66–7.67, 7.69, 7.71, 7.78, 7.80–7.82, 9.9, 9.11, 9.14, 9.20
HOK Architects, 7.5, 7.7, 7.9, 7.46

home care, recovery time, 6
hospital-acquired infections, 37–45
   aspergillosis, 54
   and bathrooms, patient, 58–59, 110
   and building construction, 53–54
   clostridium difficile-associated disease, 42–43, 58
   computer tracking systems, 37
   control of. *See* infection control
   costs related to, 39
   extended-spectrum beta-lactamases (ESBLs), 44
   legionellosis, 53
   methicillin-resistant *Staphylococcus aureus* (MRSA), 43–44
   multidrug-resistant microorganisms, 41
   myths related to, 40
   pseudomonas aeruginosa (PSAE), 44–45
   and surfaces, 39, 43–44
   susceptible patients, 39
   transmission, elements of, 41
   tuberculosis (TB), 54
   vancomycin-resistant *Enterocci* (VRE), 44
host, infection transmission, 41
HSCT, 149
human factors
   and ergonomic design, 105–106
   human-factors analysis, 106
Human Factors and Ergonomics Study, 106
humanic clues, 81
Hunton Brady Architects, 7.36–7.37
HVAC systems, 54, 7.28, 9.10
hypochlorite solutions, 42-43

I

ice machines, contamination of, 53
Idealized Design model, 117
IDEO, 97, 117, 135
immunity, neurophysiological aspects, 10–11, 139
immunocompromised patients, susceptible to infection, 39
impression, first, 82
inboard plan, patient bathroom, 7.4, 7.36
independent variables, 24, 28
indirect lighting, 65

infection, hospital-acquired. *See* hospital-acquired infections
infection control
   airborne precautions, 46–47
   antimicrobial agent controversy, 49–51
   and carpet, 55–56
   cleansers, types of, 42
   contact precautions (CDC), 46
   design implications, 47–48, 51
   droplet precautions, 47
   HEPA filtration, 53
   nanotechnology, 51–52
   and single-bed rooms, 58–59, 110–111
   standard precautions (CDC), 45
   on surfaces, 43–44, 50, 51–52
   water supply disinfection, 53
InformeDesign, 16
Institute for Family-Centered Care, 89
Institute for Healthcare Improvement (IHI), 37
Institute of Medicine (IOM), 35, 38, 141, 7.25
intensive care units (ICU), 7.83–7.91
   e-ICU (remote monitoring), 115, 7.19
   floor plans, 7.83, 7.87, 7.89
   glazing, vision-to-obscure, 128, 7.15
   ICU ready rooms, 115–116
   infection rates, high, 38
   music therapy, 72
   nature, views of, 7.83
   neonatal, 7.71, 7.82
   nurses' workstations, 7.82, 7.85–7.86, 7.88, 7.91
   patient monitoring, 122, 124, 7.19
   patient susceptbility, 41
   redesign, elements of, 99–100
   rotating boom in, 128, 7.83–7.85
   size of, 7.37, 7.84
   staffing ratios, 116
   waiting areas, 7.84
intermediate care units, size of, 123
Internet, health information on, 82, 83
Intersept, 50
interventional groups, 25
interviews, for research, 24, 97

J

Jain Malkin Inc., 5.16, 6.2–6.3, 8.1, 8.3–8.7, 9.7–9.8, 9.14, 10.3, 10.11
just-in-time studies, 29

postanesthesia care units (PACU), 9.14

recovery room area, 9.3

small/inefficient, 7.69–7.70

O

observation, research method, 24, 97

OhioHealth, 97

Olson Zaltman, 98

Oncology Care Chair, 152, 10.6

100,000 Lives Campaign, 37

organizational culture, and patient experience, 96–97

original data collection studies, types of, 28–29

outboard plan, patient bathroom, 7.5, 7.8

outpatient departments, 5.4

P

pain

reduction strategies, 72, 138

and stress, 6, 7, 138

patient care

and Baby Boomer generation, 83

and bathrooms, 126, 7.62–7.65

branding, 90

cancer treatment, 152–154

critical care, 123

data-collection on, 97–98

defined, 88, 117

dining room, 5.20

elements of, 88

empathy as design factor, 90–91

experience audit, 90, 145

experience engineering, 90

family amenities, 5.11–5.15

family-centered care, 88–89, 92–93

first impressions, 82

and headwalls and footwalls, 125–126

hospital features, most important, 85–87

ICU redesign, 99–100

impressions, clues to, 80–81

information, importance of, 91

and literacy levels, 83–84

lobby design, 5.1–5.5

and organizational culture, 96–97

patient as consumer, 85

patient-centered care, 88

and patient experience, 79–100, 144, 147

and Planetree model, 88–89

positive distraction, 5.16–5.19

practitioner/patient interaction, 92–93

process redesign, 93–96

value satisfactions, 81–82

waiting area design, 5.6–5.10

wayfinding design, 5.21

See also patient satisfaction

patient-focused care, defined, 88

patient process interface. *See* patient experience

patient rooms, 109–129

acuity-adaptable. *See* acuity-adaptable rooms

acuity-adaptable rooms, 115–116

bathrooms. *See* bathrooms, patient

CDC infection control guide, 45–47

ceiling lifts, 126

corridors to, 127, 7.34, 7.66–7.70

critical care units, 128–129, 7.83–7.91

ergonomic zones, 7.12

floor plans, 7.59, 7.61, 7.87, 7.89

footwalls, 7.13, 7.23, 7.44, 7.60

future view, 7.10

green design, 7.13

headwalls, 7.23, 7.39, 7.54

headwalls/footwalls, 125–126, 7.5, 7.7

innovations, examples of, 112–113

intensive care units, 115–116

intermediate care units, 123

LDR/LDRP rooms, 127–128, 7.71–7.82

med/surg room, 7.38–7.45

mirror image rooms, 113–114, 124, 8.8

negative air-pressure, 54, 9.10

over-bed tray, 7.16

positive air pressure, 54

prototype for redesign, 7.11

same-handed orientation, 122, 123–124, 135, 7.5, 7.6–7.7

semi-private, 7.46

single-occupancy. *See* single-bed rooms

toilet sharing and contamination, 58–59, 110

Transforming Care at Bedside (TCAB), 116–117

universal room, 114, 120–121

patient safety movement, 37–38

patient satisfaction

hospital features, most important, 85

hospital experience ratings, 86

in single-bed rooms, 109–110

value satisfactions, 81–82

pay for performance, 37

peace-and-quiet periods, 117

Pebble Project studies, 27–31, 126

Fable Hospital model, 29–30

research matrix, 14–15

Perkins+Will, 5.1, 5.8, 7.90–7.91, 10.5, 10.9

Perkins Eastman Architects, 9.16–9.17

Peterson Kohlberg & Associates, Architects, 7.43, 7.70

Phillips Lighting ambient experience, 71–72

phlebotomy, 132

physicians' lounge, 102, 6.2–6.4

Picker Institute, 97

placebo, 25

placebo effect, 139

Planetree Model Hospital project, 88–89

positive air pressure rooms, 54

positive distraction, 104, 132–134, 144, 5.16–5.19

postanesthesia care units (PACU), 140–141, 9.14

pre-admit testing, process redesign, 95

prep/recovery, 147, 9.3–9.4, 9.12–9.14, 9.20, 9.24

Press Ganey, 85, 109

privacy

chemotherapy session, 151, 10.2, 10.4

glazing, vision to obscure, 128, 7.15

and HIPAA, 69

and single-bed rooms, 111–112

speech privacy, 69–70

procedures, 137–141

cath labs, 9.11–9.12

Cyberknife, 9.22–9.23

endoscopy, 9.4, 9.13, 9.24

prep/recovery, 9.12–9.14, 9.24

surgery, 9.15–9.19

process redesign, 93–96

effectiveness of, 100

elements of, 93–95

pre-admit testing example, 95

Project Index